The Day
I Met a Lion

The Day
I Met a
Lion

by MacKinlay Kantor

Doubleday & Company, Inc., Garden City, New York, 1968

To Bea and Maury Greenbaum

Contents

Note to My Grandchildren [1958]   1

The Day I Met a Lion [1962]   4

A Dirty Little Job for Dave [1957]   14

Memorial for Mr. Vertigo [1949]   24

Two Guys from the Twenty-third [1950]   40

Assembly of the Saints [1967]   72

Time to Wake Up Now [1945]   81

The Hungriest Ones [1963]   90

Paul Revere and the Nazi Spies [1962]   95

Her Name Was Grace [1941]   104

Of Guns and Monsters [1962]   114

First Blood [1936]   118

And the Armies That Remain'd Suffer'd [1945]   124

So the Old Maid Said to the Traveling Man——[1953]   133

Not Built with Mortal Hands [1952]   147

Of Course There Are Apparitions [1965]   153

The Best Cooking of My Life [1952]   170

Lobo [1956]   184

Pretty Pictures for Tooey [1946]   223

Flight and Murder of the Multitudes [1964]   237

He Found Life Good and Left It Better [1966]   251

The Babe and the Boy [1945]   263

It Couldn't Be Pedro [1962]   267

The Time in Which a Person Shall Live [1957–61]   270

Christmas Card from Jupiter [1962]   279

The Idea of Singing [1953]   284

They Loved Me in Korea [1951]   287

Layne's Pink Lady [1964]   300

A Speech About Saucers [1962]   304

The Marchers [1955]   308

Frankie [1966]   313

The Larks of April [1967]   326

Letter to Canella [1966]   339

THE DAY I MET A LION

and other Critters; and other Days and Nights; and also certain Terrifying Events; and various Mysteries; and Scenes in a Tender-hearted Place; and some Laughing People, and some who weep; and Good Smells from the Kitchen; and sundry Dangers; and a symphony of Airplane Engines; and a Great Teacher; and a love of Woods and Waters; and Brave and Honest Policemen; and one Clinical Discussion which the prudish may find appalling; and an Apparition; and Tender Memories; and a Flying Saucer; and divers Intimate Recollections; and other Actualities which, during his lifetime, have befallen

THE AUTHOR

Note to
My Grandchildren
1958

Dear Ones:

The most interesting people in this world you will never meet on television. The most ferocious adventures, the darkest cream of mysteries, the spiciest apples and clearest creeks—these you will find seldom when you sit down before a shimmering screen.

You will find them instead hidden between the covers of books. And stimulation will come through the application of that almost forgotten art—Reading Aloud.

This is a benefit valued in those dearest hours when a family may be assembled. I remember that your mother and your Uncle Tim thought that it was a captivating rite to be accomplished in bed! . . . Many things which children enjoy doing are very rewarding to the children when the children do these things themselves; but they are not occupations in which parents or grandparents may join with any but pretended enthusiasm.

Reading Aloud, on the other hand, offers the same spice and tonic to the one who reads that it awards to him who listens. We all enjoy being actors at times; there is no happier way in which to be an actor.

Your great-grandmother was an actress before my eyes and to the response of my eager ears, and she was a good one. It seems sometimes that I can hear her yet—when she was anything from the Mad Hatter to the Lady from Philadelphia; and

back again to those delicious moments when she screamed at
Tom Sawyer as his poor Aunt Polly screamed, or when she
gave every reassurance of the Swiss Robinson mother on a
fairly enchanted island, as that good woman delved into her
wonderful bag.

In the same way I tried to be Huckleberry Finn and Long
John Silver when your mother was young. She swears that I
succeeded admirably. So, you see there is double benefit: *the
joy at the time of doing the thing; and the pleasure of being
reminded about it, no matter how many years later.* A story
shared by audience and reader is a tale many times endeared
and many times endowed. How indeed does the Bible itself
become best compelling in drama and in poetry? Surely it is
because that great Book has its tales and messages so often
Read Aloud.

In an Iowa town where I lived through those years which
I spent in your assorted sizes, we were blessed in having a fine
public library. A rich man, who boasted few close relatives, had
left his entire estate to be used for library purposes. So that
library goes on, pouring out its gifts to the community more
than half a century later.

If we did not have the noblest stories on our narrow shelves
at home, we could find them in the public library. So also may
you, in your own time and in your own public libraries. Thus
may you demonstrate the art of bringing the world of the past
—the world of delighted and delightful imagination—into your
very spirits. Thus may you demonstrate this ecstatic occupation
to others.

When the first bearded men went tramping in their cloaks
from camp to camp and castle to castle, they chanted legends
aloud. Such recital, in its way, was the Reading Aloud of early
times. Folks were benefited by a voice telling a tale . . . they
may accumulate the same treasure in this very moment, and in
hours yet undreamed. . . .

Turn off the television for the night! Boldest stallions and
fiercest dragons and the most comical hares are not the ones

which you will see posturing before you amid a crescendo of studio music. They are those which you hear about while being read to. Their rarest manes and horns and ears are those in which you yourself dress them—not the ones tailored by some unseen producer.

The richest message is not refined and filtered through a dozen other minds. It comes to you across ennobled distances, directly from its source to the happy target which is yourself —and which is as well a child unready to be born and not yet dreamed of—a child whom each of you in your own turn may Read Aloud to, in a year which lies many star-winks ahead.

The Day
I Met a Lion
1962

The Great Man was coming to our town.

The Great Man's craggéd face stared with a kind of defiant serenity from posters, from pages of our two local newspapers. Power and enigma of the African wilderness shone in his eyes . . . as if a pride of lions walked with him.

His name was Carl Akeley, and if you are too young to know his name you can look him up in the *Britannica*. It is now more than forty years since last I looked at him; through most of those years he has been sleeping his wise remote sleep on the slope of Mount Mikeno, in that distant land of the gorillas. Yet still I remember the moment when his big misshapen fingers touched my life. I give thanks, and reverence.

. . . The contrast was all the more severe because in those days I was surrounded by Little Men. My father was remote, divorced, mainly out of the picture. My maternal grandfather —hard-working, taciturn, grimly honest—was still a Little Man; so was the man who owned the newspaper which my mother edited, and where I worked, helping her. So were the bulk of those who walked the Webster City streets. There were perhaps a dozen statuesque souls in our Iowa community. But I was only a teen-ager: rarely can the gulf between maturity and immaturity be bridged to fetch a rewarding intimacy. Our Superintendent of Schools, according to common opinion, had his face set in a perpetual sneer . . . our high school Principal went bustling off into well-deserved anonymity long ago.

There was a daily demonstration of pettiness throughout the school. A few kindly teachers sought sincerely to give the best of themselves to the young folks; but they were still the few.

Life rang with the cheap tinkle of a dime-store tea-bell. It was hard to hear an organ tone, though some of our ears were open and willing. . . .

Night after night, on my way home from work, I stopped at a shop window where the powerful face of Carl Akeley looked out into space, and I recognized and bowed before his majesty. I pinched myself . . . actually I had stood beside the man, even exchanged conversation with him!

It happened in Chicago, some years before. When still a small boy I was imbued with the desire to become an entomologist, specializing particularly in *Lepidoptera:* butterflies and moths. By the time I reached Boy Scout age my insect collection was extensive; so was my knowledge of the subject, at least for a youth of my age. I entertained not the slightest ambition to become a writer, in those years. Bright-winged moths, and all the spicy mysteries surrounding them: they beat their wings through my dreams.

. . . Surprisingly my father volunteered to furnish the wherewithal for my sister and myself to attend school in Chicago. We had no second sight, no way of knowing that this experience would end in debacle. We had been neglected by our father for many years; but we believed eagerly in his promises, and made the change to Chicago. I was fourteen: tall and gangling, and ridden almost equally with ambitions to be a crack entomologist and to enlist in the Army for service overseas in World War I. Neither of these ambitions was achieved; but I did try.

On the entomological front I soon made contact with Dr. Gerhard, at the Field Museum, then located in a crumbly pile left over from the World's Fair of 1893. Why this genial man put up with me is something I will never know; but he did his best to welcome the fumbling intrusion of an enthusiastic

boy who came claiming his time on Saturdays, or late sometimes
on other winter afternoons.

One cold day, in that drafty tangle of dim hallways, I found
a small assemblage of museum officials and workmen who were,
for the moment, honored by the presence of Carl Akeley. He
had dropped in to give his opinion concerning some new exhibits, and in the rearrangement of some old ones. Gerhard
was one of the group, so I stood close and, with the rest,
thrilled to the presence, the impressive conversation of an internationally famous naturalist, explorer, sculptor, who towered
like a silver-clad peak in his field.

. . . That momentary contact had been some time before,
but I cherished the recollection. Intervening years had been
bitter, difficult, filled with pains and perils. In Chicago my
father was arrested for using the mails to defraud; I quit school
and went to work as an office boy, to help provide eating
money for the family. Then the Child Labor inspectors caught
up with me, and threw me out of that job because I was under
sixteen. We had to go back to Iowa.

All told, I was now three years behind my old class in high
school, and had thought that I should never return to finish up.
But things changed for the better, in this winter of 1921–22.
Mother's income from the newspaper venture was encouraging,
if still not adequate; she gloried in my willingness to return
to high school, and also work part time on her newspaper. It
seemed to me then, however, that school hours were barren,
profitless of any advantage to the future, just as the newspaper hours were rich in variegated experience.

(Nothing which has happened during the intervening four
decades has caused me to change my mind about this.)

Our school was filled with the squeak and quacking of parrot
voices; and the notions which were considered were parrot notions—imitative, trivial. Sometimes even now, gray-haired and a
little slowed down in wind and limb, I find myself confronted
by some dismal repetition of those attitudes still persisting,
faulty and corrosive, in a later civilization. Then I am apt to

have a nightmare wherein I dream that I am imprisoned in high school once again.

. . . I made my big mistake when I bragged that I had met Carl Akeley, stood beside him; even—I laughed—worked with him.

"Wait a minute, Mack. Who's Carl Akeley?"

"You mean to say you don't *know?*"

"Oh. That man who's coming to lecture—?"

Fervently I launched into a recital of Akeley's accomplishments. I pointed out how he had revolutionized the whole process of zoölogical exhibitions, by striving for a presentation in which specimens were set before the public in their natural posture and surroundings. I told of his journeys and writings, his fight to protect the gorillas from those who would murder them pointlessly.

"And yet I guess you couldn't call a man like that very soft —not a man who actually killed a leopard with his bare hands!"

"Bare *hands?*"

"He had nothing else at the moment, and it was a case of either Dr. Akeley or the leopard. He doesn't hanker after killing animals; but that time he had to do it."

They stood regarding me doubtfully. There were not only friends in this crew, there were Enemies as well: the ones whom we called spies . . . spies for the Principal, spies for the Superintendent. I was sticking my neck 'way out . . . should have known better, but didn't.

"What do you mean, Mack? You say you *worked* with him—?"

"Certainly! We helped to move some things out of an exhibit, and put them in another case. Everybody worked and shoved, side by side! Even the Head of the museum. So—" Again I laughed, and repeated it with all the show-off arrogance of youth (most especially youth which has been savagely bruised)— "Technically, I can say that I met Carl Akeley, and worked with him."

That time I was really asking for it. And I got it. Oh, *how*
I got it. . . .

It was the custom in such towns to request visiting lecturers
to drop in at school and speak briefly to the students. It wasn't
a stipulated part of the lecturers' visits, but very few of them
refused. No extra remuneration was involved; doubtless the majority of these distinguished people—statesmen, travelers, authors, scientists—considered that such momentary ordeal was
merely another responsibility which fame had brought to them.
(I know that to this day I will go and speak to young people,
and for free, while I refuse to step off on a professional round
of lecture platforms.)

There were a couple of hours of work at the newspaper
office, before school. Sometimes I was late, and the school people didn't like this; so I ran a demanding race on that fateful
morning . . . dashed in at the north door, threw my cap in
my locker, came up the stairs three at a time. I beat the tardy
bell by seconds.

But there were people waiting for me in the hall. I saw faces
smiling, and some of the smiles weren't very pleasant. I felt
a little chilly, but still didn't know why.

"Mack, have you seen the bulletin-board?"

No, I had not; so they led me up to read the thing displayed
there.

The home-made handbill was prepared in neatest type. There
was a picture of Carl Akeley, and the announcement that he
had consented to talk to the high school students that very
morning. Worst of all was the paragraph appended, which read
something like this:

"It may interest the high school classes to know that one
of their fellow members, Mack Kantor, once became acquainted
with Dr. Akeley, and worked side by side with him at the
Field Museum in Chicago. No doubt this will come as a surprise to many, and probably it will be an especially happy
surprise for Dr. Akeley to greet his old friend. Mack will be

encouraged to meet with Dr. Akeley, immediately after the latter has finished his discourse in the Assembly Room."

Pretty mean, on the whole, but those folks could be mean. As I said: they were Little Men, and Little Men are the meanest.

The whole purpose of this enterprise, of course, was to reveal me as a liar. In our tender-hearted Webster City of that period there was, unhappily for me, a school of thought which reiterated through the years: "Mack will probably turn out to be just like his father." I was writing my first editorials for the Des Moines *Register* in that same year. But my detractors let it be known that they didn't believe I actually wrote that stuff which appeared in the *Register* under my name: it must have been written by my mother. When I won the *Register*'s annual short story contest, open to any Iowan who had never sold a short story (I was the youngest winner in the history of that contest), the same people said that probably I'd copied the story from some source or another. Not a line about my winning the contest appeared in our high school newspaper.

. . . Often nowadays, interviewers ask if I was ever encouraged during school days. I say, "Certainly! Very much encouraged—by antithesis."

. . . There I stood, with personal and social disaster only minutes ahead. Carl Akeley wouldn't remember me, naturally enough. Why should he remember? Who could possibly, under the circumstances, recall a bony schoolboy who had been one of a throng, three years before, during a momentary encounter at the Field Museum? Akeley owned honored access to every important museum in the world. He might even have difficulty in recalling certain Fellows of the Royal Zoölogical Society, the Royal Geographical Society, all the rest. He knew intimately the British, Belgian, French, German people in his and adjacent fields. He knew officials of various lands—daring hunters, fabulous naturalists.

So he would stand there and say: "What? Who? Who's this? I'm sorry, I don't remember this young man," and the cheap poison laughter would begin, and go trilling beyond the borders of space.

There was sweat on the back of my neck, sweat under my hair. I tried to smile. . . .

"Did you hear that?" said a voice in my ear. "They've just rung the bell for Assembly. Come on, Mack. Up to the Assembly Room!"

Then I was walking . . . my footfalls sounded tiny and far away.

If only they had put up that evil notice on the bulletin-board the day before!—then I could have left school. I wouldn't have returned; wouldn't ever have entered that building again. But here I was—trapped. I couldn't go rushing away out the door, fleeing now. It was too late: headlong flight would be a tacit admission of my own guilt . . . which was not guilt, again; yet everyone except a few affectionate friends thought it was.

So we reached the Assembly Room . . . I was in a trance. Somehow I sat down, tried to grin feebly; and then the next moment the Superintendent was on the platform, with Carl Akeley beside him.

. . . Oh yes, I said to myself, dully . . . he does look like a lion. And also he must remind people of that old bull-elephant who mauled him. . . .

I haven't the slightest idea what Carl Akeley talked about, that morning; didn't know then, can't tell you now. Brief it must have been: those visiting speakers were never asked to appear for more than fifteen minutes. It seemed like fifteen hours, to me.

Frail hopes came chasing into my brain. Suppose he got mixed up in conversation with some teachers, just after he was finished? Then there wouldn't be time! If I once got safely out of that accurséd room, then maybe I could take refuge in the boys' lavatory . . . maybe even have an opportunity to drop my books in the locker, seize my cap and be gone. If only I weren't summoned to appear up front!—if only they didn't demand that I meet face to face with Dr. Akeley, while the whole Assembly Room was still filled with the doubting, the curious . . . those with sly contempt in their hearts.

Eventually we applauded the speaker. . . . A bell rang for dismissal; we all rose up and turned away from our desks, we filled the aisles.

I tried to find shelter behind others, tried to droop down, efface myself physically, and this was difficult to manage because I was tall. Then quickly . . . *oh, it will be over soon, it will be over* . . . my nickname was called . . . a single syllable like the cracking of a whip.

People hadn't yet reached the two wide outer doors of that torture chamber.

"Mack," the Superintendent called. "Come here!" And he was smiling . . . how he smiled . . . the burly Principal was grinning behind him.

Carl Akeley halted and looked puzzled. What interruption was occurring here? Akeley was headed for the door, back to the safety of his hotel room. . . .

"Just a minute, sir, if you please," said the Principal. "Here's an old friend of yours."

Somehow I'd walked that distance to the front of the room. I stood there and looked into those deep-set eyes. Feebly I was extending my hand.

"Surely, Dr. Akeley," said the Superintendent, "you'll remember someone who says he knew you at the Field Museum?"

They repeated my name again and again . . . repeated it with various inflections, and their triumphant leer was as the smirk of devils. Three hundred students stood staring, wondering what would happen; but most of them thought they knew. And all those teachers rimmed along the back of the room, and at the sides— They were watching, the world was watching.

I said, "Dr. Akeley, sir. It was only once that we met. I was with Dr. Gerhard. They were moving an exhibit—"

The expression on his face underwent complete alteration. Never have I seen so much compassion, such nobility, projected into a human countenance, and all in a split second.

He *knew!* Dr. Akeley *knew.* He knew what they were trying to do to me.

He didn't remember me, didn't know me from Adam, couldn't know me; 'twould have been impossible.

His voice seemed as coming from a cavern, a lonely place high on the African hills: a cavern of tusks and skeletons, a cavern illuminated by moonlight. . . .

"Remember you?" he cried. "Of course I remember you!"

He repeated the name they had uttered to him, the name he had never heard before, would never recall more; yet he made a magic of it.

"Of course, of course!" he cried. "In Chicago, some years ago. Yes, you've grown so much, Mack, I didn't know you! You were a friend of Osgood, right? Of course, of course—"

And I hadn't been a friend of Dr. Osgood, had only watched him in admiration, when sometimes we passed in a museum corridor. . . .

Carl Akeley moved leisurely toward the staircase, and I was moving with him, because he had his arm across my shoulders, and was impelling me on his way, which had now become my way. . . .

"Tell me," he said, "what are you doing here?"

"Well, sir. . . . I was interested in entomology at that time. But now I want to be a writer. I'm working on a newspaper, part time, and going to school the rest of the time."

"Ah, yes," he said. "Writing: sad and lonely business! But of course—" The deep eyes peered at me. "If you're determined, there'll be no stopping you." His thick arm, that arm so torn and scarred, tightened for a moment across my shoulders.

Students and teachers had parted to let us through; we were going down the stairs. I didn't see the Principal and Superintendent, couldn't see anyone but Carl Akeley just then. (I was told later, by a delighted gang of boy friends, that the Enemies looked as if someone had just told them that there was no Santa Claus, and no Easter Bunny either.)

We reached the second floor. Dr. Akeley and I shook hands.

"Sir," I said, "I've got to go to class. It was nice of you to—remember me—"

"How could I help it?" said the great voice of the Great Man. "And, Mack—you'll be at my lecture tonight?"

"Yes, sir. I'll be there."

Then he called after me once more, when he was joined by the Enemies—now so thoroughly discomfited and discredited, merely by this man's intuitive generosity. He called, "Good luck on the writing, Mack."

. . . So his voice comes down the years—all the way from the Africa where his gnarled bones rest, all the way from that challenging Paradise which his soul must be exploring.

. . . In those few minutes, by force and example, he had taught me something that I needed very much to learn. He taught me that the measure of a man's true greatness is not necessarily in the extent of his accomplishments; but in the extent to which his heart remains unsoiled, unspoiled, forever understanding.

I had been surrounded by rodents, and needed to meet up with a tawny lion. I had met one.

A Dirty Little Job
for Dave
1957

The killer spread its smelly gray body over more of the Globe, and dragged more people to ache or to destruction, than any other single malevolence amid the misfortunes of humanity. Wan doctors succumbed, the saws of coffin-makers hummed overtime in their shops, the priests prayed.

A third of a century after this horror, the observant Mr. Stewart Holbrook solidified the story with careful research, and a magazine published the tale.

In Florida a tan-faced husky man of middle age sat in his office and read the story to its cruel end. He stood up, and the sound of waves was in his ears—ocean water moving ceaselessly across the roughness of coral.

He heard the wail of gulls, the sound of his own footsteps dragging, he heard other more frightening sounds. He stood gazing out of his window, seeing never the increasing autumnal bustle as Sarasota moved into its new tourist season, but seeing other strange things he had nearly forgotten.

At last Dave Boylston left his office and strolled down the narrow private stairway which led to the interior of his big drugstore. Many people bustled behind the soda fountain and cigar counters, among the other counters laden with sundries and cosmetics—all working to supply the needs of the customers trooping in and out of the three public doors which gave access to Dave's store.

Pharmacists were busy: one at the telephone, two compound-

ing or wrapping drugs; other customers waited. Dave has been a
pharmacist since the days before his children were born.

He stepped to the wide prescription window and took a slip
of paper from a customer's hand. "Hello, Charlie."

"Hi, Dave."

"From Dr. Harris? I'll fix it right up for you." He squinted
at the prescription. "For your wife?"

The customer nodded. "Doctor says she's got flu or something."

"I'm sorry," and Dave meant it, for he had known Charlie
and his wife for years. He moved automatically to the proper
shelves, he began to take down bottles. "Did you say flu?" Once
again the crashing waves were in his ears, and the sound of
gulls.

"Boylston!" yelled the Chief Petty Officer, in the hall outside the ward.

"Yay?" Boylston was just eighteen years old, small for his
age. He was tired, his uniform was stained. The CPO was exhausted too; everybody around the Key West Naval Station was
worn to a frazzle in that distraught autumn of 1918.

Wards were full, the sick were bunched in the hallways; the
new sick were being lugged or assisted up the steps, and some
of them tried to make it under their own steam, and sometimes
they fainted along the way. Truckloads of ominous rough-boxes
stood parked directly opposite the infirmary gate—the boxes not
concealed, glaring in their newness; there were no hands to
unload them.

Like a lot of other Navy personnel, Dave didn't like the setup
at Key West. He had tried to ship out every time an opportunity
offered, or every time rumor suggested that one might offer.
Thus far he had been out of luck. Often while he lugged the
bedpans or manipulated the syringes, he had dreamed of another station, any station. But with this epidemic it seemed that
any change might be delayed for a long time.

A mocking challenge lived in the look the CPO gave him.
"You've been asking to ship out—"

"I sure have."

"Go get your sea-bag. Pack your dunnage. I'll have your orders from the Skipper as soon as you get back."

Dave didn't know whether to grin or feel sad. He looked at his wristwatch: it was about two in the afternoon. This was a blinding surprise.

"Draw some stores," said the chief. "There's some people sick where you're going, and we don't know how they're fixed on medical supplies. The message didn't say. Make it snappy, sailor."

Dave went to pack his bag, and that didn't take very long. He knew just what he would take and how he would pack it; he had packed for weeks, in his imagining. Here was the actuality . . . he was shipping out in a dream.

He drew the necessary stores. Quantities hadn't been mentioned; he had to guess. But there wasn't much room for speculation about the variety or substance. They were using a standard therapy for the flu, and it seemed to work some of the time: first, a big dose of Epsom salts; then plenty of aspirin; externally, alcohol rubs, as the patient seemed to need them—or more likely just as often as overworked personnel found time to give the alcohol rubs.

Epsom salts, aspirin, alcohol . . . Dave toted his burdens to the slip where a seaplane lay. That was all he knew: he was going by plane, he had never been in the air before. (He had worked in stores, he had worked in Walpole's pharmacy in Sarasota. There hadn't been much chance for him to study, as a civilian; but he had made pharmacist's mate first class with swiftness after he put on bell-bottom trousers.)

Two fliers waited with the seaplane—big men, glassy-faced in goggles. They made remarks which didn't encourage this frightened paddlefoot to any degree as he blundered, trying to help stow his bags aboard the craft. Armed guards, the few other people along the wharves, watched idly. The Gulf of Mexico glimmered hard outside.

The showed Dave where his seat was, they told him gruffly

how to sit in it, they fixed the safety belt; he faced speed and wind and possible disaster. The pilot was ready, the observer in his seat also; other knowledgeable young men in dungarees stood around to do their chores, to cast off the restraining lines. There was talk about switches and contacts—things Dave thought he would never understand. He wondered what Fort Jefferson was like, because that was where his superiors had told him he was going.

Big propellers began to spin, the foam was blasted, the sea-plane skated over bunching swells. It rocked and bounded, the spray flew thick, the wind tore. They headed into the sun, and for a while Dave couldn't see anything. . . . Only about seventy miles, he had heard someone say. That shouldn't take very long, because airplanes flew so fast in this modern age of 1918.

The aircraft operated regularly on antisubmarine patrol through this region of Gulf and Cuban Straits. From their conversation, Boylston knew that the fliers were to drop him at the Fort Jefferson Naval Station, and then continue on the regular schedule of their patrol.

Latitude 24 degrees, 36 minutes North; Longitude 82 degrees, 54 minutes West; there lie the Dry Tortugas. "A group of 10 small coral keys or islets," say the encyclopedias, "lying at the extreme western end of the Florida Keys, some 70 miles from Key West."

The books will tell you more, speaking of a Carnegie Biological Laboratory established there in 1904, and a Federal bird reservation proclaimed in 1908. Long ago prisoners had been confined in the battered fort. We in this age remember a movie about an unfortunate doctor who was himself a celebrated prisoner—something to do with John Wilkes Booth and the assassination of President Lincoln. The rich modern shrimp beds, the so-called "pink gold" on which Monroe County fishermen have fattened for years—these are not far away.

Sharks and other fish galore . . . great shining snappers in

shadows below the coral, the waves chewing up into the foun-
dations of the fort, mangroves tangled green on the few unin-
habited keys so close. And all around, out into the glaring wide
prairie of ocean, foam running loose when the wind blows, the
birds upended and shrill in the breeze.

Thus appeared the Dry Tortugas, as Boylston and the two
Navy airmen glimpsed them, when they smashed the water
with their pontoons that afternoon. The trip really hadn't taken
long, but it had seemed an eternity to the eighteen-year-old
tyro. He was glad to feel some kind of solidity beneath this
queer rocking machine—even the false solidity of salt water.

Their big bug ambled to a slip which extended outward from
a wider section of wharf built near the battlements. The fliers
swore because there was no one on the dock to make fast a line
for them. With difficulty they held the patrol plane against the
pier for a moment, while Dave unbent his cramped legs and
staggered ashore, and reached back for the sea-bag and other
bags which the observer handed out with scant ceremony.

They said their quick goodbyes, the line fell loose as hands
waved perfunctorily; once more the whirl of propellers began
to rift the surface. Dave stood and watched. He felt the wet
hurricane about his ears, and momentarily turned his face away
from the drive of it. Then the aircraft had taken off once more
into the wind. It rose clumsily, the legs of its pontoons spread
wide. It turned to the south; and here he was at his new station
of duty.

Dave walked along the pier, sea-bag on his shoulder, hands
straining with the other bags. He had expected to be challenged,
he thought that someone would ask him to display the flimsy
order folded in his pocket. But no one was around to ask him
anything. Beyond the old fort loomed, antique as a European
castle on a postcard. Dave observed, in secret delight, that there
were even a moat and drawbridge. Through this shadowy gateway the ugly brick buildings of the interior stared.

No challenge, no sentry. His feet rang lonely on the hollowness of the main dock; he labored into the summoning silence

of the huge unroofed interior. It was the kind of place where there must be cells and dungeons . . . bars in the apertures would be corroded, and so might half-forgotten rings in the wall, where once the malefactors were chained.

Dave looked up at the sky. He stared back, trying to see the plane which had brought him, but already it was vanished into the damp haze above the Gulf Stream. He did see a flight of pelicans, they moved in silent echelon, they made no cry. But things were so still that he fancied he could hear the pounding of their wings.

No sentinel, no Shore Patrol, no character standing around with an armband and webbed belt and bayonet and Springfield rifle. Dave stopped; he shifted his load to unwind the cramp from his hands, and then picked up his burdens again and went forward. This was odd; he felt a little discomfited.

Suppose the aircraft had put him down at the wrong island? This seemed to be a particularly old fort, and maybe it was abandoned. Maybe there was another fort behind one of the nearby keys, hidden by mangroves. He might have to hunt for a boat, or maybe even make a raft (he liked that idea, because he was young) and paddle over to his proper station when the sea became calm.

Out of a corner of his eye he saw something white blowing loose on the fortification above. That was a sloppy way for anybody to run a place—not to police it up, to leave rags lying around. But then— Was there a movement under the white cloth, and did he hear a sound not made by the wheeling birds?

Something cold touched his heart and his body. He had relinquished his sea-bag and other duffle, he was climbing. Three stories aloft . . . he was in a trance, crawling on a steep hard journey to the rim of the fort. That soiled white bundle before his eyes. . . .

There was life in this coral wilderness, if miserable life. A voice talking, gabbling in delirium; a voice asking for Mother.

Dave ran forward. It seemed that this sailor—a boy about his own age, flushed and fever-ridden—must have fallen from some higher perch, and so he was lying on the stones, and no one had moved him.

Dave knelt, touching the sailor. The boy twisted his face with its wild blue eyes, and coughed hard, and sighed again, and his jaw gaped afresh. He had made an attempt to bed himself out here; he had folded a sweater under his head; he was barefoot. In angry illness he had prayed that the wind might cool him and cure him.

Twenty feet beyond him was another man, lying in a quite different position, and then on beyond was another, and he was trying to sit up and call to Dave and wave his arm. From within the open window of the nearest barracks came the sound of more coughing. A door slammed remotely as the wind blew it.

For a moment the pharmacist's mate felt as dizzy as the sufferers who had spread themselves along the battlements in that dangerous wind. Now he knew why there had been no challenge, no sentinel at the pier. Flu had come to the Dry Tortugas. It got there before Dave did.

When he was a boy in South Carolina, Dave had to go to work very early in life. There wasn't any time left to him to seek entertainment, to read for fun. He had never read about the smallpox epidemic which swept the Blackfeet nation (and so, when enemies came to attack remote villages, they found only silent tepees flapping in the upland breeze, and every Indian, from elder chief to papoose, dried in death).

But a story did enter his thought in recollection: maybe a teacher had read it to her class when he was small. It was about a spell which came down on a castle, and so everybody lay in a trance: the scullion in the kitchen, the very dogs in the yard, the sweet Sleeping Beauty on her couch. Years passed, brambles grew high, the Prince came cutting through them. He kissed the Sleeping Princess, and then life began again for all.

. . . This was a kind of castle, here on this far dot of coral, these Dry Tortugas. The sick sailors weren't any pretty princesses, and the pharmacist's mate felt himself no prince. He was merely a lone guy with an abandoned sea-bag which he had dumped on the rocks. If he was going to work any magic, it had to be done with Epsom salts, aspirin and alcohol, and with his own two legs and two hands.

This is the hardest part of the tale to write, because it is the hardest part for Dave to remember and recount. I find, having searched up the old notes I made when I first heard him reciting the facts twenty years ago, that time has brought variations into his narrative. I asked him about this the other day, and he grinned sheepishly.

"You know how some folks are: they can go back thirty-nine years and remember every detail, as if it were cut out of stone. I'm not like that. I get confused, and— Well, at the time I was pretty tired. Busy, too."

"You'd had your clothes on since you went on duty that morning. I suppose maybe you put on a fresh uniform for the trip, didn't you?"

"I suppose I must have."

"How long before you had your clothes off again?"

He considered. "I think it was the third or fourth day. The days and the nights got sort of mixed up. I was kind of going around in a dream by that time."

"How long before you slept?"

"I guess it was quite a while. Two or three days later—something like that. By that time some of the guys could help out a little. You know; the stronger ones helped take care of the weaker."

"How had you made them stronger?"

Dave grinned. "Same old routine: fifteen or twenty grains of aspirin every three or four hours. That was to bring their fever down. Epsom salts to clean out the infection from their systems —or so we believed, anyway. And alcohol rubs."

He looked at his hand. "My hands got pretty sore, rubbing. We had good alcohol though. No, I didn't drink any of it; but it was pure grain."

The first thing he had to do was to get those scattered Sleeping Beauties in off the top of the old fortification before night killed them there. Everybody who lived through that flu epidemic remembers how it hit like a ton of bricks: a sudden aching, complete collapse, almost like a paralytic stroke. Sometimes it was as much as an hour or so coming on; but usually it struck in minutes. Sometimes, it seemed, in seconds.

Some of those men had been at work outside, when they were taken sick, and so they just dropped where they were, and felt bad and passed out. Others had sought the open air deliberately: the fever was broiling them, and they wanted to be cool. They thought that the constant racing of the wind would make them more comfortable. They had staggered outside and made little makeshift beds or pallets out of sweaters and peajackets, then they hadn't the strength to go back inside.

So Dave had to take them inside now. It was quite a job. He tugged and pulled. Whenever he found someone who seemed strong enough to help not only himself but others for a moment, he asked that man to do a little tugging and pulling too.

"How many were there, all told?" (He had said thirty in his original recounting to me, a score of years before.)

"Mack, it gets rather hazy. I think twenty-six."

"Who was in command? A lieutenant?"

"I think it was an ensign. Maybe there were two ensigns on duty there. It gets away from me because it was so long ago."

And probably because there was so much aspirin and so much bitter froth of Epsom salts and so strong a smell of alcohol; and the soup to ladle out. There was a good galley, and there were two good cooks, as soon as they could cook anything . . . and then bedpans, and the guy who kept trying to get out of bed and go back home again; he said he was going home to have his aunt take care of him, if he had to walk, and home was in Missouri, so Dave had to keep him from walking all the way to Missouri, or trying to; and then another guy had thrown up his soup; and then that fellow in the bed beyond had dirtied his bed all up, and the nearby patients complained about the odor, so something had to be done about that; and then fifteen or twenty grains of aspirin again; and Dave even tried to keep charts, so he wouldn't be giving the same sailor too much aspirin, and then two other guys maybe wouldn't have had any; and then there were a couple of guys who wanted to fight, because they were both out of their heads, and it was a job to cope with them; and it was night again and wind came harder and colder, and the sea running with it, and all the gulls quacked for miles around, talking about the storm that was coming; but in the meantime one fellow had slipped outside—to try to get cool, of course—and Dave found him and brought him back; and maybe he was one of those who came down with pneumonia at last; and then, damn it, help me go to the head, I got to go to the head; and give me something to spit in; and give me something to throw up in; and I'm not going to take any more of that damn aspirin; and what about a little soup or something; and then here was another guy determined to smoke in bed when he shouldn't have been smoking at all, and so there was a big deal about that; and my back hurts so, and my back hurts so; I want to go home.

"You say there were twenty-six?"

"Around about that many."

"How many cases did you lose?"

"Never lost a case." (That was the same thing he had told me in 1937, and so he must have been right about that.)

He took the last pneumonia-ridden man back to Key West himself, holding the man in his bunk as a small ship rolled and pitched, battened deep below decks, some hours after the weak hand of a convalescent radio operator had sparked a message to the base at Key West—after the little ship had come over to the Tortugas with more help than Dave could offer. But he appears to have offered a good deal.

Memorial for
Mr. Vertigo
1949

In December, 1938, I returned to New York from a Caribbean trip, bearing with me a well-designed but dirty trinket which I had picked up in the marts of Colon. This gaud was set with red gems and synthetic diamonds.

My wife gazed doubtfully at my offering, but she was willing to have it cleaned and appraised at a convenient opportunity. The opportunity did not arise before we prepared for a dinner date the following Friday; and Irene decided that no article from her rather meager store of jewelry would look quite so well as the brooch or pendant from Panama.

The jewels were still dulled by the patina of long neglect. There was not time to have any jeweler perform a hurry-up job. Accordingly I was despatched to a drugstore on First Avenue near the narrow five-story house at 427 East 84th Street, infested by Kantors in that year.

At the prescription desk I encountered Mr. Vertigo. He appeared at my elbow like a squat wraith materialized among stacks of Kleenex. He wore a faded red mackinaw with the belt missing, and a peaked cap with a glistening visor. On the outer band of this cap, under the peaked part at the side, were fastened two celluloid buttons of the type affected by public chauffeurs, and one celluloid button bearing the name and likeness of Alf M. Landon.

The lone pharmacist was busy with an emergency prescription. I pleaded my need to a clerk; but he said he knew nothing about preparations for cleaning jewelry.

Mr. Vertigo, then a nameless troglodyte, pressed his active talons on my sleeve. "Excuse me, but what you want is a fifty-fifty solution of alcohol and spirits of ammonia."

I must have looked doubtful, even as I thanked him. "Alcohol and ammonia? Thanks—I'll try it some time."

"Not just ammonia," hissed Mr. Vertigo in the gushing whisper he employed. He had a trick of stumbling and fumbling with his words—it was not exactly a stammer—yet he still managed to utter his speech with such rapidity that you found yourself assimilating an entire sentence in retrospect.

"Not household ammonia," said Mr. Vertigo. "Spirits of ammonia. You take some of that household stuff, like you use for washing windows or where the cat went on the floor or something, and you would absolutely ruin your jewelry. Take a tip from me. I know a man who used to work for a wholesaler."

Time was fleeting, the cocktail hour beckoned, I still had to bathe and shave and dress. I capitulated. "Could the drug clerk mix it for me—alcohol and spirits of ammonia?"

Mr. Vertigo was delighted at my acquiescence. His broad, plump cheeks spread round and full and clean to the margin of his protruding ears. His nose hung like a scimitar, with chin and mouth retreated beneath the jutting nostrils. Under bushy brows his small brown eyes glinted and danced, as if agitated by elastics pulled about by his brain.

"That makes sense," he said earnestly. "You would have to wait here too long. No, the drug clerk cannot sell you pure alcohol. I know a man down the street."

He vanished into the wintry tangle of First Avenue. . . . He returned before I could do more than buy a carton of Chesterfields and examine an unappetizing display of gum, and wonder several times whether I shouldn't have better stood in line to await the pharmacist's attention.

The triumphant Mr. Vertigo brandished an eight-ounce bottle minus label; a colorless liquid frothed therein.

"How much?"

His smooth brow wrinkled for a moment, then became placid

again. "That will be, all in all, exactly two dollars. It is good stuff, Colonel. It will clean your jewelry to a point of brilliance."

I brought out my money. "But how much for your time and trouble?"

"Colonel, the two dollars includes also my time and trouble."

At home, with the aid of the solution produced by my as then unidentified friend, I polished the jewelry to a sheen which would have awakened jealousy in the hearts of all the Blacks, Starrs and Gorhams in town. Irene squealed. . . .

(She wore the pendant frequently, swearing that she would have it appraised; but she neglected to do so before, alas, the treasure was removed from her dressing-table by a wicked maid whom we acquired near Katonah the next summer, and who also acquired my daughter's baby-ring and a lighter of mine.)

The important part of this story is not the jewelry from Panama; the important substance is Mr. Vertigo, wherever he might have come from. We never knew.

We met him next, my wife and I, about 7:40 P.M. when we strayed along 84th Street, hunting for a taxicab. We found one. It was an antique model, bedight with red stripes and white side-walled tires, and it had Mr. Vertigo's photograph framed with his license. His name was actually Francis Vertigo; and one of those citation tapes was fastened across the face of the license, declaring that Mr. Vertigo had been commended for public service.

He told us about this, as he drove dangerously but skillfully toward the Marguery. It had to do with a holdup.

"Then I seen this fellow coming out of the store and it didn't look right to me and then I seen this other fellow on the corner and then I went around the block and seen this cop and I took him in my hack and we come back and by that time both these fellows had gone east on Seventy-second."

There was more to it: there was a tussle, the policeman discharged his revolver twice, but the holdup men were captured intact and unbleeding, according to Mr. Vertigo. "They had a record not just as long as your arm but as long as five arms fastened together, Captain—that was the record they had."

I accepted the demotion in proper spirit, and spent much of the evening musing on what five arms fastened together would look like, and how long they would be.

Mr. Vertigo had declared, "I'll be around," when he left us at the hotel. We didn't accept this statement literally. We were surprised, therefore, when we emerged into Park Avenue shortly before 2 A.M. and were pounced upon by Mr. Vertigo.

"I figured I would be around," he said, "like I told you. I figured I would be around just before two."

"How did you know what time we would be coming out?"

He said negligently that he figured it would be maybe just before two o'clock; later we reviewed our conversation of a previous hour, to see whether we had given him a clue. It seemed that we had not. He owned a peculiar antic wisdom which could be perceived but never explained.

On the way home, Irene talked of a minor soiree we were scheduling during the following week; her plans entailed the use of a punch-bowl. Our solitary punch-bowl had gone to destruction in October, bursting like a crystal bomb amid Finnish shrieks, and we had not replaced it. Now, with Christmas threatening ahead of us, we could not afford to.

"You want a punch-bowl?" said Mr. Vertigo, without turning away from the wheel. "O.K., I will bring you one. What night did you say—Tuesday? Who you planning to have *do* your party, anyway?"

We discovered that to *do* a party, in Mr. Vertigo's lingo, referred to the serving of drinks, the manufacture of hors d'oeuvres, and such chores. Irene said weakly that she thought our own couple might prove adequate, with perhaps the assistance of Luella, a pinch-hitter engaged on such occasions.

"Do not get Luella," said Mr. Vertigo. "I will bring you my cousin Marie—I mean she is kind of a cousin—and she will do your party up brown. And she can furnish the punch-bowl and anything else you want."

Irene was noncommittal; but it happened that I was slightly

inebriated on this occasion, and wholly entranced by Mr. Vertigo. I forthwith told him to proceed; and we received a telephone call the following afternoon from a woman who uttered Arabic, and then there was silence.

Irene insisted on engaging Luella anyway. It was well that she did: the party kept growing and growing. People had relatives visiting them for the holidays; a troop of old friends from the Midwest came to town unexpectedly. . . .

Cousin Marie and a hideous cut-glass punch-bowl arrived at a conveniently early hour on the important day. Cousin Marie was as hatchet-faced and erect as Mr. Vertigo was round-shouldered and plumply simian; she spoke in accents undiagnosed by us. She changed into a respectable uniform and promptly commenced activities below-stairs.

When Irene came up to dress, her eyes were large. "That woman is making the most incredible things."

"For instance what?"

"For instance chives butterflies."

"What in God's name are chives butterflies?"

"That," said Irene, "is what Cousin Marie calls them."

Not the least of the wonders bespoke upon this evening was the appearance of Mr. Vertigo himself, busily obtrusive, and clad in a white coat stiff with starch but with a huge submerged coffee stain ingrained in the goods on one sleeve. How or when he obtained access to the house I do not know. I met him, to my astonishment, in the library after dinner, shortly after our houseman Carl had appeared with the brandy, and after I had requested that a box of cigars should be brought. It was Mr. Vertigo who brought them.

He whispered, when he lighted my cigar for me, "How do you like my Cousin Marie, Colonel?"

I was pleased to accept this reinstatement to my former rank; but he never awarded me a military title thereafter—not even when we met, in uniform, some thousands of miles away from East 84th Street.

Mr. Vertigo toted up a mildly appalling bill. He came to

the door and rang the bell and presented the bill in person, two nights later. I paid without a murmur, for Irene was still entranced at the mere recollection of the chives butterflies; and from then on she insisted that Cousin Marie should *do* our parties, although we gave only a few that year; and we were duly regretful when Cousin Marie announced that she was moving to Hartford to live with some other cousins, in March.

Mr. Vertigo did not move away. He dwelt, according to his own testimony, "far up on Madison Avenue," and there was a Mrs. Vertigo whom we promptly named Vertiga although we never met her. There were several children; we referred to these as the Vertigreases.

From then on we found Mr. Vertigo active in our lives, up until the time we moved down to our Florida house in the summer of 1940.

He gave up cab-driving. There was some kind of financial tangle, replete with summonses and suits. I could never understand whether Mr. Vertigo owned his own cab, or whether he was an employee of a small fleet, or whether he leased the cab on shares. He explained often, but—

"Then you see this fellow he had the cab before but there was a mortgage on it and then the fellow at the garage said he would require him to pay off at least two hundred dollars before February and you can see what a hole that put him in and me also. I do not like to call any man a liar but I must confess he could tell a lie not as long as your arm but as long as five arms fastened together."

There was the matter of the Seth Thomas clock. It had belonged to my grandparents in Iowa. It would run no longer, and a repair man in a progressive shop insisted that the works were so outmoded, so antique and generally cheap and useless, that it was impossible to repair them.

This clock was mentioned within Mr. Vertigo's hearing, and he demanded the instrument at once. He knew a man, he said. This man was away down on Second Avenue near St.

Marks; more usually the men he knew were on the upper East Side.

Mr. Vertigo and the clock vanished together, and neither reappeared until the end of the week. The clock seemed to have been scrubbed, and its moldy but handsome walnut case had been enhanced by a coat of varnish which I deplored. But it would run and it would tick; it would strike not only the hours but the half-hours and quarter-hours as well, which it had never been known to do before. It kept up such an incessant din that it drove the family mad.

Irene insisted that the clock should be banished to my workroom at 149 East 61st Street, where it spanked away with increasing melody until one spring afternoon when it growled like a dog, struck nineteen times, growled again, and stopped ticking and striking—I fear forever.

. . . Cannel coal? For some reason there was a brief famine in cannel coal that late winter. We loved to burn it in our grates, but none of the dealers could supply us. Mr. Vertigo could supply us.

He came to our door with two colored youths who drove a battered truck, and they unloaded cannel coal in quantity. Our small basement space was cluttered with sooty burlap sacks. I had failed to remind Mr. Vertigo that our lease on that house would be terminated with the coming of summer. I cannot remember exactly what we did with all the left-over cannel coal. We were taking a house for the summer in Westchester, and certainly didn't want to cart a quarter-ton of this oily product all the way up there. I remember trying to give it away; but probably several sacks were left for the mystification of incoming tenants.

When we came back to Manhattan, it was to an older, shabbier house at 522 East 87th Street, and in this we installed our own belongings. The East 84th Street house had been leased to us furnished; certainly the rented things were more handsome than our own at that stage of the game.

Mr. Vertigo displayed his disapproval by an awful silence

when first he came stalking through rooms at the new place. How he trailed us there, I have not the faintest idea. We had not given him our new address—indeed we did not know it ourselves when we moved away from 84th Street; but here he was, buzzing at the front door bell, and puzzling our new cook with a request for Mr. MacCameron.

He had called me Mr. Cameron or Mr. Canton at times before; but this was the first time that I was designated as a member of that peculiar sept, the MacCamerons. Later he confused alliteratively the names of myself and of my then publishers, the firm Coward-McCann. At Mr. Vertigo's request I had given him a copy of my novel, *The Noise of Their Wings,* which came out during the previous season. Since the names MacKinlay and McCann both appear in proximity on the backbone of the book, Mr. Vertigo might be pardoned for thenceforth referring to me alternately as Mr. MacCameron and Mr. McCann. He finally settled on the latter; yet when he came to write me, after years had passed, he had my name spelled correctly on the envelope, and the letter was forwarded from New York to my Florida home and thence to the ETO.

It reached me at the 305th Bomb Group, at a base in the Midlands called Chelveston. "Dear Friend, no doubt you will greet with surprise the knowledge that now I am a soldier of Uncle Sam and serving to the best of my ability with the Eight Air Force. Let me ask you and the misses and the kiddies to drop me a line at this faraway place which I cannot tell you where I am but the APO appears above. How are things back home? It would surprise you to know what privations is undergone by the men who serve in foreign lands; but their *morall* is pretty O.K. I cannot say as much for their *morrals.* Ha."

(I take it that the censor never read this letter. He would not have passed willingly such calumny against the personnel of the Eighth.)

"When you are sitting comfortably at home remember those who serve in foreign fields and think your gratitude to them.

We could also use a little package now and then like cigarettes
and candy and what have you. Hint."

Since I, together with a good share of the 305th, had at
that reading just returned from a tussle with Papa Göring's
boys over the north of France, I didn't appreciate the picture
of State-side indolence which Mr. Vertigo had drawn. My
little playmates to whom I displayed the letter took a very
dim view of his attitude, and were also incensed because, from
the address, we learned that Mr. Vertigo was a member of
the 306th Bomb Group at Thurleigh, adjacent to our base.

It was one of those conflicts of juxtaposition which cannot
correctly be called a conflict. Certainly the 305th was not
fighting the 306th—but they might have been at times, if one
judged from the mutual attitude expressed.

I wondered whether perhaps Mr. Vertigo had not been
clobbered during the interval that elapsed since he wrote the
letter. Two aircraft had collided in a close pattern above the
border of our field only a week before. Flames had shone,
wreckage had hurtled, purple smoke had knotted on high.
Might not Mr. Vertigo (a quaint tail-gunner, perhaps called
"Pop" by younger members of the crew) have offered the
substance of his life in such a last erratic frying?

His own letter suggested that he had not done so. He was
a T-5, and T-5s were not commonly members of combat crews.
Usually the enlisted men were staff sergeants or tech sergeants.
I shook off the protestations of friends who thought I was
crazy to travel over to Thurleigh just for the purpose of
looking up such a limp-witted joker as Mr. Vertigo must
be. . . .

They did not know, they did not know. They did not understand the glorious past which was his. They did not know
about the private automobile delivery service instigated by Mr.
Vertigo, who was alarmed at the extravagant price demanded
by a neighborhood garage for the delivery and pickup of the
two automobiles we foolishly maintained in town. He had

suggested that I pay only the regular price for storage, and leave the pickup and delivery to him.

When May Greenwell, the children's governess, left the front door to deliver Layne to the Brearley and Timmy to the Town School, she could count on the gray coupe's being there, flush against the curb, its windshield well-rubbed, its tires unscraped. Seldom did we witness the going and comings of Mr. Vertigo. He moved as a parcel of elves through a Grimm legend, he came secretly and silently and in proper season.

The fact that his charges completely overshadowed the original garage cost was something I preferred to forget.

The boys did not know, they did not know—they could not guess about the cannel coal, nor about Cousin Marie, nor about the Seth Thomas clock which struck and growled, nor about the hot spinach and the bundled-out maid.

(Our cook suffered a death in her family, and departed in haste. We took in her stead the first woman the agency sent us, and in foolhardy fashion did not check upon this woman's references. She was a psycho, pure and simple, as the cops call it. Irene and I went off to Washington, and the governess was alone with the children. Dinner was a long time in coming, and our offspring, momentarily unsupervised, invaded the kitchen in belligerent hunger, demanding food. The cook's reply was to snatch up a kettle of spinach from the gas range and hurl it at my daughter. Fortunately Layne was twelve years old, and agile. She ducked, and missed the kettle and most of the spinach, which fortunately was not boiling yet. Layne emitted a roar of anguish, and Timmy, aged seven, thoughtfully applied the butt of his toy gun to the maid's shin, forcing her into retreat. What would have happened just then I do not know, if Mr. Vertigo had not appeared with the family collie, whom he had gigoloed to Carl Schurz Park. Miss Greenwell was above-stairs when the brawl occurred; she hastened down in time to find an enraged Mr. Vertigo bodily tossing the dangerous domestic into the street. He went up himself, packed her bags after a fashion, and deposited them outside the door

a few minutes later. His bill that week included: "Taking out
Pal .50 cents. Putting out maid .50 cents.")

. . . They did not know the ravages of the private furniture
upholstering he managed, nor the pipe repairs he arranged.
He knew a man on upper Lexington Avenue, and this artisan
shaped the most beautiful hand-cut stems I ever saw, and
drilled them with a tiny hole through which I might not bite.
The fact that Mr. Vertigo's man lost or preëmpted three of the
best pipes was something I had to pass by. His workmanship
was excellent; the price, for once, was agreeable.

They did not know Mr. Vertigo. . . . I found him now behind a squadron supply counter at Thurleigh. He was a paddlefoot undeniably, and it seemed that I might have spared myself
any worry about a hero's death. Still, I could never quite get rid
of the lurking notion that he was marked for sudden and
outlandish extinction.

Before making myself known, it was interesting to wait amid
shadows and gabbling sergeants, there in Flight Equipment
Supply, and watch Mr. Vertigo functioning.

He had not slipped at all. His military accomplishments
persisted in the same spirit of mystery as those of his civil
career. A visiting Wing Commander, one of Harris's staff, was
intent on flying a daylight mission, and was being equipped
for the fray. He was suspicious of the American-style parachute
harness which they tried to fit upon him, and I didn't blame
him much. For long missions over the North Sea, I had
managed to wangle one of the RAF quick-release-type harnesses. The American webbing was commonly secured either by
heavy snaps or by little interlocking sockets and pegs: you
had to twist like crazy in order to get them free, in order
to get yourself out of the harness. In an emergency this took
up time and offered difficulties.

With the RAF type, on the other hand, the straps were all
anchored together under a movable metal plate on one's belly
or chest. You spun the plate around, gave it a quick blow
with your fist, and the whole thing flew apart instantly.

The Wing Commander regarded an American harness with loathing; sergeants shook their heads.

"We haven't got any of those Raf harnesses," they said. It was good to see Mr. Corporal Vertigo taking charge of what might have become an embarrassing inter-Allied situation. He said that he knew a man over in another supply hut, and he disappeared. He was back, and with the desired RAF harness, before the visiting Wing Commander had done much more than adjust the loose straps of his Mae West.

Mr. T-5 Vertigo's offering was inspected gratefully. "Wizard. Perfectly wizard. But— The pin, you know: the safety pin?"

Those plates usually had such a pin, attached to a small chain, and it would keep that plate from sliding around into the release position when you didn't want it to—which might be when you were dangling under your chute some five miles above the drink. In this case both pin and chain were missing.

But Mr. Vertigo got out a GI handkerchief and wound it tightly into a little khaki-colored rope. He showed the RAF officer how to tuck this stuffing between the two sections of the plate, winding it all around, with one end dangling free. It worked like a charm: the plate could not possibly turn, so long as the twisted-up handkerchief was mashed into place. One quick pull brought the handkerchief free: the plate could be turned and swatted in a second.

"Wizard!" exclaimed the Wing Commander, with appreciation exploding in his blue eyes. In this festive moment I made myself known to Mr. Vertigo. Our reunion must have been something to affect the toughest soul among those onlookers— 306th personnel though they were.

It was arranged that I should entertain Mr. Vertigo in London. He was to telephone me at a number which I gave him, and let me know as soon as he had been granted a forty-eight-hour furlough. He had never been up to London, and greatly desired to see Buckingham Palace, the Tower, the Lord Mayor, and a place which he designated as West Minister Abbey. He hoped also that he might encounter the King.

Eventually the date and hour were set. Mr. Corporal Vertigo was to meet me at a small supper club called Slavia, not far from Selfridge's store, and one which many who read this may recall. Here enlisted men could conceivably be entertained by those of us who wore officers' uniforms. I had done it before, and anticipated no RHIP difficulties.

What with double daylight time, afternoon was still with us although the clock insisted that it was night. While awaiting my guest I sat in the bar and fell into conversation with a flak-happy major and a lieutenant colonel, both intent on tasting the fleshpots of the battered metropolis to the fullest. They had wads of pay in their pockets, but lamented that they had been unable to secure what they deemed proper transportation.

The lieutenant colonel had tried to make off with a staff car for the evening, in the face of all sorts of possible dangers, but was thwarted. Two handsome London ladies, most enthusiastically described—veritable houris, if these officers could be believed—also entered into the scheme of their planning. Both gentlemen cursed the taxicab situation, and said that they would be condemned before they would submit to another night of such mixed-up ramblings and sorties while trying to find themselves the necessary taxicabs at proper intervals.

Mr. Corporal Vertigo arrived in the meantime, and I presented him fondly to the officers, who were not at all snobbish about it. They even pressed drinks on this eager little man, and alluded to their troubles in his presence.

He left the bar some time later. I thought at first that he had gone to the men's room; but becoming apprehensive when he did not return, I went back there and could find him no place. I looked upstairs on the dance floor. Mr. Vertigo was not dancing, although a great many lieutenants and pilot officers and even a few sergeants were cavorting gaily.

I came down into the hallway at last, to meet Mr. Vertigo ducking in through the front door.

"You tell them I have got a jeep, Mr. McCann," he said.

Where he got that jeep, whether he stole it, just how he promoted and maneuvered or bargained—just what devious chicaneries, in all that muddle of stringency and discipline and directives— These are speculations which must be left to a better imagination than mine.

The major and the lieutenant colonel stood in admiration on the curb. They walked around and around the jeep. They shook their heads; they tried to question Mr. Vertigo, and he offered complex explanations which didn't mean a thing.

The major gave Mr. Vertigo a five-pound note.

"It is until tomorrow morning," said Mr. Vertigo. "Then I got to give it back to this fellow. At least by eight."

"That'll be all right," said the lieutenant colonel. And to the major, "Charley, you'll have to drive this thing."

"Not me, Slewfoot," said Major Charley with firmness. "I'm going to be busy with my babe."

"Well, I'm going to be busy with *my* babe," said the lieutenant colonel.

I looked at Mr. Vertigo. I was not disappointed. He kept nodding, and flapping his cap against his thigh.

"Do you desire me to drive it for you, sir?" he offered, and they fell upon him with cries.

Not even in the British Museum, I suppose, could one find a blueprint of their meanderings during the succeeding night. Be it remembered that blackout was in force as soon as it grew purely dark—that the byways of London Town are extensively puzzling, even to the natives—that Mr. Corporal Vertigo had never been in London before—

We had one more drink. Mr. Vertigo whispered for forgiveness.

"I got to do a favor to these officers, Mr. McCann. You understand that?"

"Of course," and I bade them Godspeed when they went driving off through the dusk with a pattern of searchlights fanning the skies ahead of them, and sirens blending in a kind of 11 P.M. overture.

I did not see Mr. Vertigo again while I was in the ETO,
then or later. It might as well be said now that I never saw
him again. Lest the reader believe that somewhere in the
procession of fabled spooks that drift about the ancient town
from Berkeley Square to Bloomsbury, from Chelsea to the East
India Docks and back again . . . lest the reader believe that
in this legendary pageant of fabulous Clanking Men and Grey
Ladies and Whispering Cavaliers, there now drives a phantom
jeep containing Mr. Vertigo and two young Air Force officers
and two extremely well-stacked babes . . . lest I be accused
of sentimental romancing, I must relate a conversation which
occurred in Kingston, Jamaica.

When I first returned from overseas, I found my family
ensconced in a Fifth Avenue apartment: the plagues and jovi-
alities of Manhattan homesteading would no longer be ours.
Still, we rather expected to hear from Mr. Vertigo one way
or another. Perhaps he might appear at the rear door, proffering
tenderloin steaks or nylons. . . .

He didn't come, but he was still a figment of our family
balladry to be invoked at evening sessions round the fireside.
We wondered about Vertiga and the Vertigreases. Perhaps they
were all long since gone to Hartford, to dwell in harmony
with Cousin Marie and tribes of other kinds of cousins, amid
cut-glass punch-bowls brimming with alcohol and spirits of
ammonia mixed fifty-fifty.

Then, not too long ago, my wife and I went on a cruise,
and dallied in Kingston on our way back. At a table in the
Myrtle Bank patio, a shipboard acquaintance introduced us to
a charming gentleman: a Britisher of importance in the Consu-
lar Service or the Foreign Office, or something. The shipboard
acquaintance, expatiating as such people will, introduced me
as the man solely responsible for *The Best Years of Our
Lives,* which point might conceivably be argued by Robert
Sherwood, William Wyler and Samuel Goldwyn.

"Ah, yes," said the gray-haired Englishman, ordering gin-

and-lime. "*The Best Years* and all that. I believe we have had a mutual acquaintance," and he began to chuckle.

"Have we indeed?"

"Most certainly. Most amazing chap! I encountered him several times when he was an airplane steward for a small South American line, and I was traveling about by air. We held long conversations on numerous occasions—rather I should say that *he* held the conversations. I believe you employed him at one time in some sort of domestic capacity? He happened to hear me discussing the cinema with someone else, and he told me of the association—told me a great many things, in fact. But of course they're rather well gone out of my mind, now."

However he could still chuckle about them, and did. Irene and I pondered uncomfortably, trying to guess just what bizarre revelations Mr. Vertigo had indulged in.

We drank a toast to Mr. Vertigo in gin-and-lime and daiquiris; Irene said that it would be almost worth returning to South America at once, and by air, if indeed we might have a meeting with Mr. Vertigo.

The old Britisher shook his head. "I am afraid that's quite impossible. You see, the commercial airliner—the one in which he served as steward— Yes, it was in the Andes; there were several bad accidents about that time. Nobody got out, of course."

The news of Mr. Vertigo's shattering demise cast a gloom over us. Nevertheless, wherever he may be now, we have become convinced that he is in a good situation and in good hands. Undoubtedly in whatever strange plane or dimension to which he has been projected, he knows a man. We pray that his celestial activities may resound through an eternity not as long as your arm but as long as five arms fastened together.

Two Guys from the Twenty-third 1950

Last night about 11:30 P.M. (maybe it was night-before-last, or during the preceding week, or any night you care to name) a vigorous young man, bareheaded, with curly blondish hair and wearing a gold-checked lumberjack, came up the stairway out of New York's east side IRT station at 103rd Street and Lexington Avenue, and walked briskly north.

Concealed beneath the tails of the plaid woolen fabric swung a loaded .38 Special revolver. It was not alone the possession of this gun which gave the man a calm security in a shadowy neighborhood. His pride and his purpose stemmed from a sound physique (5 ft. 10½, 190 lbs.), a keen mind, a pride in his occupation. His name was William Klepper.

An hour earlier, Bill Klepper had sprawled asleep on a comfortable bed in Stuyvesant Town—Apartment 1-A, at 521 East 14th Street. Bill is twenty-seven years old and, like most other young men his age, a war veteran. But he has always had trouble sleeping daytimes when working at night. He tried to nap during the afternoon. He gave it up as a bad job and, with his pretty wife Dottie and plump two-and-a-half-year-old daughter Bunny, Bill arose and drove to the Bronx to call on his parents.

The Kleppers returned home before dusk, coursing swiftly down the East River Drive in their secondhand Oldsmobile. Bill passed two red lights on the way. Dottie admonished him about this, but it didn't do any good, it will never do any good. When you are accustomed to passing red lights frequently in your workaday life the habit is strong in you.

Dottie prepared dinner; they ate heartily and well, and Bunny demanded to witness a television show before she was put to bed. She and her yawning dad enjoyed a program while Dottie did the dishes.

. . . Dottie woke Bill up about 10:30. She had a snack ready for him: ham, biscuits, left-over salad and plenty of coffee. When he had dressed and eaten, Bill took his gun from a secret hiding place and his cartridges from their own nook beyond a little girl's prying fingers. He loaded the gun, belted it on, kissed Dottie, kidded her about her figure. He banged briskly out of the apartment, wondering as always whether the new baby, due to arrive in January, would be a boy or a girl.

Meanwhile, far up in Apartment 6-E at the Park Chester— 2121 St. Raymond's Avenue in the Bronx—another larger, balder young man, also twenty-seven years old, was leaving for work. He was Klepper's partner, Edwin Jackson, gray-eyed and freckled-faced, called alternately Eddie or Jakey by his friends. Ed's wife, Virginia, is an attractive blonde. The Jacksons have a daughter also—Barbara Ann, going on four. Like the Kleppers they are proud of their apartment and their television set; like the Kleppers they have a safe hideout for Eddie's gun and cartridges.

Eddie took Barbara Ann to visit bears and monkeys that afternoon, but he had it all over Bill Klepper: Eddie could sleep blissfully in the daytime, and did so before marching off to the zoo. Virginia fixed lamb stew for dinner, and they enjoyed that, and they enjoyed the cards they played after Barbara Ann had sung herself to sleep in the bedroom.

Even while Klepper's train was grinding north through black tunnels, Jackson's train was bowling south. Big Ed, just under six feet tall but weighing well over two hundred pounds, lounged in his neat brown suit in a corner of the car, with a magazine in his hand. He was on the job even so.

Some ten minutes away from the 103rd Street station, his

attention was directed to the opposite end of the car. Two
ill-favored men, both obviously drunk, were arguing loudly and
shouting obscenities. Other passengers, shocked or frightened
by the tumult, shrank away. Jackson put down his magazine
and moved forward.

"Shut up, both of you."

One of the men tried to lurch to his feet, but Jakey shoved
him back. "I'm a police officer. Pipe down and behave yourselves. Otherwise I'll haul you off this train and stick you in
the jug."

The men turned abject and apologetic. Jackson kept his
eye on them until they got off at the next station. His own
destination was just beyond. It was dangerously late, he discovered from a glance at his watch, and he sprinted up the
same stairs where his partner had walked a few minutes before.

The trivial scene on the subway train was not an instance
in which Jackson was throwing his weight around. He proceeds,
off duty and in civilian clothes, in exactly the same manner
he would proceed when in uniform and on duty. He is and
was expected to conduct himself thus, and so are all the other
eighteen thousand members of the New York City Police Department.

A cop is never off duty, for practical purposes, unless he
is on Sick Report. That's the reason the revolvers are kept
at home, whatever the risk. A policeman may not run down
to the corner delicatessen for a pound of coffee his wife requested, unless he has his loaded .38 and his shield with him.
"Carried on person at all times"—it means just what it says
in the regulations.

Patrolman William A. McLoughlin, Shield No. 4750, 87th Precinct. At about 11 P.M., April 28, 1948, off duty, in civilian
clothes, observed and apprehended two suspicious youths who
had committed a burglary in a warehouse at 143 Grand Street
Extension, Brooklyn. . . .

Patrolman William R. Cash, Shield No. 14495 and James C. Hooey, Shield No. 19707, 28th Precinct. . . . At about 9 P.M., May 2, 1947, off duty, in civilian clothes, observed and kept under surveillance, two armed men, acting in a suspicious manner. The officers intercepted the suspects in front of 22 West 99th Street, Manhattan, in which vicinity the two felons had planned to commit a homicide. When ordered to drop their weapons one of the gunmen attempted to shoot the officers, whereupon Patrolman Hooey shot and mortally wounded him. . . .

These quotes from actual citations tell the story; it is a chorus constantly recurring. Take the six posthumous Medal of Honor awards announced in June, 1948. Of those six medals, two honor the memory of patrolmen who went into action while off duty and in civilian clothes. For instance, Patrolman Winthrop S. Paris, Shield No. 10600, was spending a quiet afternoon in his own home at 936 Stebbins Avenue, the Bronx. This courageous young Negro officer went into an adjoining apartment to arrest an armed burglar, and suffered fatal wounds in the encounter. But Paris took care of the burglar before he died.

When he reached the police station at 177 East 104th Street, Ed Jackson hurried up to the second-floor locker room at the rear. Bill Klepper was nearly dressed, and fastening his shield carefully on the breast of his blouse. Their lockers were well apart and out of sight of each other; they shouted bits of personal and family information back and forth while Eddie removed his clothes and struggled into his uniform.

Other men were constantly chattering together, banging metal doors. People were kidding tall Patrolman "Pop" Gunn, who had recently come back from Sick Report with a newly healed gash and stitch marks on his skull.

"You get your alarms written up, Bill?"

"Yeh."

The men trotted down the steep old stairway to the Back

Room where Sergeant Higgins was preparing to turn out the platoon. The police formed in long ranks, facing a wide doorway. Higgins, a poker-faced veteran, called the roll and gave whatever specific instructions were necessary. Several men stepped from the ranks as he called their names, to receive slips of paper with the detail of jobs to be done, or notifications to be delivered. There were general instructions . . . employees of one small factory in Sector One were out on strike, but not picketing. The man on that post and the two officers in the sector car were warned to keep a close eye out for loiterers. . . . Nurses who lived in a dormitory at one of the hospitals in Sector Four had complained that they were being followed when they came from the Madison Avenue corner. (There was a little laughter about this.) Watch out for suspicious characters in the vicinity. . . . *Right face. Forward, march.* An officer on house duty held the doors open for the double column to proceed to the sidewalk. It was three-and-one-half minutes after twelve o'clock.

Among precinct personnel there are three tours. In the traffic divisions the hours are arranged differently. A precinct cop is either on the Day Tour (8 A.M. to 4 P.M.), the Four-to-Twelve, or the Late Tour (12 midnight to 8 A.M.). He serves six days or nights of duty on one of these tours, has forty-eight hours off, and then reports for the succeeding tour. Thus within some three weeks he has worked completely around the clock. The old-timers remark that this is a lot better than elder days when you got thirty-six hours off between tours. You can't do much, when you have only thirty-six hours off and must catch your quota of sleep; but you can relax a little on the Forty-eight. Morale in the Department is high, as a result. The men believe Mayor O'Dwyer and ex-Commissioner Wallander to be responsible for this and other satisfactory innovations, and revere them accordingly.

Jackson found Klepper as the men dissolved from formation, and the two officers moved through dimness toward the northwest corner of Third Avenue and 104th. Crews of several other cars came along, as well as individuals going toward solitary duty on foot patrol posts in eastern regions. Other cars would change crews back at Lexington Avenue, in order to minimize traffic difficulties.

Car 322 arrived, southbound on Third Avenue, and halted in front of a lighted saloon at the corner. The officers finishing up the Four-to-Twelve climbed quickly out, laden with their sticks, gathering up a stray flashlight, reaching behind the seat for their folded raincoats. It had poured briefly in the afternoon, but the autumn night was clear now.

"Hiya."

"How you doing, Ruby?"

"What you say, Ed?"

Quickly they examined the car inside and out. Each team is responsible for the condition of its motor vehicle; no team wants to accept the blame for a scratch or a bump which someone else has put there. Car 322 was a pristine joy, back in those faraway days of its first duty in March, 1949—seat covers untorn, fenders unmarred, pistons purring softly. Now, with something like sixty thousand miles of service behind it, Car 322 may no longer stand out on dress parade. There have been minor accidents, bumps and abrasions without number. Three crews of patrolmen cannot shove a green-and-white Ford around elevated pillars, among trucks and pushcarts and buses, twenty-four hours a day for more than a year and a half, without the experience leaving its wounds on them and on the vehicle they share.

If any Plymouth and Ford coupes in any city take the constant beating the radio motor patrol cars of the New York Police Department take, then I don't know where. Three tours each twenty-four hours—a mileage of from twenty-five to fifty miles picked up in each tour . . . one hundred fresh miles every twenty-four hours is the average in the 23rd Precinct. Naturally certain repairs and maintenance must be performed while on the job, but they are necessarily minor. You can change a spark-plug at 110th Street and Fifth Avenue, and

still hope to show up at a sudden Signal Thirty at 96th
Street and First Avenue; but you can't grind your valves or
take down your transmission. Car 322 has been in the garage
several times for overhauls of varying periods. Ordinarily speaking, for twenty-four hours every day and night its hood is hot,
the vapor is puffing from the exhaust.

Is there a boneyard or Valhalla where the remains of NYPD
patrol cars find their eventual rusty haven? It may be that
the mottled ghosts of the cars' temporary and permanent occupants slither there in the dark of the moon and slink amid
the tatters . . . a pretty child choking on the button she had
swallowed, a child strangling while Jackson screeched his way
across town to Flower Hospital, while Klepper administered
what first aid he could . . . the Puerto Rican with seven knife
gashes in him, his bowels oozing, bubbles bursting from the
hole in his right lung . . . a silent hard-faced man who bent
down suddenly and tried to pull from his shoe the tiny automatic they had missed when they searched him: people like
these, scores of them.

Klepper and Jackson drove south to 103rd, west to Lex,
north to 104th, joining the spasmodic parade of other patrol
cars past the House. The sergeant stood on the curb.

"Car 322 O.K., sir." They flung him their salutes. He returned the salutes and waved them on.

(Klepper was appointed to the Department in February,
1946; Jackson graduated from the Academy in April, 1947. By
this time there seems nothing strange to them about saluting
a sergeant, though Klepper was a sergeant himself, in the Air
Force, after he was washed out of pilot training for dangerous
flying. Jackson won a battlefield promotion to a lieutenancy
in France while serving with the 106th Infantry Division.)

The car turned north around the corner. Their first concern
was with the heart of their sector, Lexington Avenue above
106th Street. Everything seemed ominously quiet. Those ten
blocks, except for the regions traversed through new housing

projects, are studded with bars. They close perforce at 3 A.M. Sunday morning, at 4 A.M. every other morning. This was a weekday night. There would be nearly four hours for danger to develop amid the glare of signs, the slopping of rum and *cerveza*, the screech of Spanish songs, the horrid smells from the washrooms.

Bill and Ed now roamed Third Avenue, inspecting the store fronts as they went. (It seems to them both sometimes that their minds are a busy map, cooked by the humidity of summer nights, or iced by a dirty wind. No, not maps . . . but each mind a kind of bas-relief of the precinct in general, their sector in particular . . . a molded exhibit on a panoramic table. Their brains are adhesive in studied recollection where every scrap of paper and splintered crate is splotched indelibly.)

Gratings over the store fronts made their dark frescoes against the patrolmen's consciousness—but only because the panes of glass were gleaming solid behind them. No glass, no dirty sheen behind the diamond pattern of rusty grilles? They would halt where the glass was shattered, where someone had broken in. But not in this hour: the glass was solid on Third Avenue as yet.

They poked west along 106th, the radio sputtering harmlessly. There was work in the 1st Precinct, work down in the 8th . . . a job, a real job, a shooting far up in the 32nd Precinct . . . these remote demands were no concern of Patrolmen Jackson and Klepper. Their job was the immediate, the actual, the 23rd Precinct.

This precinct stretches from 86th to 116th Street, from Fifth Avenue to the East River. Thus it is thirty blocks long, and some eight blocks wide at its widest. There are well over two hundred square blocks in the area; the bulk of these have contributed more than their quota of homicides, suicides, and assorted felonies through the years since they began swarming with primitive, undernourished, ill-housed, ill-taught people in brown skins.

Jackson and Klepper are veterans not merely of Sector Six,

but of the neon-stained avenues that trail through the three
sectors on the west. Until the designation of a new sector, they
had the "Avenue Car"—an extra vehicle sent wisely by Captain
Savage to patrol those regions where the bars were thickest;
and consequently where the citizens were, as the cops say,
jumping.

"They'll be jumping tonight." You hear that prognostication
often around the House, especially toward the end of the
week and more especially in those times when relief checks
have just been doled out. There is a firm belief, also embraced
by the entire personnel of the 23rd, that a full moon means
ructions. Many can quote chapter and verse to prove it, and
do so most impressively.

They were jumping right now, at 108th and Lexington. Car
322 had just turned north when suddenly there appeared a
tangle of struggling figures in front of a bar. Jackson's foot
went down on the accelerator, the car jumped like a cat and
landed with a crunch of brakes, fairly on the outskirts of the
twisting mob.

Three people were the core and cause of this disturbance:
a young man in a cheap tan suit, a burly black in overalls, a
gaunt gypsyish character with a mustache and sideburns.
Klepper's door banged open, he dove into the group.

One man had just fallen to the sidewalk, but he was kicking
and slugging at space even as he sprawled there. Klepper
collared two of the brawlers, and his collaring was done quite
literally: he jerked the young man in the tan suit to his feet,
hauling him up by his necktie, and meanwhile the tough
fingers of Klepper's left hand had clamped on the necktie of
the man with the mustache and sideburns.

The burly black-faced gladiator was attempting to escape,
but he didn't get far. Jackson, speeding past the front fender
of the car, nailed him by his belt and the back of his shirt.
The crowd—wild-eyed men, squealing young whores, and a
few pitiful children—scattered at the impact of the patrolmen's
arrival and then swelled close once more.

The proprietor of the saloon was out on the sidewalk, lifting his hands in deprecation, laughing a little.

"Wha' hoppened?" demanded Jackson in conversational tones calculated to soothe, but keeping a firm grip on his prisoner nevertheless.

The proprietor grinned amiably. "They just start to fight."

"Which ones? Him?" He pointed to the youth in the tan suit, whose mouth had been bloodied. "And this fellow?"

"No. I don't know—"

"Not him?"

"No. I guess he go away."

"Knife, Ed," said Klepper. He had his hands full, restraining his prisoners, both of them sobbing and snorting. He kicked a knife toward Jackson with his foot; Eddie picked it up: a switch-blade, all right, and opened. But fortunately the keen steel was not greased with blood. Had they been a moment later—

"Who belongs to this?"

No one knew—least of all the three men who had been tussling. Jackson and Klepper searched them thoroughly . . . no guns, no more knives, nothing. Familiar faces appeared in the crowd: a barber from Third Avenue . . . the officers knew his name: Paul. But Paul could tell them nothing. He was just walking along . . . one of the waiters from Luis's Bar at 110th and Park . . . but it seemed that he too was just going past.

There was that foul-mouthed talkative little prostitute, Maria; she was forever hanging around that corner. She admired these policemen because they helped her little brother and took him to the hospital when he fell off the rear end of a bus last year. Maria lectured volubly, waving her red-nailed hands, hoisting the satin shoulder straps inside her sheer yellow blouse as she gabbled. She told them nothing—exactly nothing.

Who started the fight? Each man swore that someone else

attacked him. Each contended that he was merely defending himself.

No one but a rookie in the 23rd would ever have considered an arrest here. No case, when the matter came into Court. Merely a waste of time, energy, and the municipality's money, together with a little increment of terse censure. No policeman enjoys hearing that.

"Let's chase the whole bunch, Eddie."

The crowd scattered and fled, some of them laughing; one or two, of Communist persuasion, muttered about police brutality. The starved white-toothed children capered away in glee. The erstwhile contestants were headed in different directions, and warned against returning on this night.

Only the young fellow with the bloodied mouth insisted on arguing. He wanted to go back into the bar. He hadn't finished his drink. He was a free citizen; he had a right—

"Listen, Free Citizen," growled Klepper, "you're just lucky you're not in the jug."

The young man tottered off, mumbling curses. The officers watched him go. They strolled inside the door of the saloon and glanced coolly about. The few people at the bar settled down, drinking and conversing with that self-conscious probity which nearly all of humanity wears when under the eyes of the police.

The switch-blade went into the glove compartment—the usual repository for such trophies. The men got into their car, they went on with their job.

Men in the cars, as well as those on foot patrol, must telephone the House at stated intervals in order to receive instructions about work allotted to them. These calls are staggered so that the switchboard will not be overtaxed at any given time. Jackson and Klepper had been ordered to ring at fifty minutes after every hour throughout the tour.

12:50 A.M. is now approaching . . . they visit the nearest signal box. It happens to be Box 2339, fastened against a building wall at the southwest corner of Lexington and 112th Street. The car makes a quick U and swings close to the west curb of Lex. Klepper gets out, pencil and paper in hand; he opens the box and takes up the receiver.

"Car 322. Patrolman Klepper."

Jackson sits observing the long street, splotched with its bar-grill signs, studded with moving figures; he is watching for trouble, as always. Bill Klepper returns to the car.

"Go down Lex, Jakey. Just this side of 106th. Noisy people on a stoop."

They find there a fat Puerto Rican, well dressed, striking his fists against the bars of a basement apartment, while a woman snarls and shouts within.

They search the man. No weapons.

"A knife!" The woman shrieks through the open window in a wild spasm of Spanish and English. "He said that he'd cut my heart out. . . . Well, he *did* have a knife the other night. You come in; I show you—"

They push the man into the apartment ahead of them. He goes slowly, his arms up, hands folded in back of his head as prisoners are taught to walk in some foreign lands. Probably he has been picked up by the police many times before, and not just in New York.

In an amazingly neat living-dining room at the rear, the woman lifts a bowl of wax fruit from a sideboard. From underneath phony grapes and apples she produces a mean-looking little hunting knife with a four-inch blade. This, she insists, was the knife the man threatened her with earlier in the week. He was drunk, and she took it away from him. The man swears that he never saw the knife before.

This is a landlord-tenant hullabaloo. The man owns the building; the woman leases it from him, and rents out various rooms and apartments. It seems that at one time there was love between them, but no longer.

"Listen, lady, we can't arrest him because of this knife. He says it isn't his. We have no proof that he ever carried it.

But"—Klepper turns grimly toward the greasy face beyond the
table—"we can arrest you for disorderly conduct unless you
stay away from this building and quit making a row on the
street at night."

"*Mi casa,*" declares the man blandly.

"Sure it's your *casa,*" Jackson tells him, "but you rent it
to this lady; you just admitted that. If she doesn't want you
inside, that's her business. If you want to settle your difficulties,
go to Court in civilized fashion. If we see you bothering around
here again—"

"*Brother!*" says Klepper.

They take the man back outside, the woman uttering threats
and thanksgivings behind them.

"Keep your voice down, lady." She doesn't need to get the
idea that they are necessarily on her side in the dispute. They
are merely trying to preserve the peace, to protect life and
property, to prevent a crime before it occurs: all those things
they learned long ago at the Academy.

The man halts on the sidewalk and seems disposed to resume
the verbal altercation, but Jackson starts toward him. "Do I
have to spank you, Chico?"

The man lumbers away, muttering, and turns the corner
west on 106th. They see him a moment later as they glide
past. He has hailed a taxicab and is loading his bulk into it.

"Did you see that bank book when we went over him?
Sixteen hundred bucks the guy deposited just today. Where
would a guy like that get sixteen hundred bucks?"

"Probably he's got a string of whorehouses. Maybe he shoves
ze stuff." Marijuana, Jackson means.

"*Si.*"

"We were in there quite a while, Bill. Better give another
ring."

They call in again from Box 2327 in front of the project,
on Park Avenue just above 112th Street. No, there have been
no important signals on the air, but there is another job:
Apartment 6-E, at 175 E. 111th Street. Family trouble. They

speed quietly toward the address, stopping only once to caution the driver of a newspaper truck who is engaged in noisy discussion with a colored taxicab-driver.

"Where did you get bumped, Mac? I can't see where anybody even got his fender hurt."

"No, I stood on the brakes! But he came right in front of me and—"

"Look, folks, write each other a letter about it. And get that truck and that taxicab out of the way."

The new job concerns Mr. James Maduro and his daughter, Magdalena (one would judge from her attire and attitude that Magdalena is well named). After a climb—yes, of course it's the top floor—to the sixth apartment, east side of the building, the patrolmen tap firmly with a stick on the door of the Maduro home and declare themselves to be *policia*.

The door flies open. Mr. Maduro, in frenzy, is striving to attack daughter, wife, neighbors or even *policia* with a broken Canada Dry bottle clutched in his lacerated hand. Patrolman Klepper renders Mr. Maduro submissive with one quick slap and takes the ginger ale bottle from him.

Mr. Maduro collapses in a kitchen chair and weeps copiously, declaring that neither daughter nor wife love him, and that he will bleed to death anyway. Magdalena, in the skimpiest, cheapest and lowest-cut black satin gown in the world, condemns her father stridently and demands that the police summon an ambulance because she has an infinitesimal cut upon her oily scalp. The mother wrings her hands; three somewhat smaller Maduros, frightened from their beds, add lusty voices to what is certainly not a Greek chorus but essentially a Puerto Rican one.

Bill Klepper runs cold water on James Maduro's hand, dabs at same with a paper towel, and discovers that the hemorrhage is superficial. Eddie Jackson tries painstakingly to discover what the trouble is.

It all relates to a man named Torro, beloved by Magdalena, hated by her relatives. She has been out with Torro again, contrary to parental injunction, but since she is nineteen and the sole breadwinner of the family, there doesn't seem much that anyone can do about it. There is mention of a married brother, Pedro, who works in a restaurant over on Madison Avenue. Eddie suggests tactfully that Magdalena spend the rest of the night at her brother's apartment. By morning perhaps the whole family will have calmed down and their troubles can be more readily adjusted.

Magdalena whoops that she wouldn't walk over to her brother's place on West 112th Street alone—no, not if all the *policia* in New York ordered her to do so. There is no telephone in this apartment or indeed in the building, so Patrolman Jackson escorts the enraged young lady to a telephone on Third Avenue, trying to soothe her into sanity as they go.

Klepper delivers himself of a brief discourse on the evils of trying to settle such family contention with fists, bottles or kitchenware. He instructs Mrs. Maduro how to dress the shallow wounds in her husband's hand and suggests the Flower Hospital clinic as a recommended precaution. He trots back downstairs to find that Eddie and Magdalena have returned to the building stoop, where Magdalena now awaits her brother.

The two patrolmen sit in their car, ostensibly listening to the official radio, but keeping a cagey eye on Magdalena to make sure that she doesn't dash back upstairs to reopen the argument and thus become either the active or passive partner to a homicide. At last Pedro Maduro, a sullen pock-marked youth in a canary-colored convertible with the trunk smashed in, drives up to take Magdalena away. Peace reigns at 175 E. 111th.

"Peace in *our* time," murmur the patrolmen sardonically.

Well, that was an easy job. But getting to be a cop in New York City is no easy job. The job itself isn't easy, after you are *in* the cops or *on* the cops (the expressions are used interchangeably). Ordinarily about six thousand young men are trying to get jobs in the Department.

They work hard, they study nights, they work at other jobs

and then go down to Delehanty's Institute or some other trade school, spending tedious hours in classrooms. They try to learn how to get on the Civil Service list of appointees to the Police Academy where in turn they will—eventually, they hope —learn how to be cops.

Pay is generous, by the standard of some other towns; pay is not so hot in comparison with more remunerative professions and skills. Your 4th-Grade Probationary Patrolman, newly appointed to the Academy, receives $2,400 per annum as his base pay, together with an additional $750 granted several years ago as a "temporary" cost-of-living increase.

This take-home pay of $3,150 has risen to a total of $4,150 by the time a patrolman reaches his 1st Class top grade; this occurs automatically after three years on the job. From then on he can hope for no higher salary unless he rises in rank. The climb to a sergeant's chevrons and to the gold shield of lieutenant is arduous. It means years of study, years spent in grade, and with no blemishes on the aspirant's record.

Both Eddie and Bill are studying in their spare time, hoping to get on the Sergeants' List. In 1948, when I first met Jackson and Klepper, neither one desired to ever leave the uniformed division. Like many of their mates they rather scorned a detective's job.

Now they are not so positive about it. A 1st Grade Detective earns exactly one thousand dollars a year more than a 1st Grade Patrolman. Furthermore both young officers have seen enough of the detectives' work by this time to realize that the field of investigation offers entrancing possibilities.

A man cannot be blamed for not desiring to spend the entire young years of his manhood crowded in a sweaty radio motor patrol car, or consistently drenched by rainstorms, fried by the sun at a crossing, sliding about on sleety rooftops, crawling from sagging fire escapes to slippery window ledges, forever and eternally climbing the noisome stairways of New York's slums.

It's always on the top floor. This is an axiom among the

patrolmen who guard congested areas of walk-up tenements. Why this should be true, no one knows exactly; yet the rookie learns soon that it is no fallacy. Night after night, day after day, the jobs will all lie on the fourth, fifth, sixth or seventh floors, with emphasis on the last two. A job on the first floor— be it homicide, family trouble, an accident, a borning baby, or a dying old man—that is something to wonder at, and to take grim satisfaction in.

Some people have theories to explain this. Jackson and Klepper, along with a lot of other patrolmen, feel that it may be because rents are cheaper on the upper floors, and therefore a more shiftless, broken-down or savage class of tenant is apt to be found in those regions. After fifteen months of first-hand police work, I evolved my own theory, at least where family quarrels were concerned.

Family quarrels account for a goodly percentage of the jobs in the danker regions of the city. . . . A man and his wife are quarreling in a first-floor apartment. The man slams the door and walks out into the street where eventually his rage may cool itself or be dissipated amid various distractions at hand. . . . A man and his wife are battling in a sixth-floor flat. The man does not go out on the street. Six flights are a long way down, and a worse journey coming up again, so he stays in the grim two-room apartment. His rage is fed by this hateful proximity. Eventually he snatches up the ice-pick or the can-opener and goes to work on his babe.

Two-Three Precinct. An alarm of fire at Lexington Avenue and One Hundred Eleventh Street. Box 1344. Authority C.B. 2:14 A.M. WPEF 69.

This is important, not because it's a fire, but because it's smack in the middle of their own sector. Car 322 is crawling north on Park just below 115th when the alarm comes over the air. The boys swing east to Lexington Avenue on 115th— against the traffic, this would be, but there isn't much traffic at this hour.

A truck hogs the path through the middle of the housing project that bulks on both sides of Lex for three solid blocks. Klepper pushes the siren menacingly. The truck edges over to let the green and white car past.

Ruddy lights have already been shafting abroad, the squeal of trucks has sounded. Fire equipment is all over the street at 111th and Lex. A battalion chief comes whining up in his bright sedan; he must have been cruising nearby.

Jackson and Klepper have already parked, and are out doing their job, halting traffic or waving it on as seems essential.

One by one the police cars ooze swiftly in past the fire trucks. The nearest sectors have all responded, and of course the sergeant too.

It's just another falsie. Helmeted firemen group around a box at the southeast corner of the intersection.

"Tag We're It again," says the battalion chief. "This is one of the worst boxes." Behind him Sergeant Dunnigan nods his gray head. There have been three falsies at this corner during the week. Klepper and Jackson now recall them: one last night, one two nights earlier, one the afternoon before that. . . .

Trucks growl in their departure, the sergeant goes away, the police cars are all moving again. But Jackson and Klepper have an idea.

They have spoken about it before, in speculative conclave. Now they get into 322 and drift toward the corner where the last remnants of the crowd dissolve. These people they watch carefully. They observe the stocky dark-faced husband who leads his limping wife away to continue a midnight stroll homeward. They see the younger men and cheap-clad girls who scamper toward the nearest neon-lighted bars.

And more than this: they see a thirteen-year-old boy in a khaki battle jacket too large for him. His saffron face is thin. He has deep haunted eyes, but just now the eyes are too bright.

The boy lingers near a doorway adjacent to the corner. He

does not notice the police car; he is staring after the last shiny truck that grunts its way west in 111th. Jackson and Klepper know that they have seen that same face with the freeze of concrete in its expression, on that same corner in the season of other false alarms.

The boy turns his back on the deserted scene of recent excitement and walks slowly through the shadows of East 111th Street. The green and white car glides after him.

Klepper leans out at the side. "Hey, kid."

The boy keeps walking.

"Hey, *amigo*," says Bill Klepper, and then he whistles.

"That's him." Jackson appraises the sudden frightened anguish of the face turned toward them in the gloom.

They stop the car and get out. They approach the boy—two giant figures confronting his nervous frailty.

"Quite a show, wasn't it, Johnny? All those big red trucks. Quite a thing to see."

The boy arches away. "I didn't do it," he explodes rapidly, in better English than they had thought he would use. "I didn't turn it in!"

"Goodness sake!" Klepper says. "We didn't accuse you of turning in any false alarm. Here—stick around a minute—don't run away. We want to talk to you." His fingers are tight on the drab sleeve. "What's your name, son?"

"Eddie."

"Eddie what?"

"Eddie Rios."

"That's a coincidence," says Jackson. "My name's Eddie too."

They move along with the boy, farther from the glare at the corner, deeper into the anonymity of shadows.

"You live around here, Eddie?"

The boy cannot speak. He manages to indicate the steps of a building a few doors farther on. The officers can see someone standing there as they approach: a youngish woman with a face darker than the boy's, and she has the tattered relic of a cheap fur jacket around her shoulders. She speeds down the steps and trips forward to meet the patrolmen.

"*Policia!*" She chokes. "No trouble? Please! My boy—my boy—have trouble?"

"Oh no," says Jackson easily. "We just want to hire him for a spy, that's all."

The woman and the boy seem whispering the words inside their souls.

"You see, we wanted to talk to someone here in the neighborhood. A kid—nobody would notice him too much. Now, lady, what I want you to do is to ask your boy to keep an eye on that fire alarm box at the corner for us, whenever he can. You know—whenever he's home."

Klepper asks graciously, "Does he work anywhere after school?"

The woman shakes her head. The boy stands stiff. "I did work at José's," he bursts out. "You know—José, up the street?"

"That little grocery and meat market? Why don't you work there now?"

Haltingly, the boy explains. The mother breaks in with quick phrases—terrified Spanish, some disordered English . . . yes, Eddie had worked for José, the grocer. But he was burning some cartons out in back—he got them too close to the shed. It caught fire, a little bit; José had to put it out with a pail of water. So he discharged Eddie.

Jackson says sagely, "I guess you can't blame José too much. His whole place might have burned down. Did Eddie ever have any trouble like that before?" he asks the mother.

"Trouble?" She pretends not to understand.

Klepper hunts for his Spanish. "*Con los fosforos?*"

Her hands are crimping together and then twisting apart. She breathes hoarsely. . . . *Si.* There was trouble once before. Well—maybe more than once. He was very small then—only so big. He used to play with matches and—

Klepper says, "But you don't do that any more, do you, Eddie?" The boy shakes his head.

"O.K.," says Jackson. His tone becomes charged with a deep and whispering confidence. "What I want you people to do is to keep an eye on that fire alarm box for us. Somebody or other—maybe a boy—is pulling that box all the time. It costs the city a lot of money to make these runs. And then there's the traffic hazard. There might be an accident; somebody might get run over and killed while the fire trucks are answering a false alarm."

Klepper adds, "There's a pretty stiff penalty for a thing like that. Such a kid, if we caught him—or her—" He inserts the second pronoun to rob the threat of its obvious sting. "Such a kid would probably be put away for a while. Sent to the reformatory."

The mother tries to swallow. She makes a dreadful sound.

"You see," says Jackson, "that would be an awful thing to happen. A kid like that—not really murdering anybody—but yet committing a serious crime. Just so he could see the fire trucks come to this corner! We want you to keep an eye on that box for us."

Klepper says briskly, "Report any suspicious activities to the man on post around there on Lex. The policeman. He'll be looking out too, of course. But if you see any boys hanging around here just tip him off, will you? I think that ought to do the trick, don't you, Ed?" and he glances at his partner seriously.

Jackson nods. "I hope it does. We'd surely hate to have to take a boy away from his mother and send him to jail. You can help us to prevent it by cooperating. Will you?"

The woman gasps, "*Si, si!* We help. We watch. We help you, *policia!*"

"How about you, Eddie?"

The boy is looking at the sidewalk, not at the officers. He nods slowly.

"That's fine." They swat the boy on the shoulder so hard that he staggers. They wave a salute to the mother, and climb back into their patrol car.

"The hell with us," says Klepper, as they watch mother and son disappearing speedily through the doorway of their building. "Aren't we stupid? If we just kept watching that little character, one of us might see him actually pull the box and get ze traditional reward."

"A day off," Jackson agrees. "I could use a day. How about you, Fat Stuff?" They both laugh as they go wheeling away. "I've got a hunch," says Jackson, "that we won't have so many falsies around here from now on."

There are three designations for the regular signals given over the air. "Calling all cars—" You may hear that when you go to the movies, but you will never hear it when you are sitting in one of the NYPD patrol cars. A Signal Thirty is an armed felony; stickups fall in this category. A Signal Thirty-one suggests a felony in relation to a motor vehicle.

I chose *Signal Thirty-two* as the title for my novel about the New York cops because a Signal Thirty-two embraces the remaining gamut of human iniquity and peril. A Signal Thirty-two is ominous, titillating—and, above all, urgent. The alarm has come in usually in such confusion and haste that Communications Bureau has no opportunity to assay it. It could be anything: a brawl, an attempted suicide by gas, a maniac chasing children through hallways, an old man crushed by a truck at a street corner, a puppy fallen into an elevator shaft—anything, everything puzzling, ridiculous, horrifying, compelling. The Thirty-twos are a bizarre pattern of the city's misery and threat.

Such a call stammered out from the radio a little after 3 A.M., when Jackson and Klepper were just crawling back into the car after giving a traffic ticket to one of Marcantonio's disgruntled followers. The man had driven carelessly through several red lights while angling his way across town; he nearly ran over an old couple at 108th and Park. Jackson and Klepper had to chase him well up into the 25th Precinct, far past 116th Street, before they brought the runaway car to a stop.

On top of all that, the man had the nerve to boast about his political connections, and began to whine and apologize only when a trip to a cell seemed imminent.

So they were just opening the doors of the patrol car when they heard the Signal Thirty-two, and it was an "Assist Patrolman." No officer lets any grass grow under his feet or any moss form on his tires when he hears those two words. Sadly enough, there have been times when even the speediest radio cars were unable to reach a scene of conflict in time, and thus the only assistance men could render the unhappy patrolman was to serve as pallbearers a few days later.

Bill Klepper was driving, relieving Eddie at the wheel; the little car sighed down Lexington Avenue with unholy speed. Other cars were congregating ahead of 322. They had had to come a long way, but both Bill and Eddie were grimly disappointed at arriving so tardily: this call was in the middle of their own sector, near 110th and Lexington. While they were still a block and a half distant the sound of a shot ripped out, together with a tinkle of shattered glass. Klepper and Jackson had their revolvers drawn before they were out of the car. They shoved their way along with other officers into a smelly restaurant, their feet crunching glass splinters as they ran.

They saw the blood-smeared features of Patrolman Cormany, one of the newer men in the precinct. He sagged against the lunch counter, gun in hand; a big man lay motionless on the floor in front of him. Cormany had a bad cut on his head, but his condition was not serious.

It took a few minutes to get the story. Cormany was alone on patrol post down the block, when he ran toward the restaurant in response to the proprietor's yells. Two men were fighting. While Cormany wrestled them apart and twisted a knife from one man's hand, another man crept up behind him, seized the officer's nightstick, and gave him a vicious blow over the head. Cormany toppled; he said that he was dazed by the blow, he couldn't act or think clearly for a moment. A young veteran in the crowd, enraged at the attack, caught hold of the malefactor and managed to retain his grip until Cormany staggered to his feet and drew his revolver. The man who had struck him was just breaking loose, and his friends were threatening close even as police cars began to squeeze their brakes in the street outside.

Cormany lifted his .38 and brought the barrel down against the skull of the hoodlum who still brandished the nightstick. But—there was a little laugh in this—the dazed patrolman neglected to keep his finger outside the trigger guard as he swatted with the .38. The result was a simultaneous explosion of the cartridge in the chamber, and a broken window-light.

"I bet that character thought he had his head blown off."

"Well, he *ought* to have had it blown off."

Bill and Eddie did not linger on these premises. The precinct must not be left unpatrolled; Sergeant Dunnigan sent new cars away as fast as they arrived. Car 322 returned to the slow dark process of creeping along Third and Park and the cross streets in between.

The men talked a little about Cormany and the incident in the café. Then they forgot all about it when an old woman came jabbering from a dark doorway, a lame woman with her dress half torn from her body, a drunk and idiotic old woman dripping tears because some young men had manhandled her and carried off her purse.

. . . Family trouble at 78 East 113th. Uh-huh—the top floor. That was out of their sector but the crew who should have attended the case were busy on another job. A husband had come home from work late. He had found himself locked out of his apartment, his clothing and radio-repair tools dumped into the hall. He was trying to kick the door down when Jackson and Klepper reached the scene. The wails, the swearing, the neighbors pushing close, the baby that rubbed its sleepy eyes, the angry wife in her wildness. . . .

. . . Aided Case at Mt. Sinai Hospital—a taciturn well-dressed young Italian. There were deep scratches all over his left cheek, his left eyelid was badly torn. There were scratches on his arm too. What had happened? "A cat," he said soberly, and repeated it again and again. "It was just a pet cat. I picked it up in my arms, and it started to scratch me."

Patrolmen and nurses exchanged glances. This patient was not fooling anybody, though they couldn't get him to change his story.

"What will I put down on this Aided Card?" demanded Jackson. "Attacked by angry cat? Or should I say ferocious cat, or a dangerous cat? How about it, Mac? Blonde cat or brunette cat?"

The young man stared coldly ahead, with his good eye while the nurse dabbed at the other. "I don't know what color it was," he said.

. . . Food, up on 116th Street. A little all-night place where the patrolmen were greeted hospitably by the elderly proprietors. It was their favorite place, reasonably clean for that neighborhood. They never ate much during the Late Tour anyway. They took turns sitting out in front with an ear to the radio. Jackson had a sandwich and milk, a small dish of ice cream; then Bill went in for his milk. He thought he would have perhaps a bowl of corn flakes. He was just pouring cream over the flakes when the siren snarled and he dashed out.

"What we got, Jakey?"

"One-seven-six-three Madison. In the rear. Might be a leaper."

It was a leaper, at first glance. They crouched in a filthy courtyard behind the building where the crushed figure of Oggie Smithfield lay. (Oggie Smithfield. Age, 25. Color, black, etc., etc. That was what his identification said when the police examined his wallet.) Oggie's eyes were glazing as he stared aloft and made soft mooing sounds. He was peering far up into the ragged night, past seams of clothes wires and crooked fire escapes, to the high roof whence he had flown.

Two patrolmen came out of the building and spoke to the sergeant.

"Where is she?"

"Right here. We brought her down from the fourth floor rear apartment. Says her name is Davis."

Mrs. Billy May Davis twisted thin brown hands as she talked to the sergeant in a low voice. Yes, Oggie was a boy friend of hers. No, he hadn't fallen from the window of her apartment. Nor— She didn't know how it happened. Yes, Oggie was in there with her, and then her husband came and began to knock on the door and demand to come in; no, they weren't divorced, but they had been separated for six months; and Oggie said that he didn't want any trouble with that husband of hers, so he climbed out on the fire escape and went up two stories to the roof above; seemed like about the same time her husband seemed to go away from the door, and she thought she heard his footsteps on the stairway; maybe he went up to the roof too; and then pretty soon she heard a kind of yell and then she heard something fall; she didn't know it was Oggie until the police came and knocked on her door, trying to find out where Oggie had fallen from.

But already people had searched the roof and there was no one, no one.

"I guess this is one for the Detective Division."

"They're already here. I just saw Detective Maurer go up the stairs inside."

"Looks like a homicide, all right. I don't think he's breathing any more."

The young Negro intern from Harlem Hospital got up off his knees beside Oggie Smithfield and put away his stethoscope. "Homicide? Yes, gentlemen, you got your homicide."

The sergeant said, "O.K. Everybody except 789 and 930 resume your posts."

What makes a cop? Why would anyone want to be a cop?

Jackson's father was and is a cop—a lieutenant with a fine record. So Ed had an illusion before his eyes, a tradition which he embraced willingly.

Klepper's father was a cop for years. He left a long time

ago and went into the Fire Department. Now he is a captain there; Bill and his father wrangle heatedly about the respective risks, merits, and general charm of the two careers.

It would be easy enough to let it go at that—to say that this was merely an attempted emulation, a devoted identification of a young self with an admired ancestor. It is not so easy as that, nor so simple.

I know dozens of patrolmen who are of a generation to possess grown sons. Many of their sons are not in the Department at all; they are dentists, tellers, cigar store clerks, airplane pilots, real estate salesmen, anything and everything except cops. I know dozens of younger officers as well, and many of them have parents who were appalled at Junior's choice of a career.

There is a mysterious impulse and determination which makes a man a policeman in New York City today. He is not asking merely for a pension-sustained old age. He could find that more easily in various other types of state, municipal, or national service. And if you accuse the New York policeman of possessing a simple masochism in his nature, a desire to risk his body and his soul in divers ways, you are falling into the common trap of the parlor analyst. There is much more chance of his being maimed if he serves in the Fire Department!

No, it stems from something more complex. I will ascribe to the veterans, who today wield their majority among New York's squads and precincts, a peculiar curiosity—a desire to observe and share the heartbeat of human existence. Your doctor witnesses but a portion; your policeman sees all. No other entity except God Himself may glimpse this fascinating panorama of human courage and depravity. And after one has worked alongside these sophisticated and able young men, he cannot but endow them with the basic virtue of benevolence—no matter how they might try to shrug it off.

I am not talking about the disgruntled, foot-sore ignoramus who snarls from his traffic post when you make the left turn you were not supposed to have made. I am not talking about the fat-brained dullard who has been hanging onto the job which he stupidly regards as a sinecure because he is a little sadistic at heart, and because he dreams of retiring at half-pay in two more years and buying a share of his brother-in-law's bar out on Long Island. Such oafs exist in any group of human beings selected or unselected. It would be impossible to assemble eighteen thousand men and not dredge up a few fifth-rate humans among them.

I am talking about the earnest people who comprise ninety-odd percent of the modern Police Academy graduating classes and who are replacing the thick-skulled automatons whom we have resented. These men are rich in their assimilation of danger and basic human values. Silver Stars and Purple Hearts are a dime a dozen among New York policemen today. And so they carry into their civilian careers the devotion and patience which they learned the hard way in other theaters of activity.

They are human; they are not gods. Among them are the weak, the venal, the opportunists. Among them, too, are saints and Sergeant Yorks—folks who perform arduous or horrifying tasks simply because these things are their job and the fulfillment of duty is expected of them.

The night wore itself away. The parade of the ailing, the miserable, the angry and perverted unwound in a strange harmony before the patrolmen's eyes.

A hollowness of dawn appeared. . . . Broken glass sounded on Third Avenue, but Klepper and Jackson were not there to hear it. They were investigating an eccentric driver at 107th and Park, trying to determine whether his peculiar fashion of motoring was the result of mere momentary weariness or a dangerous alcoholic state . . . the gong sounded within the façade of the hock-shop. Petty thieves had fled before Car 322 reached the scene. Search as the officers might, they could find no trace of the fugitives nor of a portable radio snatched through the broken window.

Both men now rode in the seeming torpor which overwhelms people at the end of a tour—especially perhaps at the end of the Late Tour. They had been climbing, cautioning, counseling, chasing through hours when the bulk of the world slumbered, and when they couldn't.

Eight o'clock was not too far away. The windows of clean apartment buildings which had replaced cluttered tenements of the project area were gleaming in cold sunlight on the west side of Lex.

The car crept north. . . . The radio popped, the radio was alive.

Two-Three Precinct. The address: IRT subway station at Lexington Avenue and One Hundred Sixteenth Street. A Signal Thirty-two. . . . Twenty-third Precinct. The address—

They were only a block and a half away. As the car gushed ahead Jackson and Klepper envisioned what might be in progress in the thundering tunnel underneath the street. A stickup, a fight, an attempted assault, an accident? All these things they had encountered in subway stations at one time or another in the few years past.

There was no clue in the alarm. Sometimes there wasn't a chance for the voice at Communications Bureau to get any hints into a call. *Proceed Quietly.* That would have meant a holdup most likely, or some dangerous men to be apprehended and searched. *Use Caution.* That might have meant danger from electricity . . . these thoughts crackled through their minds in the few seconds it took for the car to halt at 116th Street, rocking back on its frame as Eddie slammed the brakes.

No clue about which platform . . . uptown side, downtown side . . . many blocks away they heard sirens haunting the dawn. Other cars were coming, but this job was theirs: Car 322 was first on the scene.

Jackson bounded across Lex and dove for the downtown subway stairs. Bill Klepper was already springing down the stairway that descended to the uptown platform on the east side of the street. They had their guns drawn; they did not know what to expect, though there were yells to greet them, and the roar of a receding train, and the remoter mumble of another train advancing toward the station.

They emerged on opposite platforms simultaneously, and raced toward the turnstiles. People were there, only a few. It was a colored woman who was doing the screaming; she did not seem to be hurt.

"What's the matter, lady?"

A wild-eyed youth caught at Klepper's sleeve. "There! There! Him—"

They saw the limp figure from their opposite vantages: a long body in dirty attire, workman's clothes, draped over the third rail cover, and tipped with fresh pink at one of its lower extremities—a redness like raw veal where the cleaving wheels of a train had torn the right foot from the leg. Yes, there was the foot itself, lying several yards distant—another pulp of meat in its butchered leather.

But the man moved. He was alive; it seemed that they could hear him moan.

From the west platform Jackson dropped lightly down to the track. He stepped across the housing of the downtown side third rail, and crept past supporting pillars of the tunnel. Klepper anchored his gun in his holster and vaulted to the tracks. Both men were acutely conscious of an oncoming deep-throated clank and palpitation from the long shaft that bored away behind them. Another train—

"Third rail, Bill—"

"I know. Go easy, yourself—"

The sprawled figure with the bloodied stump made a cooing sound. They thought the guy was through, for a moment. His shoulder seemed to rub fairly against solid metal: the third rail, with its devilish charge of volts. But no, he was still moving, he hadn't touched it. Maybe just some of his clothing, not enough to transmit the last glaring shock into this miserable body.

Rails, ties, spots of oil, the dimness, the smell of grease and disinfectants, breath of the IRT . . . it all swam past them.

They were beside the man who had fallen from the platform of a moving train and now lay unalert to the mighty scramble of wheels which rushed to make a final mincing.

Other patrol cars had reached the scene, they were halting in the street up above, the feet of other patrolmen rang on stony stairways. Jackson and Klepper heard voices they knew, but they were first, this ugly job was theirs.

"Easy," they croaked to each other. "Easy. . . ."

They held the dusty arms. Slowly—oh, too slowly, it seemed —they worked the sodden body out of its proximity to the third rail. Glaring metal: here it was, a finger's breadth away, so close, so close. One touch, and you get your picture in the papers, but you won't be able to look at it . . . only Virginia and Dottie will see it, and the others left behind; and the pictures can be cut out and pasted in sacred little scrapbooks for Bunny and Barbara Ann to cherish when they grow older. Just as close as that. . . .

Inches grew and spread. They could get their arms around the heavy buttocks now, they could lift and haul beneath the shoulders, they could exert more of their own weight. *Easy.* They had him up, riding on their straining arms, and the tunnel was alive with thunder as the new train pounded close.

It seemed like a long expedition, an obstacle race wherein they moved as a team, crouching and hauling together . . . vealy stump dripping with arterial hemorrhage, and the man's big head hanging foolishly, his dark mouth making strange jabberings, and the train booming closer.

Back in the tunnel a motorman stared at them, the automatic yelps of the warning whistle came. Metal began to grind against metal. The train was trying to stop, but there they were, hoisting that character up on the platform.

Other blue figures, kneeling, bending to help. Guys from the other cars: Festa, Hoenicke, Gunn, Hirschhorn, Fitzpatrick, people like that. The glare of shields, the reach of strong eager hands—

The moaning burden was torn from them. Together Patrolman Edwin Jackson, Shield 9492, and Patrolman William Klepper, Shield 11661, swarmed up over the edge of the platform. The train roared, screeching, braking its way out of the tunnel, and came to a shuddering halt, filling up the space where they had leaped and labored.

You might think that would be good for a Commendation in anybody's language. Correct. It was.

Assembly of
the Saints
1967

. . . Suddenly streets and sidewalks of a city would bloom with a quaint and strangely beautiful crop of wilted human flowers.

They grew thickly around public buildings, grew in front of every hotel. Mainly they were garbed in blue and brass, and most of them wore black slouch hats. Their beards were kinky silver, and laughter came ringing, and under all was the reassuring, implacable booming of drums.

The Grand Army of the Republic had come to town for its annual Encampment.

This phenomenon was witnessed with joviality and tears in many Northern cities of middle size and, rarely, in the larger places. It began nearly a hundred years ago . . . then the participants had young sweat and keenness. It ended near the middle of this century, when a bare handful of sages could be assembled, and boosted into automobiles—when newspaper cameramen flashed their final bulbs, and the painted drums were stilled at last.

Those of my own generation remember with adoration and pride: we can recall a time when many younger Civil War veterans were of the age we now bear. But there were always older ones . . . there had always *been* older ones. There were older ones in the War itself. I own the official rosters of many regiments, on a shelf in my library. One of those volumes is sacred to the nature and exploits of the 37th Iowa Volunteer

Infantry, called the Graybeards because the majority of personnel were "above the age." The eldest man? His name was
Curtis King, and he was eighty when he enlisted.

Santa Claus came to town when the GAR came, and you
might even believe that the Apostle Paul moved in as well.
The Seven Dwarfs came, and Davy Jones, and Davy Crockett
and Daniel Boone. Here was a concentrated dose of gunpowder-
flavored America, and every fife screamed like a high-flying
hawk.

In the wake of these actual veterans there trooped a muster
of other organizations, all stemming from the parent whole,
and full of their own legends and fabrications and rivalries and
trivialities, just as groups come banding in assembly nowadays.
A convention of patriotic lodges always has a noble excuse, a
noble motive and myth, though often much of the nobility is
assumed or insincere. But there was a kind of immaculate serenity about the Grand Army of the Republic—and in their
own month and region, about the United Confederate Veterans
—which choked the human throat with gladness that we who
watched could call ourselves Americans too.

The trumpery of the United Nations hung before no one
in those days. There was merely the joy that we were a Nation
united. Even the most die-hard old Rebel, ready to demonstrate
at the drop of a cob-pipe how the yell of the Louisiana Tigers
differed from the ordinary Rebel yell— Even he admitted this.

I know. I used to attend the Encampments as often as I
could, North and South.

The saints assembled . . . that meant that every born liar
and tall-tale teller and happy exhibitionist who was worthy of
membership in the GAR or some fringe organization— He came
along too, or she did.

. . . Let's say that it is 1922, and the place is Des Moines.
More than twenty thousand strangers have come to town. These
include not only throngs of Civil War veterans, but Daughters
of Union Veterans, Sons of Union Veterans, Women's Relief

Corps, Ladies of the GAR . . . all the acolytes, all the attendants, eager wives and grandchildren.

It is September, the traditional month for the reunion. Sun
falls kindly as a summer sun but without its hurt. From their
train windows as they approach, stealing across river valleys or
down them, the visitors can see that woods are bright in patches
with the red of vines already turned. There is a perfume of
corn and oaks in the country air.

The Polk County Courthouse has been made into a general
headquarters . . . there's room to maneuver in, there. Halls
and lobbies roar with human triumph, with muttered campaigns. People are passing out cards and posters. *Vote for Smith
for Commander-in-Chief . . . J. D. MacTavish, Our New Commander . . . Nugent from Nebraska.* Why should it mean so
much to be elected to a high post in the organization? Ah, but
it does, it does.

Bob Spunner, picturesque with white Buffalo Bill hair, mustache, and imperial— He has had his picture taken for the
eleventh time since the Encampment began, and is even now
telling an admiring throng of high-schoolers that he will be
one hundred years old on his next birthday.

Twelve feet away, Eben Collins, once of the 16th Vermont,
is breaking into righteous wrath, peering over his shoulder and
then turning to wave a purple-veined fist in front of Harry
Kuppner, ex-68th Pennsylvania.

"That old Spunner is lying again! Listen to him! He ain't
a hundred years old any more than I am! I remember hearing
him at the Encampment a couple of years ago, telling folks
he was just about to be *ninety*. I tell you, he ought to be
exposed as a *fake!*"

"Oh, don't pay no attention to him, Ebe. He's just weak
in the head."

On the stairway leading to the second floor, a ladies' quartette is singing. The women wear gowns of identical pattern,
but varying in shade, and each has a red-white-and-blue scarf,
and is bedizened with badges relating to her membership in

the Daughters of Union Veterans. This quartette is an institution. The Girls, as they are called, have been singing at Encampments for many years. They have their own nickname proudly flourished . . . we'll call them the Columbus Canaries, or perhaps the Aberdeen Angels, or the Kalamazoo Korus. It doesn't matter. They seem to have more teeth than most women of their years . . . but they practice that untrained harmony of people who love to sing for singing's sake.

> *Tenting tonight, tenting tonight,*
> *Tenting on the old camp ground. . . .*

They own a rival in the shape of Aloysius Boyle of Brooklyn, New York, who some fifty-nine years ago fought on the Union left with the Irish Brigade on that glaring July second at Gettysburg. Mr. Boyle loves to sing, himself, and has done so consistently at every Encampment since he first began to attend in 1888. During the evenings he is apt to burst into Chauncey Olcott ballads without any urging at all, but now a patriotic number is suggested by the activity of the ladies' quartette.

In eagerness Mr. Boyle does not wait for their applause to die down. He has established himself seven steps on the stairway above the ladies, and is holding one hand over his heart and one extended toward the crowd. His seamed pink face is alive with compassion, the silver hair around his pink scalp stands out like a halo.

While the shot and shell were screaming upon the battlefield,
The boys in blue were fighting, their Country's flag to shield—

A yell of fifes, a bombardment of drums like thunder beyond the gates of Heaven: these serve to drown Mr. Boyle out, and to make his eventual speech about his own designation as an "Irish nightingale" fall on deafened ears. The Pasadena Drum Corps has tuned up outside the main entrance. People go flocking around. The Pasadena Drum Corps is noted, has long been noted.

Still, there are those snobs among the National Association of Civil War Musicians who demand that the Pasadena Drum Corps be placed at the *end* of the annual parade, "so's they won't disturb the rest of us. They got those blame fifes in the key of C! Everybody else has got B-flat!"

B-flat or C, it matters not at the moment. They are playing *The Raw Recruit* as if the entire military past, present, and future of the United States of America depends on it. The crowd falls back, laughing in a storm. The Pasadena Drum Corps has decided to march through the door and play *inside,* and this they are doing. The elderly graystone building quivers in its roots.

'Way over across town, at the State House, shuttling bands of veterans and other visitors are sightseeing. They wander happily from cannon to cannon on the spacious grounds. Uncle Mel Gartway sits resting on a concrete ledge, surrounded by a flock of schoolgirls. The children are in awe of his empty sleeve and the badge which proclaims his one-time participation in warfare with the 13th U. S. Infantry; and awed as by a miracle when their teacher points out the Congressional Medal worn by Mr. Gartway.

He shows off a polished lead minié-ball which hangs from his watch chain.

"Weighs just an ounce. Or used to. . . . I reckon some of the weight has wore off by now. But that was the reason they had to take off my arm. 'Twas at Vicksburg, nineteenth of May, Eighteen sixty-three. . . ."

Back across the river, at Sixth and Walnut, the Michigan Drum Corps has tuned up, and the Michigan Drum Corps is something to hear. They are nearly forty strong, and they boast a snare drummer—a squat, solemn, bearded man—who can beat the Long Roll for a full three minutes without tiring, and does so without even being asked. With a hundred others, Mr. George Warner Young, local insurance man, and Mr. Harvey Ingham, local editor, stand entranced in the crowd. So do the Reverend Frank Chalmers McKean, local Presbyterian, and Mr.

Henry A. Wallace, local farm journal publisher. They will all be late at their offices, coming from lunch, but nobody cares. This is more important than being on time.

Tribes of children congregate everywhere, following the veterans like *Kinderleine* lured by the Pied Piper. Truancies rise to a new high this week, but at least it is rumored that the schools will close officially for the grand parade.

Fresh-faced housewives, members of one of the local Ladies' Aid societies, are progressing slowly along the sidewalk, laden with baskets of home-baked cookies which are being lightened with speed. "For veterans only," they cry, shaking their heads at other hands extended hopefully. "Sorry. Veterans only."

Fat old Werner Larsen, one-time 1st Minnesota, wants to know how many cookies he can have. He is awarded two big thick brown ones. "My wife used to call these hermits," he says wistfully, "when she was alive. And— Do I get a kiss, lady, to go along with 'em?" Yes.

The little bearded man from Michigan has finished his Long Roll, and finished the jig he does along with it. The street is resounding with shouted requests from the thickening crowds. "Play *Yankee Doodle.*" "Hey, mister! Play *The Girl I Left Behind Me!*" "Play *Marching Through Georgia!*"

"*Marching Through Georgia*," says one gray-haired rawboned fifer to another. "They don't seem to realize that wasn't written 'til after the War."

"*Girl's* all right, and so's *Yankee Doodle*, but they're chestnuts. Let's give 'em something regular. *Eighteen Twelve* or *Gilderoy*."

But—

"*Village Quickstep*," calls the Fife Major, and holds his instrument aloft in signal. The music begins . . . long slow movement first. It was popular as a guard-mount during the War.

(I remember starting to play it on my fife, at an Encampment of United Confederate Veterans, in Richmond in 1932. I had been ensconced with some shaggy North Carolinians who demanded, "Give us a tune." So I began to play, and the next minute was threatened by a long-haired gentleman from Arkansas who descended with waving cane. "Stop that damn Yankee quickstep!" We became fast friends within the hour. Mr. Reeley and I exchanged annual letters for years following. Until the day I received that inevitable missive from a niece: "I am sorry to have to tell you . . .")

Let us walk, let us push our way along sidewalks and go into the street itself. Traffic moves at a crawl . . . old soldiers are limping everywhere. Old ladies, too. All the local children underfoot. . . .

A drum corps from Pittsburgh is playing in front of the Savery Hotel, a drum corps from Massachusetts in front of the Kirkwood. We might eventually elbow our way to the counter of a narrow restaurant near Third and Grand—one called the Bon Ton Cafe—and try to sustain ourselves with a cup of coffee. Mr. Gust Zanias is the proprietor. With a wide grin, Mr. Zanias is contemplating three veterans of the 5th New Jersey Volunteers—the only ones who could find each other at this Encampment, although there are believed to be others of their comrades around. They have laboriously counted out change, to pay for their late midday dinner.

"No check, Pop," says Gust. "Not for you folks, not here today. No check."

Des Moines has taken the visitors to its heart, just as Grand Rapids will do in 1934, and Rochester in 1935, and Washington itself in 1936. Not so many in the Michigan Drum Corps in 1936 . . . not so many in the Pasadena Drum Corps. What you might call a corporal's guard from all the GAR drum corps, even with Sons of Union Veterans helping out. And fat Bert Child, National Secretary, marching slowly in the lead, no longer able to beat his drum. . . .

What about the little old fellow who used to play the Long Roll? You know . . . he kind of danced around while he played it?

Oh, yes, I mind him well. But he's gone. Gone for years.

It is 1922 again. A clear morning, not too warm. Maybe there is an imagined smell of hickory nuts along with native coal smoke in the air . . . Jonathan apples are ripening in orchards north of town.

Locust Street is a pulsating river of black slouch hats and ragged whiskers. Uncle Mac McGeehan slides his shriveled wrist inside the thong of his bass-drum club, preparing to pound long and heartily.

We find the beauty of bugles here . . . tarnished brass fringe dangles heavily from treasured flags. And some infirm among the color-bearers will allow sturdy Boy Scouts to lift the weighty staffs instead. But others will never yield, they won't give up the chore. Arms are strained, shoulders bent and aching . . . the stirrup in which the flagstaff rests grows hard and hurtful. But they will not give up. Never, never. They go tottering on, and applause roars like a waterfall.

Herein is apology for nothing. This is the patrolling of a valiant Past.

We have but to stop and think, and recognize that there must be dullards and cheats and even cowards somewhere in the unsteady ranks—men who treated their wives with cruelty, who were stupid with their children—men who lied, and stole from their partners, and are yet alive and talkative about war careers which are from first to last an extravagant falsehood.

Yea, there are bound to be a few of those.

But in the main we know also that here we are observing Thanksgiving Day and Ground-Hog Day and Arbor Day and Memorial Day. Here marches the grease and greenness of an elder America.

Because we own illusions, captivating and vigorous ones. Our illusions have not been washed away (a nation grows more confused in each hour that its illusions are drowned).

Drums continue steady, strong as a lumberman's heartbeat. Fifes shrill out their messages of *Jefferson and Liberty* and *O Lassie, Art Thou Sleeping Yet?*

We consider the blue-coated sire who sat calmly with his

newspaper in the Fort Des Moines Hotel lobby an hour ago. His scanty beard was black, his hair black as a crow's wing. And people said, "Oh, he can't be a Veteran. He must be one of the Sons."

So we went up and asked him. He put down the paper with tranquillity, and smiled a welcome and a dismissal. "Ninety-three years old next November," he said. "Never took no water in my whiskey."

. . . And we know that their late enemies possess the same bliss and assurance: those men who wear tiny Maltese crosses in everyday coat buttonholes, just as the Grand Army men wear a coin of reddish-bronze.

There are the words of General Stephen D. Lee resounding from a Southern city, years before, when he spoke of angels "with things like chevrons on their wings." Stephen Dill Lee asked his rhetorical question out of a regional heart, as proud as these activating the hoary ranks before us, from our own Upper Mississippi or Upper Ohio or Upper Hudson areas.

"When the pale sergeant comes, we shall listen for voices in the upper air, saying, 'Welcome, Comrade. Do they love us still in Dixie?'"

Oh indeed, they loved them down in Dixie. And we Yankees loved our own dark-jacketed throngs through all the years they marched, until they were only a trickle and then but a memory.

But it seemed that the very act of gazing upon them conferred a Degree in Patriotism, an ability to weather the future scorn of people who hold that it is essential to consider the honor of some other State before we consider our own. People who declare that the Flag is a mask held in front of a façade of trickery and deceit. . . .

Forty-five years are vanished. We worship in the glory of September. Drumsticks press their fervor against taut skin of the drums, the lame feet shuffle on, and we follow in rapture.

Time to Wake Up Now
1945

That chilly March afternoon we got back from Germany around four o'clock, and promptly I went to my barracks and packed up for Paris. I was leaving the 344th Group of medium bombers, based at that time in a windy valley stretching from Cormeilles to Genicourt.

The 344th—especially the 495th Squadron, with which I had been flying—boasted a swell bunch of boys, and I was sorry to leave them. (Editorial Note by Author, 1967—Funny. Every squadron I ever flew with, in two wars, seemed like "a swell bunch of boys." Shows I'm queer for squadrons.)

But more than that I found myself worrying about a gang of Germans I had never even seen or talked with.

Maybe they were good Germans; I didn't know. I was convinced that a lot of them must now be good Germans in the traditional sense of the word (borrowed from our pioneer past: i.e., the only good Indian is a dead Indian). The trouble was, I couldn't decide just how good those Germans at Olpe were, in the more ordinary sense of the word, before our B-26s came flashing overhead that afternoon.

We hadn't intended to go to Olpe. We had been briefed for a target called Bad Oyenhausen, away up northeast of Hamm. The boys made a lot of cracks about this, naturally: they said they'd rather go to Good Oyenhausen, if such a place there were. Bad Germans, good Germans, Bad Oyenhausen, Good Oyenhausen . . . it was all rather mixed up in my mind.

As we twisted along the narrow road toward Paris in Colonel Witty's car, I considered the facts of the matter. Some friends named Durato and Fender and Brady were riding with me, and we had a bottle of rather green cognac. Fender had finished his missions that day, so of course he was planning a celebration; indeed was already embarked upon it. I could talk with the others, and take an occasional swig with them.

I wished that I could get over being concerned about those Germans at Olpe.

I had flown with a very sharp pilot named Ehart, and I remembered how we all cussed when the order for diversion came crackling in over the radio. We were across the bomb line by that time, or almost. I know that we were across the Rhine, and in those faraway days of March our bomb line still lay close to the Rhine. A bomb line is an imaginary barrier set up for the protection of ground forces; it is changed from hour to hour. You cannot drop your bombs on the nearer side of the bomb line: only on the farther side, for fear of killing your own troops on the ground. Sometimes mistakes are made. That's the way General Lesley McNair got killed.

Anyway we were diverted, and at first we thought we were going to have to turn around and go home, but more information followed. We were told to attack Olpe instead of Bad Oyenhausen.

That was fine. Olpe was close at hand, and Bad Oyenhausen was a long way off, and we had been warned about a lot of Luftwaffe in those northeastern areas. So we would proceed at once to Olpe and get rid of our bombs on top of the road junction there; and we would receive credit for a mission after all, and we would be home before we had expected. As the RAF would say, "Good show, good show!"

Well, we reached Olpe in short order; our window-ship was right ahead. When I saw his bomb doors pull down, I went back and opened the door into our bomb bay. I had always enjoyed watching bombs fall on our enemies. In the 17s I never got to see much of that sort of thing, because there I flew as right-cheek gunner in the nose.

Our bomb doors were wide open when I looked, and patches of cloud scudded past a couple of thousand feet beneath. Even as I looked, the bombardier pressed his switch up forward, and the big brown plummets sank rapidly and purposefully toward the overcast. Then miraculously clouds opened to admit them. And I saw Olpe—a little place with a lot of peaked gable roofs, pinkish tile roofs, such as they have in most of those towns in western Germany. I thought again, "Good show," and closed the door, and went up front to watch the flak which was already beginning to appear in startled black and silver buffets ahead of us and below us and to the left.

Also I started to worry about those Germans on the ground.

I imagined many old ladies, and they were simple dumb honest souls. They had the kind of wrinkled Teutonic faces which you see on old farm wives in Pennsylvania counties . . . their teeth gone, the flesh on their lips all squeezed like brown flower petals around their thin mouths; and their little blue eyes were bright, as I thought of them. They wore lace caps, or maybe shawls over their heads, and they liked to keep coffeepots warm and ready on the backs of their stoves. They had flowers growing in spring gardens and maybe there were kids who called them *Grossmutter*.

Then I started worrying about the kids. I saw them with yellow hair and engaging little faces, and I imagined them playing with cats or maybe picking up bright pebbles in the road to play with on their mother's doorsteps. I put myself down in Olpe. I stood around while the bombs went wham and the bricks flew this way and that way, and the concussion blasted my ears. I thought I heard people crying.

This wasn't like bombing those flak gun positions south of Limburg, which we had attacked the previous Sunday when I was flying with Tal Pearson. Then we were after our old flak enemies—those bastards who threw the black-and-silver at us, and had at one time or another torn to bits certain airplanes that we loved and certain people who rode in them—people whom we loved also. No; and it wasn't like attacking a Jerry fighter field or a locomotive works which had been reconditioned to make Messerschmitts. This was attacking a town with harmless civilians in it. Our bombs had undoubtedly closed (for the moment) a very important transportation bottleneck. But a lot of noncombatants must have been killed.

These thoughts lingered unpleasantly with me all afternoon. They didn't vanish even after we reached the cool tired misshapen boundaries of Paris and felt a thin spring sunset on our faces.

I went to my hotel lugubriously. When I found that I couldn't have a room to myself I was more lugubrious than ever.

The *concierge* shook his head, and got out a register with a long list of names on a certain page. "All the singles are taken. You'll have to move in with someone who's already registered in a double room. Do you know any of these people, Monsieur?"

Halfway down the list I saw the name of *Grammer, S.*

"Is that Stan Grammer from Press Wireless?"

"*Mais oui.*"

"O.K. I'll move in with him. I've known him for years."

And so I had, and so had most of the other correspondents in the ETO. Stan Grammer is a dapper Englishman, middle-aged, and he manipulates Press Wireless with a skillful hand. I used to know him in London earlier in the war, when he wore civilian clothes, when we used to play poker down at the Savoy night after night while the sirens screeched outside and the windows shook in their casings.

Now Stan was wearing an American correspondent's uniform, people had told me, with his Raf wings from the last war neatly stitched on the right breast of his blouse; and I supposed that he must be having a very good time in this war, because I was sure that he rather liked war.

The *concierge* said, as the porter gathered up my bags, "You are fortunate. You will have the room to yourself, after all. Monsieur Grammer is with the Army at the Front—has been, for weeks."

About ten o'clock I finished with dinner and with what reading I had to do; I crawled into one of the two beds in our room, and smoked for a while. I contemplated the miscellaneous chunks of luggage piled on top of the wardrobes, and I guessed rightly that Stan Grammer's room was a repository for stray bits of personal belongings left there by other correspondents who had drifted off in one direction or another. I say, I tried to count the pieces of luggage and speculate as to their contents; but I couldn't get those old *Grossmuttern* and minor yellow-haired *Maedchen* out of my head.

Finally I turned off the light and went to sleep, but that gang of Germans came all the way from Olpe and climbed into bed and crowded me. They were dead and bloody, and still crying as if their hearts would break.

Then I was awake, and it was twelve o'clock. Someone was pounding on the door which I had bolted before I went to bed. I got up and tramped groggily to the door and looked out into the hall. There stood Stan Grammer and a porter with Stan's luggage, and we blinked at one another for a few seconds and then I welcomed him into his own room. The porter went away, and still Stan and I were saying that it was good to see each other again. I got out what was left of my cognac and we had a couple of drinks.

"How are things up at the Front?" I asked him, but even then I was wondering why he had that big wad of cotton sticking out of his right ear.

"Front, hell," said Stan. "Who said I'd been at the Front?"

"The *concierge.*"

"Nonsense. I've been home; on leave, in Britain."

I told him, "I'm going over tomorrow or next day, to go back to the 305th."

He made a wry face. "See that you go quickly to Chelveston, old boy. Don't linger in London. It's not nice."

"What do you mean? V-2s?"

"They've been damn bad all week. Look at this." Stan touched the cotton protruding from his ear.

"What's the matter with your ear? Don't tell me you got *hit?*"

He walked around the room, swishing the brown cognac in his glass. It was chilly; I got back into bed and watched him.

"No," he said. "I didn't get hit. It was concussion. It cracked my eardrum. It's painful, and a damn nuisance, too. I have to keep putting medication in my ear."

He said, "Larry Rue and I were just coming out of the Savoy when the thing hit. It was up in High Holborn. It was just about noon."

I watched him twisting a tuft of cotton into a sharp point between his thumb and first finger.

"You know how the Savoy is: there's that little court where you come in off the Strand? We were in that court, and I guess that made the difference. The concussion gave us a bloody hard wallop. I didn't realize anything had happened to my ear at the time; but later it got to making noises and paining me, so I went to a doctor."

He drank the last of his cognac, put down the glass, and began to take off his clothes. "God," he said, "I'm tired! Frightfully tired. I had a frightful time getting back to Paris, frightful trouble with transportation. All the damn fools there are in the world . . . I'm sick of this bloody war. Aren't you?"

He put on his pajamas and got out the medicine with which to dose his ear, and went into the bathroom. I picked up a cold cigar butt on the ashtray beside my bed, lighted it, and lay there with my hands behind my head, until Stan came back and began to turn down the other bed. He said, "We counted one hundred and ninety-six bodies."

"In High Holborn?"

"Yes," he said, crawling into bed. "It was about noon, and all those old clerks and little office girls were just going out for their bite of lunch. The street was full of them, when the thing came down."

. . . It was the girl in the light blue dress that bothered him more than the others, I think. He kept talking about her after we switched out the lights, and lay there marked only by the orange stare of our respective cigar and cigarette.

It was the little girl in the blue dress, and she had a kind of pink bow on the dress—rather like a necktie—and her hair was brown.

Stan said that they hurried to High Holborn after they had gulped back their breath; and they stood around and watched—they watched the ARPs and the ambulances—watched London taking charge of its dead and its living in that kind of fumblingly, bumblingly efficient manner which London employed in such matters all through the war. Stan said that many of the bodies didn't have a mark on them. No blood, no wounds, no nothing.

That's what happened if you were within a certain radius of the spot where a V-2 came down. You died quickly and explosively, but it was only air which killed you: blast air. If a building fell on you, you would be squashed flat, but this blast air came just as hard as a building falling on you. It crushed your chest and still it didn't leave a mark.

So all the prissy, middle-aged clerks, shabby grey bookkeepers in their shiny office coats, they were laid out in rows on the sidewalk, and so were the women laid out. The fat old dame with straggly hair, who'd just stepped out of that milk bar around the corner; and the trim young upper-class mother in her rough tweed suit, and the two little kids who had been tripping along the street with her, and had tripped into Infinity fresh-faced and capable by their mother's side. And all the little Waafs and Ats who had errands in the neighborhood, they were laid out, too—the Ats with the ugly yellow-ribbed stockings which would never worry them again, the blue and khaki uniforms in slow-settling plaster and brick dust.

The two-day-old carnation in the worn lapel; the shabby well-mended shopping bag; the malacca walking stick; the crumpled pink handkerchief that it cost a coupon to buy. They were all there on that sidewalk in High Holborn, said Stan Grammer; and distant bells pealed the cry of noon, and dust drifted its powder on everyone who came into the area.

And there lay the girl in the blue dress, the one whom Stan admired, the one he talked about so much. I guess that maybe he fell in love with her after she was killed . . . he'd never known her before.

She had brown hair and long lashes, and her eyes were properly closed: they weren't open and staring. They weren't the peeled-grape kind of eyes which dead people have so often. They were just pretty sleepy-time eyes with soft heavy lids and lovely long lashes; and the girl in the blue dress was sound asleep.

. . . He said that she might have lain that way on a couch. You could imagine that you loved her, because she was so very young and had such a candy-flower smell about her, and her legs were very pretty too; the knees were especially nice. You could see her knees because the dress was pulled up rather high as she lay there amid a powder of window-glass.

You could imagine that she was on a couch, and perhaps you and she had been making love; and then you had both gone to sleep, and then you awakened and looked over and saw her. She was still asleep—brown hair and white little ears and slim throat and everything.

So you stood beside her and you said, "Wake up, dear. Please wake up." You said it very softly so as not to awaken her too abruptly; but she didn't stir; and you had to keep whispering it and whispering it with your lips and in your mind.

"She was very beautiful," Stan said, there in the dark; and then he turned over and rubbed out his cigarette in the ashtray. "Just as if she were asleep. You couldn't believe that she was dead. God," he said, "I do hate the Germans, don't you?"

"Yes," I said.

"Just as if she were asleep," said Stan, turning over in his bed and flouncing around until he made himself comfortable. "You wanted to keep asking her to wake up. You wanted to say, 'Wake up, dear. You've been asleep a long time. It's time to wake up now.'"

The smoke arose from his cigarette ash a few minutes longer; I could smell it; I had put out my cigar sometime before. Finally I heard Stan snoring, and then I turned over and went to sleep.

The Hungriest Ones
1963

Bring me meat and bring me wine;
Bring me pine logs hither. . . .

This happened a great many Christmases ago; but still I should conceal the name of the city and the newspaper, and the name of the newspaper's editor. No use looking in *Who's Who*: it doesn't list all the publications I've worked for.

We shall be screamingly original, and call the busy Northern town Jones City, and call the newspaper the Jones City *News*; and also we shall call the editor and publisher Mr. Jones.

Our big Christmas charity deal on the *News* was called "The Hungry Fourteen." Everybody on the paper was cautioned to keep his eyes open for a hungry family. These had to be outstanding, shuddering, freezing cases of bare-boned agony . . . the *News* was like that: nothing second-handed about our publication. We didn't go around and try to crib names from lists of local charity organizations; in fact, such behavior wouldn't have been countenanced. Let the charitable organizations find their own hungriest and neediest, and let them find their own donors, too. Our newspaper played a very private game. And we were housed snugly in a neat baby skyscraper, complete with annex, easily one of the finest structures on Ojibway Street. Employees of the *News* had originality, energy, and verve.

This is the way the Hungry Fourteen worked: in columns of our newspaper, one by one, were related sad stories of the fourteen families believed to be the most miserable in all of Jones City. The public would be invited to contribute money for the relief of these families, and we would try to go over the top with twenty-seven hundred and forty-four dollars. Divide that fourteen ways and you get one hundred and ninety-six dollars. Such was the sum set aside for each of the families selected. They didn't receive their money all at once—we had to guard against their breaking out in a rash of Jordan almonds and chromium-plated tricycles. So the money was gifted to them, week by week, for fourteen weeks of winter.

We young people at the *News* were not more cynical than the average for our time and station, but still we were pretty hard-boiled. Among ourselves we made a game out of the Hungry Fourteen. Everybody contributed a dollar—which, when all participants were counted, amounted to a kitty containing a good round sum. Each would then try to come up with the worst—the most aching-voidish empty-stockingish bare-cupboarded case to be found in any annals of the needy. Charles Dickens didn't stand a chance, not with us.

Bear in mind, please, that this all occurred before the days of Federal Relief, before the days of Social Security—long before any such foam-rubber gadgets had been invented to cushion the shock of Man's falling on his stupid face. We dealt in a world just about as stark as that in which the Cratchits shivered. You produced, or you didn't eat . . . you toiled, or you didn't have fuel for the fire.

> *Bow down, bow down, O cherry tree . . .*
> *and give the Mother some.*

We had a fellow named Freddy Greenleaf, whose title was Special Assistant to the Editor—at least that's what it said on the door of his little coop. Actually he was trouble-shooter for the entire organization. When matters went wrong—when anyone had to be fired, when anything had to be investigated, Freddy Greenleaf was the man. He was an able politician, a

keen detective, and withal had a genial heart in his breast and
a splintery active brain dancing around within his shiny pink
skull. It might have been expected that Freddy would win the
prize in our search for the very Hungriest; and so he did.

He'd learned of a widow, a grandmother. She was lame—had
suffered infantile paralysis when young. Her husband had been
dead for many years, and Grandma's estate consisted of a
shrunken cottage down on the southeast side (bad side) of
town. There was a daughter, and there were three grandchildren; and the daughter's husband was in a mental institution.
Daughter was a superb seamstress, and the family had gotten
along fairly well until the previous autumn. Then an old kero-
sene stove exploded. Daughter burned both hands: she wouldn't
be able to sew for a long time, maybe never again. She couldn't
do much for her children either; and one of the children was
a spastic cripple. . . . Grandma had slipped and fallen on the
ice, and she was additionally lame from that. But still she had
to go to work. Her job was scrubbing. She scrubbed six nights
a week in a building downtown. Her wage for the week was
nine dollars.

This case of Freddy's won our contest, hands down.

We all had a part in writing accompanying stories for the
Hungry Fourteen, and garnering in pennies from the public.

"Office employees, Primex Chemical Corporation. $4.67."

"Brownie Troop, Grace Church, fudge sale. $2.54."

"Miss Teal's English class, Irving High School. $2.13."

We pulled and hauled and we wrote, we made people weep,
we made people contribute. Thus we went over the top with
our fund on the day before Christmas. Believe it or not, it was
snowing too.

When Freddy Greenleaf came into the cubbyhole which
passed for my office, he was smiling.

"In addition to winning the dollar pool," he said, "I have
just cut out a job of work for myself."

"How so?"

"It's like this. Mr. Jones"—he was speaking of our publisher
—"Mr. Jones is in a towering rage."

"What about, this time?"

"My case—the one I won on—the Starvationest of all the
Starving Fourteen. . . . The daughter's hands are burned.
Grandma slipped on the ice and hurt herself, but Grandma
still has to go to work and—"

"Look," I said, "I remember the case."

"Grandma earns a buck-and-a-half each night from her floor-
scrubbing. . . . Mr. Jones is going to go crusading, first moment
I can equip him for the fray."

"How are you going to do that?"

"I'm going to find out," said Freddy, "who the critter is who
pays Grandma nine dollars a week for scrubbing floors all night.
Then we are going to pillory him. We're going to make a public
example."

I thought it over for a minute. "Freddy. By any chance, did
you invent that Hungriest story?"

"Certainly not! I got it from the woman who does my mother's
laundry . . . has for years. Completely trustworthy and—"

I said, "Then probably you can find out."

There happened to be several of us in Mr. Jones's office that
afternoon, when Freddy Greenleaf came in, looking odd.

Then bring Him incense, gold and myrrh . . .
come shepherd, king to own Him. . . .

Mr. Jones glared across the desk as if Freddy, personally, had
been responsible for the plight of all the Hungry Fourteen.
Mr. Jones had that kind of look about him normally; but now
that he was planning to rend a reputation, why—

"Did you get the dope?"

"Yes, sir," said Freddy.

We three kings of Orient are.
Bearing gifts, we travel afar. . . .

Mr. Jones took off his glasses with a characteristic gesture, and began to polish them, as he stared and nodded at the rest of us. "I'm going to show this character up! Here's a lame old woman, traveling over snow and ice, without any reindeer to help her! And walking two miles every evening, and working all night, and then limping two miles home again to take care of those children. Nine dollars a week, that man pays her! I'm going to blow him sky-high in the paper!"

He turned to look at Freddy again. "O.K. Who is it?"

"Sir," said Freddy, "it's the Jones City *News*. It's this building, sir. It's this paper. It's—you."

Paul Revere and
the Nazi Spies
1962

. . . Some acquaintances dropped in at my house and whispered ominously about a new couple whom I shall describe as being named Ivanovsky. The Ivanovskys built a house on our Florida key last summer, but nowadays they are keeping very much to themselves. At night strange blue lights glow in a workshop behind the garage; sometimes Mister goes away on mysterious trips. He was seen boarding a jet at Tampa, briefcase in hand. . . .

To the notion of my acquaintances, the Ivanovskys are most certainly tools of the Soviets; likely they are working on some new pocket-size version of The Bomb. Evidence seems conclusive to the Browns, and might so seem to me—if I did not know that Peter Ivanovsky served the United States brilliantly and courageously during World War II, and has been summoned back into quasi-official service by our Government because of his skill in certain matters requiring unquestioned loyalty.

But I didn't laugh at the Browns when they departed. Instead I sat myself down on a sober beach chair and considered that in all honesty this might be deemed a case for Paul Revere.

In months to come (especially in Florida) any innocent soda-water-charger-cylinder will be identified as a bomb. Flashlight beams waved by Girl Scouts through evening picnic groves will become flying saucers. Simkovitches and Petrovskys without number will be shunned, pried at, preyed upon, talked about,

sniffed after, or pilloried. Horrific injustices will be perpetrated
in the name of a militant Liberty.

But no Paul Revere will go loping amid the eerie darkness
of our palm-shadowed neighborhood. There was only one modern Paul Revere.

Folks, I knew him, and knew also the Nazi Spies of Pacific
Palisades, California. I shall now recite the peculiar role played
momentarily in history by Joseph Cotten, the actor, and to
humble degree by myself; and that means going back some
twenty-one years and more.

. . . It was right after Pearl Harbor. People who dwelt on
the Pacific Coast in those scurrying weeks will recall the credu-
lous confusion that reigned.

General Stilwell's published papers state that at least two
Jap fleets were prowling California waters at the time. If the
Brass in command of the area believed that, there is little wonder that we motion picture employees were jumping out of our
moccasins whenever we heard a spring creak in an agent's
swivel chair.

We recognized some Nazi spies right there in the film colony,
and they were really something to look at. They took bracing
constitutionals with mechanical regularity. No troopers of the
German-American Bund, the *Reichswehr* or the *Volksturm* ever
paced with more threatening cadence.

They were assorted as to sex: one male, one female—pre-
sumably husband and wife. Always they were accompanied by
an evil-eyed dog—a German shepherd, no less. The male member of the duo had his hair clipped into a Prussian fuzz, and he
wore iron-bowed spectacles with lenses half an inch thick. He
boasted also walking boots and plus-fours, and carried a cudgel;
and probably he wore a corset under his clothes. There were
dueling scars on his face, or so we told each other with glee.
All in all, it was what they call type-casting. This character
might have just walked off an old set of *The Kaiser, the Beast
of Berlin*.

His female partner can best be described as a dead ringer

for those ugly photos of Irma This and Ilse That, which brightened our newspapers in days to come long afterward: the jolly days in which the beasts and beastesses of Belsen, Dachau, and Buchenwald found short shrift in a cell or at the end of a long rope.

The house of Joseph Cotten used to adorn a pleasant road called Monaco Drive. Down this drive the Nazi Spies would parade at stated intervals. From behind the mesh of the tennis court, from sprays of oleander bushes and bowers of lemon branches, we heard the pound of Teutonic iron heels. We saw the grim cheekbones and tight-screwed hair of the steel-jawed Frau; we heard guttural grunts with which the master adjured his *Teuffelhund.*

"There go the Nazi Spies again!"

"Oh, gosh, the end of another day—I see the Nazi Spies are out for their evening stroll!"

"Say, the Nazi Spies almost got hit by a truck this morning," and more of the same.

In those first taut weeks of confusion, Jo Cotten had enlisted proudly in the auxiliary fire force of Santa Monica's civilian defense organization, and I enrolled in ranks of the Westwood auxiliary police. Ardent though we might be in our service, Jo and I could not hope to attain the heights of devotion whereon the neighborhood air-raid warden strolled.

I misremember his true name, but we had one for him, just as we had for the Nazi Spies. We called him Paul Revere. The first whine of warning sirens might catch some of the civilian defense people with their pants down, figuratively or literally; but not Paul Revere.

. . . He has gone to Valhalla; he dwells no longer amid the canyons and swimming pools of Los Angeles County, but

> "... *borne on the night-wind of the Past,*
> *Through all our history, to the last,*
> *In the hour of darkness and peril and need,*
> *The people will waken and listen to hear*"

the speeding footsteps of the air-raid warden as he rushed from
house to house, from wrongly-adjusted-blackout-curtains to
light-left-on-in-the-garage to lights-left-on-in-the-tennis-court.

Paul Revere's face was kindly but stern. No one more than
he appreciated the responsibilities burdening his shoulders, yet
no one more than he was willing to accept them. He would
countenance no deviation from the emergency code hastily
scrabbled together by the heads of Civilian Defense. . . . The
helmets of some volunteers were smeared with grease stains
accumulated in their patriotic avocation, but Paul Revere's helmet was as white as a hemisphere of ice cream on a slice of pie.

Some heckling souls of the neighborhood resented Paul's
ministrations. Certain ladies declared that the warden was
eagerly ubiquitous in times of siren-induced peril only because
it gave him an opportunity to chin with the movie stars on
temporarily equal terms, or even on terms where the air-raid
warden was emperor and the movie stars his frightened vassals.
I shall nail these rumors for what they were: the cheap bicker-
ing of fishwives—acid from the poisoned tongues of viragos.

Jo Cotten and I understood Paul Revere. We knew what
made him tick. It is not often that one encounters in one small,
busy body the nobler qualities of Molly Pitcher, General Philip
Sheridan, Sergeant York, and the little Dutch boy with his
finger up the hole.

Friends in uniform came among us in that season. One was a
long-geared Army Air Force lieutenant whom I had known
since he was a boy. Tom Ridgway was stationed in Colorado.
Colorado was but the toss of a C-47 from California. . . .

Often young Lieutenant Ridgway might wangle his weekend
leave in Colorado, hitchhike along with some accommodating
pilot, and thus stand beaming upon our California doorstep
the next morning. Him I introduced to the Cottens, and the
satisfaction was mutual. Our main problem was how to get
Tom back to Colorado again after some Hollywood charmer
had obligingly tried to build up the Air Force morale during

gay weekend hours, and before Tom's CO discovered that he was gone.

On one of these perilous missions over the target of the Beverly Hills-Brentwood area, the lieutenant showed up well-reinforced by the FBI. An agent of that Bureau, one William Clothier, was a Philadelphia boyhood pal of Tom's, and was at that time assigned to the area. Clothier was a good companion, a more than good tennis player, and thus he found great favor in Jo Cotten's eyes. (Jo was a kind of unofficial tennis impresario.)

I am certainly not the athletic type, nor is my wife. Jo and his first wife, Lenore (who died in Rome years ago)—Lieutenant Tom Ridgway and the eagle-eyed Clothier of the FBI . . . they played their sizzling doubles until they melted the gut in their rackets. Irene and I merely turned over in our chairs and waved our tumblers in feeble encouragement.

Came a Sunday evening when the war shrilled close above Pacific Palisades once more, spouting its menace in every twist of sirens. We had had the pleasantest Sunday imaginable. The tennis players had alternately perspired and showered. Irene and I had alternately sipped and mixed. We smelled the flowers, we watched the Nazi Spies slogging militantly along Monaco Drive on one of their Top Secret errands preliminary to German-American *Anschluss*. Someone should have hung a sign on each of them: *I Am A Nazi Spy,* and let it go at that. . . .

Well, it was about nine by the village clock when the telephone buzzed. It was a yellow signal; so Jo tugged at his turtleneck sweater and overalls, and got out his other fireman's gauds and necessities, while I scouted in my car-trunk for pistol, helmet, and white slicker. Instructions for us auxiliary policemen were, if we were away from our home base, to go on duty at the nearest busy intersection.

We had not even scrambled into all our equipment before here came the red signal, with sirens wailing across the plains of Santa Monica and West Los Angeles. Cotten, booted and

spurred, pedaled madly through chilly blackness toward the fire
station; I went scampering down to the corner of Monaco
Drive and Sunset Boulevard. Only by a stretch of imagination
could this be deemed a busy intersection; but once in a while
some cars did show up, trying to sneak home with or without
headlights. These malefactors I soon held, halted and petulant
at the curb.

Meanwhile, impatient to mount and ride, the neighborhood
warden had left his nearby home and gone galloping through
every Middlesex village and farm, and if you think I am kidding
about Middlesex you just don't know your Hollywood. It must
have been about nine-eleven by the village clock when Paul
Revere showed up at the Cottens'.

The Army Air Force and the Federal Bureau of Investigation were keeping Mrs. Cotten and Mrs. Kantor company in a
blackout chamber which Lenore had prepared in the basement
of her home. This room was draped with heavy curtains, was
hoped to be more or less bombproof, and contained a large
supply of refreshments with which the ennui of fear-stricken
sessions might be dispelled. The two ladies, with Lieutenant
Ridgway and Mr. Clothier, were busily dispelling, when there
came a pounding at the door.

All in his pristine helmet, his trench coat, and snowy gloves,
Mr. Revere was ushered in by the hospitable Lenore. He was
operating on the pretext that beams of tell-tale light were stealing out (this according to his detractors in the neighborhood);
but I am confident that his motives were of the highest. Nevertheless he showed a disposition to tarry briefly in the well-
stocked blackout room. He seemed thrilled at meeting, in the
flesh, representatives of the AAF and the FBI—the latter most
especially. Still he did not neglect his responsibilities.

With critical eye Mr. Revere examined the mechanical preparations made by the Cottens and pronounced them adequate.
He departed, after admonishing all personnel to remain alert
and prepared for any emergency.

The All-Clear sounded at last, and Jo and I repaired to his

home with the proud solemnity of men who had served their Country as she should be served. Mr. William Clothier conveyed Lieutenant Ridgway to an air base where he might beg a ride for Colorado.

. . . Before very long, Ridgway went winging overseas in one direction, and I went buzzing in the other. The sequel to this astonishing episode did not reach my ears until many years later, when it was divulged by Mr. Cotten himself. . . .

I was driving up Monaco through the dusk, and spied Jo shall we say botanizing amid his shrubbery. I halted while he came to reminisce.

"How's your tennis?"

"Terrible!" groaned Jo. "By the way— Remember Tom Ridgway and Bill Clothier? Remember the Nazi Spies?"

"Certainly."

"And Paul Revere—do you remember him? My friend," said that low steady voice, familiar to millions, "I shall a tale unfold."

. . . It was during WW II, a good while after Mr. Revere's casual meeting with the FBI in the blackout room—a good while after Ridgway and I had gone off to listen to Guns Fired in Anger—that Paul Revere called Mrs. Cotten one night on the telephone, in a high state of excitement.

"I *must* speak to Mr. Cotten."

Lenore chattered out a few mild discouragements. Jo was very busy, she said. He was studying a new script. Couldn't she take the message? Couldn't she—?

"I *must* speak to Mr. Cotten," said Paul Revere. "This is urgent," and reluctantly Lenore went in search of her spouse. . . .

"Mr. Cotten," said Paul Revere, "remember that night when we had a blackout, and you were gone to the fire station, and I came by to see about your blackout curtains, and you had an Army officer and a man from the FBI visiting you?"

"Yes."

"Well, what I want to know is, who was the man from the FBI? I must get hold of him at once."

Jo tried to stall a little. He knew that Bill Clothier had his work cut out for him; he didn't want to interfere with Clothier's professional devotions. Couldn't he deliver a message? Couldn't he relay to his FBI friend the news—whatever it was—which Mr. Revere wished to offer?

No, indeed! Revere was determined to reach the unknown FBI representative, and immediately, and in person. Jo was compelled to yield up information concerning Bill's name, location, and telephone number.

Jo was under the impression that the warden mumbled something about this being a great thing for the Country. Certainly this man's patriotic ardor was of the highest, but Jo wondered a little about his acumen.

Some weeks afterward, Bill Clothier, released for the moment from pressing and secret duties, called the Cottens and spoke wistfully of tennis, and was invited out to polish off a few sets. While Clothier and Cotten were dashing about the court, Jo bethought himself of the Midnight Message of Paul Revere.

"That fellow," he called across the net, "the air-raid warden. Remember him? I was afraid you'd be bothered; I tried to stall him off, but I couldn't quite manage it. He insisted on knowing your name and—"

"Oh, yes," cried Bill Clothier, snatching up a ball and batting it toward Jo. "Your serve, isn't it?"

"Yes," said Jo, receiving the ball. "Well, did he get hold of you?"

"Yes, he did. What's the call? Forty-thirty?"

"No, it's add here. But I wondered what he wanted—I mean, what was it all about?"

"Oh, yes," said Mr. Clothier, returning the low serve which Jo slammed across the net, "he got hold of me all right. My, it seems good to be playing tennis again!" and that was all Jo could get out of him.

I mean, that was all Jo could get out of him just then. The war was crackling on its course, the Nation was in danger; machine-guns were rattling all over the Globe. . . .

(I knew what was coming . . . the Nazi Spies! So finally Paul Revere had spotted them—the silly couple we saw stalking along Monaco Drive week after week, and seeming to mutter the *Horst Wessel* song even as they stalked.)

"Jo, don't tell me that Paul Revere got hold of Clothier, and had him sic the FBI on that pair of spooks!"

Yes, that was just what Paul Revere had done. They appeared most palpably to be Nazi Spies. To Nazi Spies he had but one answer: the FBI.

So, in response to his importuning, several carloads of brisk young men surrounded the spies' house. They took the pair by surprise; they whisked them into custody. They whisked also a whole cargo of short-wave radios, documents, instructions, cryptograms, codes, and Heaven knows what all. Listen, my children—they *were* Nazi Spies.

Her Name Was Grace
1941

My own private American squirrel-stew was cooked to pungency by a schoolteacher who built a hot fire under the pot. She was an enormous woman, unwomanly in every movement and gesture, lumbering through middle life as if her feet hurt her. And probably they did.

For she had the size and proportions of a heavyweight wrestler. Her black hair, coarse and kinky, was turning slightly gray. Her tiny red-rimmed black eyes lived deep within a perpetual squint. A faint mustache curled on her upper lip; and those few portions of her flesh not covered by her ample gowns showed the swarthiness of a Moor. Her walk was something between a fat lady's waddle and a plowman's stride.

And, God love her memory, her name was Grace.

I stared in amazement, the first time I ever saw her. When she had quaked up into our school building, I asked another child, "Who on earth is *that?*"

"That's Old Lady Bed-slats."

The boys called her that—Bed-slats—a far-fetched jest upon her name, which was Bidlack. She was the most impressive visitation the boys of Webster City ever experienced; and without doubt she will be remembered worshipfully by them when their grandsons trot to school beneath elms serene and elderly.

I don't know where our Superintendent of Schools found her. Mr. Kelly's intuition was as long as a prairie furrow. . . . He had found Miss Bidlack somewhere, and brought her to us.

She began to set her brand in our skins and souls; the proud marks she made will be there until we die.

When I entered her room as a student, she had already become an institution. Bidlack, Bed-slats, history books, the merry-go-round, parliamentary drill: all these were now regular departments in the life of Webster City boys.

Miss Bidlack would not teach girls. If she did not completely despise the dulcet feminine whisper in all nature, at least she chose to ignore it. The female eighth graders had been relegated to the stewardship of a truly feminine woman; and Grace Bidlack, that disgruntled blacksmith masquerading in petticoats, built a high wall around her boys and barred the gate.

The gods had visited her cradle in the village where she was born, and had wafted their endowments to her even while her homely infant face was wrinkled in sleep. They had given her the power to teach young boys, to teach them well if strangely. She spent her natural life doing just that. I never met a human being with more single-minded purpose.

To begin with, she worked fifteen hours a day. She had demanded a key to the school building, and she toiled up the street from Mrs. Letts's rooming-house each morning long before the school janitor arrived.

Lunch, to Grace Bidlack, was a midday annoyance to be disposed of hastily with an apple and a moldy sandwich or some such equally disgraceful weapons. Supper was something that you gobbled hastily at Mrs. Letts's table so that you might lose no time in assaulting the mound of papers waiting to be corrected, and probably those papers would occupy you until ten in the evening. And then came sleep. (I wonder if she ever dreamed, and what her dreams were.) Then came seven o'clock, and the schoolhouse.

Usually, however, she didn't sit alone during those early morning hours. There were boys with her much of the time, and for a considerable period I was one of them.

Old Lady Bed-slats had exclaimed to me, in her hoarse but nasal voice, one winter day a few months after I came to her:

"I can't make anything out of your arithmetic paper. It doesn't make sense. No arithmetic paper should be this bad."

I sulked.

"I don't understand it," she persisted, coming down the aisle with her quick, massive tread. "Some of these examples are things you must have done in the sixth grade. Your long division is no good. And you can't multiply a simple decimal."

She got the truth at last, and so did I. It was a horrid thing to face, there in the eighth grade. Never adept at numbers, I had been passed through several grades with only a meager knowledge—not even a working knowledge—of the simplest mathematical procedure. My former teachers seemed to have been charitable but utterly incompetent.

"There's only one thing to do," said Miss Bidlack. "You've reached the eighth grade somehow. Here you are. Your papers were terrible all fall, but I thought maybe you'd improve. Well, you haven't. You're getting more fuddled as the work advances. One thing to do: you'll have to stay after school every night."

"I can't," I wailed. "I've got to carry my paper route."

She was utterly impassive. "All right. Come mornings, then. Come tomorrow morning; every morning. Be here at seven o'clock."

. . . Sometimes there was snow beating through the darkness as I ran to school. Sometimes the snow had already fallen, and lay trodden into ice beneath my overshoes. No matter how I hurried, Grace Bidlack was always there before me. Once I very nearly beat her to the schoolhouse door . . . a massive squaw wrapped in an old plush coat, trailing stubbornly through the drifts.

The heat wouldn't be turned on yet. It could be very cold, at seven o'clock in the morning up on the third floor of that rickety building. We would sit, she in her coat, I in my mackinaw, and the staunch columns of decimals would march before us. Later I would go to the blackboard and do "examples," with the cold chalk squeaking like a banshee under my thumb.

An hour or an hour and a half of this; then we would have

breakfast, and historical discussion along with it. I, munching
the sandwiches and fruit which my grandmother had prepared;
Miss Bidlack, chewing at a slab of dry bread or coffee-cake
brought in a little paper sack from Mrs. Letts's rooming-house.

I grew to know Mrs. Letts later—a shrewd and salty old
woman who enjoyed good food. Certainly she did not prepare
those clammy morsels with which Grace Bidlack fed her great
body. Probably Miss Bidlack had a private bread-hoard in her
room. Through motives of economy, I think; since she was paid
something like eighty or eighty-five dollars a month, and had
an old mother to support in her home town.

But if she did not feed herself on succulent fare, she fed
me with arithmetical sustenance. I was never betrayed by a
fraction or a decimal from that year forth. I am no mathemati-
cian, but I can manipulate complicated sums if I need to; an
income-tax holds no horror for me, except the natural dread of
having to pay it.

However, arithmetic was a side-line with Miss Bidlack—
something to be tossed off in the dark watches of a winter
morning, perhaps, but nothing to sustain interest and emotion.
She had one almighty interest and emotion, and she gave that
to us with violence and purpose.

It was America: the benefits, trials, excitement and beauty
which had come to the people living here.

Miss Bidlack's America was not a matter of railroad sub-
sidies and corporate indolence and legislative dawdling. Doubtless she knew that these fat vices had flourished in the past and
might bog our Nation down in the future. But she disregarded
completely any evils of which her historical sophistication may
have made her aware.

The America she gave her boys was a heritage of sweat, bullets, tattered flags, war-whoops, red footprints in the snow. To
children who previously had found stimulation in the exploits
of the Harry Castlemon heroes, she suddenly discovered the
thrill and significance of our national past.

We galloped with Nathaniel Bacon. We snaked through the

swamps with King Philip. We ate horse-meat with Benjamin
Church. We paced the chilly streets of Philadelphia with
Robert Morris, ringing doorbells, demanding money for the
ragged Continentals. We struck and fled through the live oaks
with General Francis Marion. With Lawrence and Decatur we
tussled against African pirates, and at last we flung ourselves,
dying, with Bowie and Crockett in the Alamo. We wrenched a
cane from the maddened statesman who attacked the delicate
Sumner, and we shivered beneath the oratory of Clay and
Calhoun.

A guidon snapped in the wind, the minié-balls squealed
around us. Historical slogans. Catch-words. Gigantic and appropriate (and God knows, oftentimes fictitious) utterances beat
against our ears. Don't fire till you see the whites of their eyes.
There are the British; we must beat them today or Molly Stark
is a widow. Open, in the name of the great Jehovah and the
Continental Congress!

Tippecanoe and Tyler too . . . Remember the Alamo . . .
Fifty-four-forty or fight . . . Go west, young man, and grow up
with the country . . . That's Stonewall Jackson's way . . .
Find out what kind of whiskey General Grant drinks, so that I
may send a barrel of it to each of my other generals . . . Now he
belongs to the ages . . . Remember the Maine . . . You
may fire when ready, Gridley.

They come shouting at me now, dream voices of the American
past: the dreamer's America, the child's America, the patriot's
America. And, most certainly, Grace Bidlack's America.

I am by no means tricked into falsehood along with my
sentimental recollection. I have not lost touch with my youth.
I see others of Miss Bidlack's boys every now and then, and we
always talk of her.

Every boy had a history book. Not a textbook, although we
had those too, but a blank paper notebook in which to paint
and inscribe his own version of national heroics with red and
green ink, with every shade of wax crayon. We embalmed
history within those books and within our memories. We made

maps showing the penetration of European explorers upon this continent, and the areas where their possessions lay. All these maps were colored alike, after the rhymed key the great Grace taught us:

"Englishmen red, for the blood which they shed."

"Frenchmen blue, for their dealings true."

"Yellow we'll use for the Spaniard bold, who spent his time in search of gold."

"Purple for Italy's sons so grand, who won much fame but kept no land."

"Brown for the Dutch, whose native soil is wrest from the waves through years of toil."

"Green for the Swedes, who fought with the Dutch. Though trials they had, they didn't keep much."

Throughout the school year we maintained a contest. There were five rows of seats, and each row was named after a motor car. A chart, crowded against the wall among flags and battle scenes and pictures of Washington and Lincoln, showed the progress of each car along the rocky road to good citizenship and decent scholarship. Ford, Mercedes, Chalmers, Chandler, and Lexington: they were speeded on their way by good deportment, willingness to learn, activity in programs and speaking contests, and by model behavior of the occupants when they moved outside the schoolhouse walls.

There were a lot of tabus; if you violated one, it could put your car in the ditch for days and arouse the fanatical wrath of your car mates. Did Merlin Clark cut across the courthouse grounds where the new grass was trying to grow? The Mercedes went into the ditch and stayed there awhile. Did Buster Fassett carelessly throw a scrap of paper into a schoolyard flower bed, and was it found by the janitor, with Buster's name upon it? The Ford went into the garage for repairs.

How she kept this excitement and interest alive in our hearts for nine mortal months, is something I do not yet understand. But Grace Bidlack did it. It seems to me now that there was something symbolic in the fact that she was the dominating presence for a nine-month period at the termination of our childhood. We were fastened to her by an invisible umbilical cord. On June first we came forth from the womb of her teaching, hearty and lusty, excited beyond measure by the valiant masculine experiences awaiting us.

And meanwhile, as we grew and strengthened, Bed-slats had been dosing herself with the tinctures and tonics which her unholy habits of eating made necessary to her peace of mind and body. I found out all about this in after years, from a teacher who was intimately associated with her.

Miss Bidlack visited a drugstore each week, and bought practically every kind of worm elixir, emulsion, vegetable prescription, golden medical discovery, antacid, vermifuge, chill tonic, alterative compound and blackberry balm known to the imagination of quack manufacturers. With this repulsive array of bottles she felt equipped for existence, and she sampled the dosages continuously throughout the school year. At the end of the year, it was her habit to have a grand cleaning-up—and probably a grand cleaning-out—as well. It is literal fact, sworn by those who knew her habits, that, annually, in one week, she made away with the leavings in her entire dresser-full of bottles.

On occasion, her colleagues were compelled to fear for her life. But after a period of agony, she arose ready to wrestle with demons again. Master of every patent-medicine in the decalogue, she had the stomach of a goat.

Possibly due to a secret anguish which she never mentioned, no one of us ever saw her affectionate or tender. Often we did see her with temper flown wild, with brows knit and breath coming angrily. Often we felt her huge paws upon us. Often we tasted the chalk dust of the schoolroom floor.

She would no more brook insolence from a boy than she would interference with her manner of teaching. When she felt impelled toward castigation it was a fearsome experience for all concerned, not excepting the spectators. She didn't exactly beat boys. She whirled them around. . . . I have always thought of "trouncing" as a fit term for this ceremony, though perhaps that implies more in the manner of blows than she was accustomed to give. She cuffed and wrestled, she flung the boys into the air. The brawniest dullard, man-grown but still boy-minded enough to be a student in the eighth grade, could become a quivering pulp within Bed-slats's clutch. The whirling frenzy to which she treated the recalcitrant was called in schoolyard legend, "the merry-go-round." No boy ever wished to ride upon it, but only a few escaped.

A shocked parent whose family dignity had been torn to as many rags as his son's shirt, waited upon Superintendent Kelly in apoplectic ire. He poured out his tale. He cried that corporal punishment should be a thing of the past, that no two-hundred-pound woman should "pick on" a thirteen-year-old boy. With all of which Mr. Kelly agreed in theory, but his final shrug and retort left the angry father silenced.

"That's all true, Mr. Sanderson! But she makes the boys *learn*. And they *like her*."

Her garb was as masculine as the law and ordinary custom of that day and place would allow. I think that she wore no more than four costumes throughout that entire nine months; probably four were all she had. A gray woolen dress, piped with red; a red woolen dress, piped with black; a black dress with the plainest and ugliest embroidery imaginable; and, for warm weather in fall and spring, a shirtwaist and skirt. And all of these were high-collared, long-cuffed; worn solely to conceal the powerful body which she hated cordially because it had been made according to the wrong pattern.

She shook us, she wiped up the floor with us. And somehow in the process she communicated a portion of her forthright eagerness for America. We had never known what it was to Address the Chair, to Rise to a Point of Order, to make a senate of our classroom and senators of ourselves; but we performed even that miracle a generation ago. By these means, and in other manners as well, Miss Bidlack was equipping us to live

in the Nation of which we were a part and of which she was
so proud.

In her we learned trial by ordeal and trial by gooseflesh
as well. Sometimes it seemed that reincarnation was occurring
before our eyes: thirty-three pairs of eyes, that never left
Grace Bidlack's face as her man's mouth rolled out the words of
Daniel Webster.

"When mine eyes shall be turned for the last time to behold
the sun in heaven, may I not see him shining on the broken
and disordered fragments of a once glorious nation. . . ."

It seems that this should read "my eyes," and not "mine."
Perhaps it was a faithful transcription of Webster's reply to
Hayne— I know that oration only as she gave it to me. Or it
may have been an archaic fancy of her own. But that was it,
always: the hoarse voice, throaty and yet somehow coming
through the nose; the fury and fire behind it. The glinting gaze,
seeing the United States Senate chamber which in fact she had
never seen.

"When mine eyes shall be turned. . . ."

We left her at last. We left her eagerly, for most of us were to
enter high school in the fall. Yet high school and all the
novelty it entailed seemed flat and futile the next autumn,
when we walked the halls of an unfamiliar building and knew
that last year's seventh-graders had succeeded to the history
books, the parliamentary drills, the chilly morning sessions and
winter twilight tutorings which had been a part of our especial
existence.

We struggled on through high school, and to the America
awaiting us, and to the other lands where some of us went.
Grace Bidlack stayed and taught in Webster City. It was something she had said that she would never do. She said frankly
that a three-year stint was enough for any school-ma'rm in any
town, and that she would leave at the end of her third year;
she had always done so.

But Mr. Kelly and the school board prevailed upon her to
reconsider. They raised her salary; another year or two went by,

and then more years and another raise. All the time she was growing old. A long time afterward, when I was in the East, I learned that she was dead, and I experienced a physical shock at the news. It was as if the illusion of Lincoln were dead too; as if the Declaration of Independence had mildewed into vanishment.

Miss Bidlack gave us the America of which so many children dream; we were able to keep that shiny, chevroned notion of a bold America longer and more ardently than those who were never taught by her. She would not have countenanced a slogan like, "Tell Woodrow the Yanks aren't coming," if such heresy had been published abroad in those days.

Some of her boys went out to support personally the legend she implanted in their hearts. Some of them died in muddy ravines where the machine-guns were pounding, or in barracks where the flu walked thick. I can't get over the notion that they witnessed a wild, bugling, American marvel when their eyes were turned (like the eyes of Grace Bidlack and Daniel Webster) for the last time to behold the sun in Heaven.

Of Guns and
Monsters
1962

In 1938, when we spent the summer digging up Indian mounds with a retinue of eager young archaeologists out in Iowa, our family had a kidnaping scare. It was complete with mysterious cars haunting around at night; equally mysterious telephone calls; all the rest of it. Our children were small, certainly vulnerable to kidnaping, and there had been enough local and State-wide publicity about the Indian mound project to attract the attention of any halfwits who might think I was richer than I was.

Finally one night at 3 A.M. I was up with a toothache. Glancing out of the window, I saw an unlighted car crawling around the corner near the big house we had rented. I got a .44 Special and a flashlight, and went out to drive my own car alongside the other vehicle. The light washed over the faces of four unpalatable-looking male specimens—who didn't say a word, but stared straight ahead. I made a U-turn, in order to have another look, and get the license number. At that moment the suspicious vehicle took off with a great scream of tires.

The Webster City police and I scouted through highways and byways for an hour, but the car had vanished.

Irene and I were sufficiently apprehensive to go up to the courthouse and get permits, as required by Iowa law, to carry concealed weapons. I bought her a little .22–.32 S. & W., which she carried in her bag whenever she was out with the children; and I had my own gun in my own car.

Returning to Florida at the end of the summer, we thought it wise to continue these defensive tactics. I went to the Sarasota County courthouse for that purpose. Young Sheriff Doug Pearson seemed a little puzzled by my request. "Why, I don't rightly know," quoth Doug, "just what you do about getting a permit." He called for help, and, after some cogitation by everyone in the sheriff's office, it was decided that I should go upstairs to some local official—I can't remember his name, rank or office—but he also was bemused when I got there.

"Pistol permit? Well, let's see—" He led the way into a vault; and after searching the steel shelves, he pulled out an impressive-looking volume and blew the dust off of it. "You see," he said, "we don't get many requests for this kind of thing." He thumbed through the pages, and thus we learned that the last pistol permit issued in Sarasota County had been applied for just twelve years previously.

There seemed an awful lot of nuisance about the whole thing: bonds to be put up, character witnesses to be produced, and I don't know what all. The official, bless him, was not given to palaver. He closed the book with a bang. "For goodness sake, Mr. Kantor," he said, "why don't you forget about this business, and just carry your gun when you think you'll need it, like anybody else?"

Well, come the next May—that would be in 1939—I was still carrying the gun in the car when I was in Florida. My friend John Upton Terrell, a writer, had accompanied me down from the North. Second morning we were home, I needed to have my car checked over by Harry Spence, down at Cooke's Oldsmobile garage. Harry gave me some sort of old jalopy to use while they were working on my car.

It was about 10:30 in the morning when Johnny and I set out for Siesta Key. We swept around the first corner after crossing the hump-back bridge from Bay Island, approaching a region adjacent to the Siesta Key fish market, where a man named Lonnie Blount then presided. Of course there was an infinitesimal fraction of the traffic in this region that there is now, so the road was deserted except for our car.

As we came around that corner—dead sober, in broad daylight, and possessed of mutually good eyesight—there was the biggest snake I ever saw, writhing across the road, from east to west.

The reptile filled the roadway completely, from side to side; which I suppose would make him at least twenty feet long. And he was proportionately thick in body. . . . Color? It seemed to us then and afterward that it was a mottled brownish-green or greenish-gray.

Johnny and I both gasped. I put my foot down hard on the accelerator, planning to collide with the monster, and maybe bump across him with enough impact to injure and hold him. If I'd had my own car I might have done it; but this ancient loaned sedan gave a couple of coughs before the acceleration took hold. Then we managed to make it—just off the west shoulder of the road, and into the palmetto scrub; but the snake had beaten us by a yard.

Automatically I grabbed for the glove compartment, then stayed my hand: my gun was down there at Cooke's garage in the other car.

I thought of Lonnie Blount at the fish market—knew he had a shotgun handy. By that time the serpent was thrashing off in the direction of Bayou Louise and the Gulf—not a single house in there, in those days—and it looked as if someone were driving a team of mules through the brush, the way that scrub tossed back and forth.

Johnny screamed, "I'll follow him!"

I ran for Lonnie Blount, yelling at the top of my lungs, "Lonnie! Get your gun, get your gun!"

Blount was an old World War I 13th Engineers type who didn't ask twice. He raced into the house, and then came hastening toward me, loaded shotgun in hand.

I yelled, "The biggest damn snake I ever saw!"

"Where is he?"

"Gone across the road!" So Lonnie and I traipsed in that direction.

We were greeted by an anguished Terrell, gesturing in an attitude of defeat. "I couldn't follow him!" he cried. "He's gone. He went so fast I couldn't even catch up with him."

With Blount we prowled the whole area, and could see where the snake had traveled through weeds (it was an erratic furrow which he made) and then he'd vanished into the mangroves. Lonnie Blount told me later that he hunted the region for days without success.

We telephoned the winter quarters of the Ringling circus, miles distant, on the mainland and beyond a bay filled with wet water. Nay, they said. No serpents lost, strayed or stolen.

. . . I recalled a book on early Florida, written by some U. S. Naval officer. It was entitled *Across the Everglades*, and in this volume the author declared that there had been (and maybe existed still) enormous snakes in Florida—creatures unrecognized and unlisted by modern herpetologists, but known to the Indians. . . . Maybe so. Sounds queer. . . .

I don't know what our snake was, or what ever happened to it. Nobody else reported the critter subsequently, to my knowledge. I'm just telling you what we saw on the Siesta Key road that day in May, 1939. See it we did.

First Blood
1936

I was born to a mother whose fingers itched for the pencil or typewriter keys. Since she would early gratify her ambition among the smudged galleys of a small-town newspaper office, my difficulty was not so much in getting into print for better or for worse, but in learning to write anything truly fit for print.

After all, there was plenty of time for infantile apprenticeship. Mother did not become associated with our daily newspaper, the Webster City *Freeman-Tribune,* until I was eight or nine years old. During those earlier years she worked in a dry-goods store, and for Mr. Scriven, the bearded grocer.

I went along to Scriven's hopefully each time my grandmother pinned on her hat, gripped her reticule, and started on the gruesome round of robbing Peter to pay Paul. It was a thrill to enter the store, to smell the gunpowder-tea and starch and barrels of sugar; it was strange to see my mother, severe in a white shirtwaist, sitting at the high cashier's-desk sacred to the telephones (there were two services, even in so small a town—the Martin and the Independent) and the spindles of grocery bills. There was something awesome in witnessing a business relationship between my mother and my grandmother, with Mr. Scriven looking on, under and over his glasses. But the climax came when Mr. Scriven scurried to his proper station behind the candy counter, opened up the portals of Heaven, and half-filled a small, purple-striped paper sack with two or three kinds of candy—the standard perquisite allotted to one paying a bill, or an impressive part thereof.

Still, Scriven's grocery store did not smell anything like the noisy office of the daily *Freeman-Tribune*, and Mother's editorial burgeonings were still some years in the future. So were my first literary attempts. Certainly I must have written the usual labored scrawls required by the teachers in Number Five, Number Six, clear on up to room Number Eight in the old north building.

In the meantime Mr. D. L. Hunter, the newspaper editor, had mumbled a suggestion to my mother—"You ought to come over to the *Freeman* awhile, Effie, and see how you like it." She liked it well enough. It was about 1913 when she went over to the *Freeman*; after that came the *Herald* and the *Daily News*, and in the final stretch, her little small-town magazine, *Community*. When she died, late in 1931, her lean fingers were knuckle-knotted from incessant manipulation of her typewriter. I wept not only that she was gone, but that I could not believe in an Immortality which would grant her a desk and shears and an L. C. Smith to be handled through the ages, while Kelly presses roared in the clouds.

Well, she tried anxiously to rile me to the endeavors of composition, when I was still very small. But after I got over wanting to fight Indians in Nebraska, I wanted to be a curator of Indian relics and Civil War muskets; and if I couldn't be that, I wanted to be an artist. My sister, indeed, did entertain the Fatal Ambition for a brief spell. She was mystical about it, but forgot all such yearnings when she fell in love with a talented young Campbellite, who would take up the Bible long before his father laid it down.

I do remember coming through one of those blood-chilling Iowa winter evenings, when the sky tightened with blue and beetroot and black, and the snowy wind howled across Willson Avenue, fresh come from Dakota. "Some day," I told my sister, dramatically, "I shall paint a sunset like that!"

Virginia's face grew dreamy, or at least as much of it did as could be seen over Grandmother's old stone-marten muff, which she hugged against her nose. "That will be wonderful," she said, "and I—I shall paint that sunset in *words*. You will paint it with paints, and I with words, and—"

"And we'll put them side by side, and see which one's the best," I cried. But she thought, wisely, that that would be a terrible way of doing.

The bug may have nibbled at me a time or two during my childhood; I scarcely think he did more than touch me with his antennae. I was well gone into my adolescence before I became severely infected. When I was twelve, however, I did write a group of poems—four, I think—and all in one week. One was about a fern, one about the flute-playing of George Barrere (we had him on a victrola record) and another concerned, "Thoughts as I stood on the supposed site of a town built by the mound-builders." All of them were pre-Elizabethan in spirit. "Play on, thou master," I said to George Barrere, and I cried at the fern, "Oh, thou little fairy tree!" The one about the mound-builders ended up with "Whence? Whither?"

To my mother, these were gems of a high order. She posted them to Bert Leston Taylor, then editor of the Chicago *Tribune*'s Line o' Type, and got them back by return mail. For future amazement (B.L.T. the satirist, B.L.T. of the acid tongue, B.L.T. who shouted to the doorman when his contributors called on him, "Keep the lice outside!") B.L.T. had scrawled in red pencil on the back of the slender manuscript, *Very good. B.L.T.* and the date.

That was something, even for a proud mother who did not know B.L.T. or recognize what unique blarney she had received. She kindly forbore having the verses printed in the *Freeman-Tribune*—not because Mr. Hunter would object, but because the townspeople might laugh at me.

I had just slid into high school, a year or two ahead of my contemporaries in age. My advancement was due neither to good deportment nor to general scholarly attainment, but solely to a more or less phenomenal ability at reading the printed word. Thus I had been jumped from second to fourth grade, all in one season, and managed by hook or crook to hold my place with that class.

Now I wrote prose, perforce. Miss Ethel Swanson was our teacher of English and Rhetoric, and when I presented her with my themes, as they were called, the English may have been sour but there was a wealth of Rhetoric. I have some of these manuscripts at hand now. "We set out across the pasture, rejoicing in the glow of the early morning . . ." "When the incident which I shall relate took place . . ." "It was but the work of a moment to reach up my hands and grasp that object firmly but carefully . . ." "I beheld an impressive view." And the subject of one theme was, *Moonlight on the Orinoco.*

That was Rhetoric, as taught in the high school of Webster City and many other high schools, and as believed in and practiced by me. The stain is insidious and far-reaching, or so my publishers and the critics tell me at times. And my mother told me that she could read what I wrote, without bias or prejudice, and that nearly everything I wrote was very good indeed. I not only forgive her now—I thank her from the bottom of my heart. For difficult family situations were at hand: I had need for the encouragement toward mere living, and for whatever idolatrous plaudits she poured upon me. I think that in such times, and where very young people are concerned, it is the better part of wisdom to be very foolish indeed. After all, she was sober-minded and critical in many matters, but she had only one son and one daughter, and little else in the world.

Now the rumbling old presses of the *Freeman* were waiting for the eight lines of verse which I would give them, but the onset of battles fairly drowned their wheezing. Iowa was well represented when the first load of cannon-fodder was forked into the grinding silo of war. Merle Hay of Glidden was one of the "first three"—the 16th Infantry, I think, and during November of 1917. The next batch were blown aloft early in March in the Champagne Sector, and a Webster City man was among them.

I don't remember much about Jim Wedding. I do remember his father—a quiet-voiced old man with muttonchop whiskers, who was long the color-bearer of Winfield Scott Post, GAR. Jim Wedding was a sergeant, and a trench mortar found the exact range of his dugout. After the war his was one of the first bodies to be brought home; the arrival of the flag-draped coffin was attended by prayers, volleys, and oratory. Some of the ex-soldiers, especially those from Wedding's regiment, stood around in the crowd and whispered. It seems that at the time of his death, Sergeant Wedding became honored in a manner not unusual for that time and place: he had seven graves. Yet it was reliably stated that his body had been identified and now reposed beneath the flag and the birches and cedars of Grace-land Cemetery. A lot of the ex-soldiers were so profane as to wonder just what was in that coffin, anyway.

But I am getting ahead of myself. I am concerned (or should be, as I was then) with that Sunday morning in March, 1918, when a telegram came to a little house on Superior Street and the news was whispered around at church. I was just fourteen, and wanted very much to go to the war, and hoped to manage it before the year was out. I ran home from Sunday school, and wrote my poem on the piano stool while my grandmother was making cabbage salad. . . . The beef-boil smelled very good, I remember; I thought it a harsh dictate of fate that Sergeant James Ernest Wedding should never again partake of beef-boil —an Iowa beef-boil, cheap and tough, but cooked all morning until it was tender, and served up with carrots and white turnips and many onions.

Something about the beef-boil, perhaps, and certainly something about Iowa should have got into the poem. But they didn't. I was still studying Rhetoric under the tutelage of Miss Ethel Swanson. I wish to do Miss Swanson no injustice. Quite likely she might have approved of the introduction of both beef-boil and Iowa, in the poem, but I am sure that she approved of Rhetoric the more.

I called it "Killed in Action," and shrank at the notion of

signing my name. I wanted local fame, the adulation and approval which might come to me; but I could not face the joking, the pool-room guffaws, the patronizing neighbors' smiles which would surely come as well. So I signed "Anon." and mailed it in hand-printed form—not to the weekly *Herald*, which my mother was now editing for Senator Cady Chase, but to the daily *Freeman-Tribune* where she used to be.

It was published the next afternoon, in a black mourning box. Tuesday morning, when the students of the English and Rhetoric class were asked what they had read for "outside reading" during the past few days, Evelyn Channer got up and said, "I clipped this out of the paper last night, Miss Swanson."

She read it aloud to the class, half of whom giggled, and some of whom were serious, and some of whom were perfectly blank—as is the fashion with such classes. My face was hot. I thought that they would all spy on me, and reason it out and say, honestly or jeeringly, "Well! We got a poet among us!"

But nothing of the kind happened. Miss Swanson called on Herbert Arthur to read his theme, "My Walk to School," and not even Evelyn Channer knew that she was touching the hem of the garment of genius. You see, I believed that every poet was a genius. On the way home from school I said to myself several times, "You're a genius!" But the words had a hollow ring; I feared that I could never be convinced.

I told my family; they took it in their stride; were calm and, I hope, proud. I clipped the poem from Monday's edition and put it in that little drawer in the secretary where my mother kept postage stamps and rubber bands and, for some reason, a dried-up buckeye that my grandfather used to carry in his pocket.

And the Armies That Remain'd Suffer'd 1945

All that night the lilacs were last blooming in the dooryard, but if you lay asleep you couldn't smell them, and you couldn't hear them blowing in the cold wind.

It cleared up, sometime before dawn.

This is something to recall in a late autumn month and on a day when bugles are sounding, and rifle volleys; and people stand with their hats off in memory of a certain moment. It is something to remember and I will remember it now and always: a bitter wind in the before-dawn meadows, the high ground between Bedford and Northampton, the bases with their thousands and thousands of people still fighting a war, still working hard to keep the engines hearty—the ones on the ground with their hands greasy with war, and those of us who went into the air still frightened at the memory of the many who had died.

It is a powerful thing to remember: the orderly's steps sounding in the hollow hall; the vague, heavy voice and the hand that tugged and shook at the covers; the voice saying, "It's seven-twenty now; Briefing is at eight-thirty; you can get chow any time," and my own voice, wearily, "Oh, thanks a lot." And the discipline of pushing my body out of bed and climbing down, moving carefully so that I would not step on Murray's feet; and then realizing, halfway between my bed and the floor, that Murray wasn't asleep in that lower cot, and that he had spent the night on leave in London.

And out to the latrine and the cold water that made the gums
tingle and the jaws ache; and a childish satisfaction in knowing
that I didn't have to shave; and wondering why an oxygen
mask might make your face sore if you had just shaved. And
then putting things into my pockets—the little things that most
men take with them: a leather folder of photographs, and a
medal of St. Joseph of Cupertino Who By the Grace of God
Did Fly (it was a medal a nice girl gave me long ago, before I
had flown any missions at all); and also there was a tiny red
horseshoe, a sort of celluloid button off one of my wife's old
frocks; and she had said: "Want a horseshoe for good luck?"
and I had said seriously, "You're damn right I do."

Out into the wan wet sunlight, and tramping along down to
the corner of the site, and I could not smell lilacs anywhere . . .
just chilly grass of an April dawn, the thin green smell of war
and England. The sky was bluer now, the sun was yellow coming up; and if the great star droop'd in the west, I had never
seen it, because I went to bed at ten the night before.

But also there was that brown figure out in the road, moving
away from the 422nd site where I was living; and that was
funny—to live with the 422nd when I was flying with the
364th. But I did it because of the old days, and because of the
people I had known who used to sleep in those same rooms—
people long since transmuted into cracklings and clinkers,
people nibbled in their fat leather flying jackets, nibbled by
icy fish of the Channel or the North Sea, and vanished away
by tides and heavy depths until there was nothing left of them
now, and even the fish had forgotten them.

There was that lieutenant in the road, and he saw me coming.
He hesitated, he turned and waited, he stood beyond the corner
of the last barracks, and he wasn't anyone I knew: he came
from away out in the wild woodland yonder where there were
Nissen huts that had not existed in 1943.

His name was Friedman—Lieutenant Friedman—and he told
his name a few minutes later because I asked him for his name;
I wanted always to remember the name of the man who told

me; and that was funny, too, because if I had heard the news over the radio I would not have cared to know the announcer's name.

There in the road we stood, and Friedman told me. He had his back to the east as he talked, and I could see larks sailing up and down beyond the nearest hedges and could hear their song and the song of other birds—British birds, the names of which most of us never knew. Maybe they were throstles and lapwings and nightingales; and they kept singing just as if it had not happened, just as if a man had not died.

We walked down the long road, going north past the officers' club, past water tanks to the mess hall; and we didn't talk much—we just muttered obscene words now and then: the things you say when you see two planes colliding in the air five hundred feet short of home and safety. You say those words when people are washed out vengefully, at the sudden end of a job well done—because they will never be able to look back on their job and realize just how well done it was, how wearying and frightening a task, how important to all future tenderness, all future stability, all dream forever.

People didn't talk much in the mess hall either. There was that box of oranges which came to us miraculously in this plush-lined war of 1945—the oranges we would have bid pounds on pounds for, in an earlier year; but now there were oranges all over the mess hall, waiting for the combat crews; and oranges rolling around in the airplanes, being squeezed flat by the weight of flak suits, oranges being only half-sucked and cast away and neglected because we had so many of them. We stood in line and got our pancakes and the rancid-tasting pork which was dignified by the name of bacon, but it wasn't real bacon. We had our generous brick of butter on the table, and someone kept a fire going in a small stove nearby, and we would put chunks of bread right down on top of the stove and let it scorch brown on both sides, and we called it toast.

We ate. We couldn't eat a lot. We went back to the big coffee tank for refills, and I looked at my watch and it was after 0800 hrs. Briefing was at 0830, so we had better get going. . . . I used to ride down to Briefing with Jonesy, a slow-spoken weather man from Vermont—a pink-faced, bespectacled weather man who made everyone laugh by just being the way he was, until he began to command the respect and attention of crews who found out how much he knew about weather. Jonesy was already gone away in his jeep; so we went out and started to hike—a navigator and a bombardier and I—but we knew we'd have to hitch a ride because the field was too far off . . . we weren't worried; they always ran plenty of regular transportation to the field at such hours.

And we waited at the road's turn and saw a truck coming, and we stood there swinging our arms and blinking at the future, not being able to see it at all. We talked in flat limp tones, we all said we could not believe it; even hearing other people exclaim about the tidings over and over again, we still couldn't believe it.

The navigator said, "By God, why do we have to fly a mission today? By God, it's Friday the Thirteenth!" and then the bombardier said, "Yes, but he didn't die on Friday the Thirteenth. He died on Thursday the Twelfth." Then we all said, Why, that's right, it was around ten o'clock last night, our time, when he died.

The truck stopped for us and we climbed up, we pushed in among solemn faces, the people who could not believe that this was true any more than we could believe it ourselves.

But that truck wasn't going all the way down the line. It let us out at the entrance to our headquarters site area, and then we started walking again. I guess we were looking at the ground as we walked, and thinking hard, and saying to ourselves, "But what will happen now? What will become of us?" and then the bombardier said abruptly, "My mother died when I was only five years old," and we all knew what he meant and what he was thinking, but we didn't say anything ourselves.

We only said it in our hearts . . . no more the strong, round voice, no more the jaunty hat and cigarette, no more the laugh for the movie camera and the still photographers; no more the

slow figure helped upon the stage; no more the great boss, the
captain, the broad-faced admiral, the personality guy; no more
the mighty priest to whom we entrusted our salvation; no more
the name that enemies hated, the name they shot out in
three hissing syllables like a Teutonic curse. O no more the
red-hot comet, the core of our little universe—the whiz, the
force, the energy that ionized an admiration or a hatred in
every breast; no more these things that had lightninged in our
lives so long. And here it was Friday the Thirteenth, and we
were flying a mission just like any other day, and we wondered what the score would be.

We were all looking down at the ground as we walked, and I
guess I was walking a little ahead . . . because they came right
out into the road in front of me—three pairs of legs marching
steadily, and one pair were officer's legs and the other two were
GI's. They held their steady military pace for forty or fifty steps
ahead of us as we walked, and then they wheeled to the
right.

The officer halted and stood while the two MPs marched
mechanically down the middle of a cinder path bordered with
little stones. We could see where they were headed: toward the
flag-pole . . . all of us in the road automatically quickened our
pace. We were going to hurry and try to get out of range, so
that we wouldn't have to stand at salute the moment the MPs
got to fooling around with that flag.

And then in the next breath we realized simultaneously
why the MPs were going to fool around with that flag . . .
this wasn't *Retreat* . . . they wouldn't be sounding *To the
Color* or any of that stuff, the way they did every evening when
we went to school at Bovingdon. No, they were going to do
something quite different; and none of us had ever seen them do
this peculiar job with the flag for such a peculiar reason before.

We stopped, we were facing toward the flag-pole, and we
could feel our heels snap back and our shoulders stiffen; and,
while their officer watched, the two MPs went to work on the
halyards. They brought the flag all the way down, then they

spread it out. The light morning wind caught the bunting for a moment and held it like a picture-book flag, and then they ran it slowly to the peak of the pole and brought it down halfway and tied the halyards.

No audible word was spoken. No order was given. And yet, watching with frozen gaze past the pole and the red-and-white stripes and the stubborn faces of the MPs, we could see that all life was suspended in the area. Trucks had stopped, the boys had stepped down and discarded their bicycles, the boys coming out of huts beyond the road had all solidified. They had turned to stone, as we people in the road had turned to stone. Sharp edges of their hard palms were bent like iron at their foreheads; and so we stood and watched, and tried to guess at what this might mean to the future and to the present; but we couldn't really guess at anything.

We went on to Briefing, and there was a delay, as so often occurred. Officers were crowding in the hall outside the interrogation room where they gave us our briefing, and I found my pilot there—a boy named Chick Kuhl, from Washington, D.C., and his co-pilot, Bob Law from Springfield, Missouri. There were others I knew, sitting around, and while we waited the main talk was about this new guy in the White House.

What would he be like? What would he do? How trustworthy was he? Some joker kept reciting a lot of stuff about how many million dollars the Pendergast machine had stolen in Missouri; but I don't remember how many millions he said. Still we took him up on it, whether we knew much about Kansas City politics or whether we didn't. Mostly we didn't.

Then the door had opened and we were filing in, and they were handing out the pilots' flimsies at the door, and I got one. I always took a flimsy but I didn't know what half the stuff on those little sheets of paper was about. Mohawk Baker Leader, and Mohawk Baker Low, and Mohawk Baker High and all that material. Authentication: Pepsi . . . 1st Division Recall: Flashlight—Pat—Aunty—Corncrib. . . . There were plenty more: three pages of mimeographed words and figures, but right then we weren't paying much attention to the flimsies. We were looking instead at a huge map with a red ribbon traced across the North Sea and across the Netherlands, all the way to a target called Hagenow.

And these weren't like the missions we had in 1943, when Heaven knew who or how many would come back; or—out of those Forts which came back—no one knew who or how many would be lifted silent or squeaking out of the airplanes, and wound in gray blankets and carried away on the meat wagon. These were comparatively easy missions now. There wasn't much flak and not many fighters, although a bunch of jets had hopped our low squadron the Saturday before, when we were coming back from Wesendorf.

Also there was the normal operational hazard of having about seven fields in the same traffic pattern; and it was all right to be told to take off in a heavy fog and do a ninety-degree to the right at the proper moment, but we never felt quite confident that those boys from the 92nd Group were going to make their ninety-degrees to the right as they came swishing up in the opposite direction, and probably they felt the same way about us.

Anyway, it was one more mission to fly, and we were glad we didn't have to go all the way to the borders of Czechoslovakia or the edge of the Alps; but still it was Friday the Thirteenth, and still a man had died in Georgia the night before, and none of us was feeling too cocky.

O nevermore the cute fellows who pretended that they were doing imitations of a radio broadcast and saying, "Mah friends"; and none of the gossip about Elliott's wives or Madam Perkins —that would all calm down and dry up and blow away . . . and who would make a wisecrack about Fala now, and why? And who would make a great joke out of the fact that the President's wife didn't exactly resemble Miss Greer Garson or Miss Jennifer Jones? And what would the Chicago *Tribune* and the New York *Daily News* live on—what kind of air would they breathe, now that their fetid food was available no longer? . . . No more the Navy cape around the shoulders, no more the strong infectious chuckle, no more the Harvard accent grown so familiar to even Oklahoma ears. Not ever again the great good meaty face with the wart on its cheek; no more the stamp collection; never again the ship models and the desk of gadgets.

And so time went by, and we had our squadron Briefing later, and then our weary walk down to 364th Supply. Before long we were hanging the handles of heavy bags over those hooks that sprouted from the sides of the big truck. . . . We swung and crowded, the chill wind blew, there were clouds. . . . We wondered whether we would be scrubbed again; and then we were at our dispersal point, with J976 looming up on the vertical stabilizer of the big Fort.

We started engines, we taxied, we took off, we formed up. We were part of a long droning line; we climbed across England; we climbed above the sea. We loaded our guns and fastened on our masks, and watched the blinker lips going back and forth—a strange little white mechanical movement so obscenely suggestive, so reminiscent of a kiss, a manifestation of human organs somehow—and we always hoped that it didn't mean the kiss of death.

And before we went on oxygen, the toggle-eer (an ex-divinity student whom we called "Deacon" Stanley)—Stanley and I both told each other how we felt, and it seemed a little better to be able to say how we felt.

And also before we went on oxygen, the navigator (he was Fred Tate, and he was twenty-one and came from New Albany, Mississippi)— The navigator and I had our legs rather tangled up together and we kept apologizing and trying to move out of each other's way.

He said slowly, "It's like a big black cloud," and I knew what he meant. I told him Whitman wrote something like that . . . a big black cloud, and a dark train moving across a dark nation. Now the same thing had come to pass, in another war; but we were far away from our country, far away even from the smell

of English lilacs whether they bloomed in the dooryards first
or last.

We were rocketing between clear heaven and the deadly
ocean water beneath. There were enemies who hated us . . .
we drove, shafting through space three miles a minute, hunting
for the flak which would await us in some degree even so late
in the war, fearful of the Messerschmitt 262s which might
doom us even today. We were bereft . . . we traveled swiftly
and in peril; and far away in Georgia, a paralyzed man had
died and left us, and we felt very lonely and unled.

So the Old Maid Said to the Traveling Man— 1953

The afternoon leaps into recollection. I was at my desk in the library of our New York apartment, and my tow-headed son (nowadays he has gilt bars on his shoulders and silver wings on his chest; but this was circa 1946) came up the hall and peeked in at the door.

"You're late coming from school, Timmy."

"The bus broke down and a bunch of us had to wait. Busy, Dad?"

"Not particularly. What are you giggling about?"

"Oh, it was kind of funny. . . . Remember that story you told last night?"

"Which one?"

"About the black cow and the white cow."

"Sure." It was the one about the idiot boy on the farm, who was supposed to stand guard while two choice cows were bred. I remembered Tim's sheer delight at the tale—the way he lay on the couch, gasping with glee, kicking his feet in the air. "It's a good story."

"And how! Well, we kids from Horace Mann were waiting for the bus, and some of the guys got to telling stories. So I told that one. Gosh, you ought to have heard those boys; they just about blew their tops. Soon as he could manage to talk again, Bunny Shimer said, 'Kantor, that's a wonderful story. Where did you get it?' I said, 'Dad told it last night.'"

His eyebrows went on high. "Well, you could have heard a

pin drop. They just stood there and stared at me, and Bunny's jaw dropped a mile. Then he managed to gasp, 'Your—your *father?*' I said, 'That's where I get most of my stories.' You know, Dad, I guess half of the kids don't believe me yet! Especially Bunny."

Tim picked up his books and headed for his room. He turned and gave me his sly grin. "And, Dad—Bunny Shimer—he's the one who is suspected of being the character who writes dirty words on the wall in the lavatory at school."

I meditated long. Another picture came to memory; it was painful; I could recall the raw, biting taste in my mouth. . . .

The scene was an Iowa kitchen, maybe about 1910, and I had just come from school. I bounced into the room and recited to my mother a limerick learned on the playground. It was about the old lady from Wheeling who had a peculiar feeling.

. . . Mother stands before me, frozen in stark horror. She cannot believe her ears. Her son— Her little darling, spewing out words like that! Well, she knows the answer. Soap and water are waiting, and the sink stands by. In another moment I am dragged sinkwards, and the best lather which can be manufactured through the genius of the Fels Naphtha company is forced into my yelling mouth. . . .

It still burns my tongue, and well it might. I violated two of the cardinal rules which should be laid down for raconteurs. First, I had been unwise in my choice of material. The old woman from Wheeling is not at all funny; she is simply a nasty harridan who behaves in a disgusting manner, witlessly, pointlessly. She accomplishes nothing. She merely befouls the room.

Had I recited—say—the one about the young girl from Detroit or the young lady from Kew or the Young man from Glens Falls, at least I would have been distributing fun instead of putrescence.

And, secondly, a mistake perhaps even worse. I had not picked my audience with care.

Mother was no audience for any teller of bawdy stories or

rhymes. In later life she might smile mildly over some brief myth about the hick bridegroom who was asked if he wanted the bridal chamber (like many Midwestern ladies of pioneer stock she possessed a response to simple, earthy, peasant humor) —but to her dying day she recoiled from the sound of a four-letter word. Four-letter words spelled vice to her, and vice was not amusing. Vice was ugly.

My playmates might have shouted with joy at the stupid rot which I mouthed. Not Mother. The soap-and-water treatment offered one good lesson: that was not to go around chattering obscenities to unreceptive ears.

I have a daughter as well as a son. From the time the children were old enough to be diverted by such colorful legendry, I offered it eagerly. Why not? For something like thirty years of maturity I have gone through life in schools, offices, studios, bars, clubs, homes—in peace and war and so-called cold war— to be greeted constantly with, "Hey, you got any new stories?" This is an accolade of which I am proportionately proud.

We all like to transmit our skills to our offspring. Had I been a champion skater or golfer, doubtless I would have taught the kids how to skate or how to play golf. As it was, I taught them to tell good stories—to tell them ardently, aptly, artistically.

This was appalling to some of my friends. One man in particular, of conservative background but not necessarily of conservative tastes, lectured me severely.

"I think you should be ashamed. You oughtn't to have told that one about the circus performer who had to undergo an amputation—not while Layne and Tim were in the room!"

"No? It's funny as hell. They understood it. It came within the realm of their experience, or at least within the realm of their active imagination. They loved that story, just as you folks did. You heard them shout."

"Nevertheless you should have waited until they'd gone to bed. I wouldn't tell a thing like that in front of my daughter and son. If I did I ought to be court-martialed."

His wife said, "I agree."

My wife said, "I don't. I think Mack's right. Children are bound to hear off-color stories anyway; just think of your own school days. They might better hear funny stories rather than merely filthy ones. They'll soon learn to discriminate between the clever and the disgusting. If they hear them told well, they'll learn to tell them well by example."

My friend was unpersuaded. He stood as a traditional slave to the duplicit standard which is common in our civilization today.

It happens that my son is now serene in his hazardous and demanding existence as an officer of the United States Air Force. My daughter is a busy and beaming wife and mother. . . . I wish that the children of my friend were as warm in the sun of fortune, but they are not. The boy was married and hastily divorced in his early twenties, and now wanders morosely from painful love affair to painful love affair. The girl is drifting among jobs and men, unsatisfied, unfulfilled; her pretty face, at twenty-five, grows sullen and petulant.

I'm not so absurd as to suggest that my children are well-adjusted simply because I told lewd stories in their presence. But I do declare that if you rear young folks under the bell-glass of an antique etiquette, you aren't equipping them very well for the modern world. The same casual give-and-take light-heartedness which allows a humor to be shared between parent and child is very apt to shine in a home where affection, trust, and understanding are the natural course of life.

But let's get down to the serious business of dirty stories as such. That term must be employed because that's what people call them, though I hold it to be incorrect. Soule's Dictionary of Synonyms says, "Dirt: filth, foul matter." Captivating tales of the category I have in mind are neither filthy nor foul. They are the toy, the quaint diversion of some of the best minds of our age or any other age. Like maybe Sir Winston Churchill and the late F.D.R.?

Most women can't tell a bawdy story for shucks, though lots of them try to. The majority of men, on the other hand, are convinced that they are experts. Most of them aren't. They have no gift of recollection, no proficiency in dialects, no skill at pantomime or mimicry. Unfortunately the jovial task of telling dirty stories requires every one of those virtues.

Nothing is more painful than having to sit and suffer through the ineptitude of the clumsy story teller. Nothing aches in your ears like the halting, "Now, let's see— Oh, yes— So the old maid said to the traveling man, 'Arrah, did ye say dat you vanted to stay all night?' And den Sambo said—"

Trouble is, story-telling is a kind of sexual symbol to men. It is associated with their notions of male prowess, like driving a car or slaying a dame.

You can say to a man, "Listen, that's not the way to hold your fishing rod. Hold it like this," and the novice will thank you meekly and humbly. But just try to tell someone that he is a duffer at story-telling . . . look, chum, you just told that Irish story in a sort of bastard-German-Mexican dialect. You didn't sound like a guy who hated Orangemen, and anyway the story is a thousand years old, and every soul heard it before he was ten, and anyway it isn't very funny. . . .

Try that, in even the most diplomatic fashion, and you have made an enemy for life.

One might think, from observing the list of skills mentioned above, that professional actors would one and all be excellent story tellers. As a matter of fact, many fine actors are lousy story tellers. At best they have three or four tales which they have learned toilsomely, word by word. The majority of actors are helpless without their lines. They have to be cued, they have to know exactly what word and intonation and gesture will follow; they have to have the thing by heart. They cannot improvise beyond a sentence or two.

There are a number of notable exceptions, but by and large their minds are too filled with the parts they played before the cameras that afternoon or behind the footlights that evening. They are concerned with the morrow's Sides and Takes, the morrow's make-up and lighting. Such concern does not make for social anecdoting.

Robert Preston is one actor who tells a story beautifully, and so is Joseph Cotten, but I think these gentlemen are more or less limited in their types of tales. Out of a New York existence which goes back to 1932 and a Hollywood familiarity which began in 1934, I will offer a palm to one actor of those I know, and I know quite a few.

José Ferrer. That's the guy. Like Salome in the old RAF song, he can run, jump, fight, something-or-other, push a barrow, wheel a truck— His fund is colossal, and he brings to the job every nobility of experience and native passion. I knew him only briefly during the summer of 1948; I have not seen any of his recent plays or pictures; but he couldn't have been any better than he was out at Burl Ives's ranch, going from idiot to Deep South to pawnbroker to Vermont apple-knocker; and every story replete with its nuances of tone and gesture. It was something to shoot at. You look at Goya for a while and the Museum of Modern Art doesn't seem so hot.

Well, José Ferrer can't make a living just telling stories, and I think it's rather a pity. So-called dirty stories are the common fare of mankind, and apparently always have been, and I trust always will be. Once again it is a curse of our phony warmed-over-Puritan-Victorian mores that we don't openly admit the fact.

Out in Iowa when I was a boy, we had old Father Barry. He was the good-natured priest of an admiring parish, and—by virtue of his pitiful lack of skill as a golfer—he sometimes found himself paired in tournaments with the worst driver and putter in Webster City, which was me.

One way or another I discovered that Father Barry loved stories. Most especially, Catholic stories. I am not a Catholic, but even at the age of seventeen or thereabouts I had acquired a fund of tales which one might not, perhaps, recite to the Pope, but with which one could make the existence of broad-minded Romans a little more lively.

Many a mile did Father Barry and I trudge together over the clipped green fairways, butchering our Spaldings and Baby Dimples with cruel cuts of our mashies, but with sun in our hearts and laughter on our lips. I had learned a bit since that day of soap-and-water at the sink. On occasion I could pick my audience with care, and my audience had turned out to be a smiling and respected priest.

Nothing offers quite the same trivial treasure as the realization that you have told a good story and told it well. I thrived upon the Reverend Father's appreciation; it gave me self-confidence then so sorely needed. And the crowning happiness came when he would see me walking down Water Street, and would leave his gardening to come over to the hedge and whisper eagerly, "Got any new Catholic stories?" Rest your soul, Father Barry, and flowers to your memory!

Parents are studious about equipping their young with graces and manners. By all means let us teach Daphne how to enter a room properly; let us instruct Donald not to blow upon his soup; let us even, coping with elder teen-agers (once again, in the liberal environments), teach Donald how to mix a decent Manhattan, and warn Daphne against lethal Gibsons.

But how well briefed is the average American on what he should contribute and how he should contribute it, in those jaunty hours when the social ice has fragged, and people—blooming with the lovely fever of young maturity—are prepared to writhe in delight at the plight of the man who got caught short in Radio City Music Hall, or the Southern colonel who criticized his daughter's approach to Southern hospitality?

To be accurate, he is not briefed at all. He has to pick it up, like a Stone Age Indian herded into a drawing room. Ah, yes, Mom and Pop told stories at home; they shrieked and squealed on plenty of evenings along with the Johnsons and the Smithers. They ganged boisterously in the kitchen, filling their bodies with cold ham and olives and beer, and filling their souls with merriment. But Pop and Mom and the sisters and the cousins and the aunts—they did their recounting and their reciting and their shrieking and squealing long after all adolescents had been salted into their beds.

No young lady from Kew, who one day had nothing to do: not for Daphne. The moppets at school might have tee-heed out a far rockier limerick than that one, and on that very day; but the parents were stolid in their determination to keep dainty Daphne aloof from such corrosions—at least at home.

Was bright-eyed Donald allowed to participate in the revelry surrounding the hunter who wanted to kill a bear in hand-to-hand combat? He was not. He was inoculated solely with sanitary humors adjudged proper for a stripling—and turned loose to measure his future glee by the yardstick of whatever snickerings assailed him in the showers at the gym.

A string of obscenities and stinky epithets are not funny at all, and no one knows this better than a good story teller. I have available a fund of several hundred stories, picked and culled and sorted through the years—nuggets plucked from the sand of the thousands I have heard. These should be called Class A tales. And of these Class A tales, a good half have not one obscene word in them. Many don't even have what might be called pornographic situations. It *is* the situation which counts —*and* the characters, the essential contrast, the rewarding ludicrous cartoon, the humanity.

If there is another neighborly art which can pay such agreeable dividends, then I don't know what it is. Gruesome stories, stupidly related, can ruin the best convivial hour which ever dawned. On the other hand, a whee of a story plumped into a roomful of folks in proper season and moment, can rescue the perishing.

One night, in Japan during the early phases of the Korean War, our crew had just returned from a bombardment mission. I shared a room with the aircraft commander, Moe Cronin, and we were both in the bathroom, scrubbing sweat and fear off our hides, when a lieutenant-colonel came up the stairs.

He was Ralph Wanderer, our 325th Squadron commander,

and he had a new Bronze Star swinging on his shirt. We hailed this gong with some raillery. It seemed that Major General Emmett J. O'Donnell had decided to decorate all three squadron commanders, and was staging an investiture over at his cottage.

Wanderer told me seriously, "Look, you've got to dress and get over there right away."

"What for? I wasn't invited."

"General sent me to find you. The party's going to hell in a hand-basket."

O'Donnell, in true Rosie fashion, had invited—not young officers, but sergeants, to witness the honors awarded their commanders—honors which, as everyone well knew, could not have been honestly won by the commanders if the sergeants hadn't been doing a terrific job too.

Ten representative M/Sgts., T/Sgts., and S/Sgts. had been selected by lot or vote from each squadron, and these thirty Top Threes were now jammed into Rosie O'Donnell's cottage, acutely conscious of their stripes and of Rosie's stars, and wishing like anything that they were back in their own club.

Rosie is a superb host, but no application of whiskey and cold cuts had been able to melt the freeze. He went beaming around, offering drinks and sandwiches, uttering jocular remarks, trying to make things roll; but the guests were cemented into the armor of Perfect Behavior. . . . No, thank you, sir, I guess I don't care for another drink. No, thank you, sir, I guess I won't have any more sandwiches. . . .

"Let's see, Sergeant. Your face— Why, sure! I remember you back at March AF Base—"

"I guess not, sir. I never served at March."

So it was rough, and so old Dr. Kantor was called in, and was old Dr. Kantor proud and pleased. The moment Wanderer towed me into the stiffly crowded little bungalow, Rosie was at my side.

"Tell Argo. Quick!"

"What—?"

His whisper was violent with anxiety. "Tell Argo. Tell Wa-

terloo Bridge. Tell about the colonel who had the three kids.
Tell anything, but hurry up. This party is dying on its feet!"

He shoved me into the center of the room and I found myself
telling Argo. I got the story long ago from Mike Ryan, who
used to make with Irish tenor songs at the Asti Cafe. It's about
a radio announcer who tries to conduct a program from Grand
Central Station; and you may have heard it long before I did,
or you may have been one of those sergeants who had never
heard it before.

The roar which went up was said to have frightened the
APs who guarded the gates, there at Yokota. It was balm to
my sensitive nature, which fattens on approval, and don't all our
natures? Rosie looked his gratitude while the Top Threes were
still staggering in each other's arms, and directed me to tell
Waterloo Bridge. I told Waterloo Bridge, and as soon as the old
constable had toted the Nazi parachutist off to Scotland Yard,
we had sergeants gobbling potato salad and sergeants lapping
ale and sergeants all trying to tell their pet stories to the general.
How Kantor won the war. I'm still waiting hopefully for my
own Bronze Star.

Those were tired men living under strain, so even the most
hard-shelled deacons will perhaps excuse such recourse to the
lewd. But don't deacons ever have toothaches? What of illness,
worry, financial vicissitude, bereavement—the whole horrid tangle of misfortunes? How good to be able to chase the Horrors,
even for a moment or two, by considering the man who used a
green pumpkin for a toilet seat, the babe who ordered lettuce
for the breakfast-in-bed of her male companion!

There is truly little need for anyone to point out the
therapeutic values of such diversion. The bawdy story dwells
with us, and nobody had better blind his eyes and ears to the
fact, and everybody had better pray that the story is a good one,
well told—not a dull one, dismally told.

Of course some people hurt the story business terribly. Take
Bennett Cerf. He happens to be my publisher and we are very
buddy-buddy. But I deplore that weird ambition which makes

Bennett skip around gathering stories, scrubbing them, dry-cleaning them, and then impaling them on pretty pins in his cute little books and his cute little lectures. I call him Cerf, the Poor Man's Alexander Woollcott. I call him Cerf, the Cannibalistic Vulture Who Picks the Bones of His Pals.

I won't tell him stories any more—not unless they are so bedewed with intrinsic obscenity that it would be impossible for even his clever brain to whiten them up. Forever he struggles to ruin a perfectly grand dirty story by making it into a perfectly god-awful parlor story. Not long ago I told him the one about the fellow who was trying to find his way into Heaven, and selected the wrong door, and fell into a lake of you-know-what. That is the narrative which ends up with the line, "Wait until the Devil comes by in his Chris-Craft!"

Bennett said winsomely, "I know. A lake of garbage!"

"It wouldn't work, and you know it."

He sighed, he shook. I swear he looked ten years older than before. "I guess you're right. Garbage wouldn't work. It has to be you-know-what."

I was cruel, and with purpose and justice. I needed to be revenged. Bennett has ruined all too many of my stories by bawdlerizing them. He puts them in his column in the *Saturday Review* and then later they find their way into the *Reader's Digest*. The steaming casserole has become cold porridge, the rare meat has turned into Nestlé's Food. . . . I try to tell my swell story, and folks look bored and pained, and someone says, "Oh, yes, I read that in the new *Reader's Digest*. But you're trying to make a dirty story out of it."

Trying, hell. It was a fragrant, tasty dirty story until Cerf got his claws on it. That one about the oldest captain in the Air Force—the character who trained an orang-outang to sit in his cockpit— Well, there it was in the *Digest*, scrubbed like Orphan Annie on her way to church.

Angrily I protested. Cerf squawked, "What are you kicking about? I gave you credit, didn't I?"

"Credit—for that asinine version? Discredit. You could smell the Lifebuoy a mile off. And what about the major out at Lackland who told it to *me?*"

Trouble is, he gets paid for that stuff. It really burns me up.

Guilty of such mayhem, Cerf is definitely not on my list of Noble Deed Do-ers along with the celebrated Señor Ferrer. On the contrary, Freddy Pearson is. He's the F. S. Pearson III, who wrote all that Fractured French. Freddy is not Jewish, but he is just about the best Jewish-story-teller I ever met, and I'm not excepting Georgie Jessel or the late Jolson.

Forrest W. Seymour, editor and Pulitzer Prize winner, can tell a story like crazy. Edward W. Beattie, Jr., whose exploits as a war correspondent and Central Intelligence Agency minion have in no way damaged his nature or his name, is a story teller of the first water. So is General Carl A. Spaatz (Ret.). So was the late Albert Payson Terhune. So is Terhune's nephew, F. F. Van de Water, himself the author of many books. I would call him a story teller of the first Van de Water, but puns are unpopular with people who didn't think of them first.

Instead I shall proclaim a list of rules and regulations for young and old, and folks should study them and stick to them. Plenty of people sixty years old are downright greenhorns trying to play in the big leagues.

1. If you don't thoroughly enjoy telling bawdy stories—if your spirit does not bubble and your eyes dance and your heart skip like a little ram—then for godsakes don't try.

2. Some unfortunates are acceptable socially until they try to tell stories. Then a loathsome odor begins to permeate the room. Mind you, they have good recollections, good mechanical skill. But there is just something about their personalities which doesn't permit recourse to the Sinful & Lewd. It's too bad, but they should take warning and stick to their Breviaries & Psalters. . . . I guess the only way for them to find this out is to wait and see if they're invited back.

3. Filth is filth and fun is fun, and sometimes they are all mixed up together, and sometimes they are not. Be certain of

your ability to discriminate between Napoleon brandy and rat poison.

4. Watch the audience angle carefully. I used to be very naughty about this, and had to learn the hard way—even long after the Father Barry years. If you don't know the crowd too well, tread with care, especially among the Female & Senile. A lot of senile females of gentlest birth dearly delight in the art of the D.S. A lot of them do not, most emphatically.

5. For the love of Chaucer and Balzac and Mark Twain and Falstaff and Eugene Field and Gene Fowler, *know* your story before you start it. I don't mean that you should practice in front of a mirror and that you should learn the lines throughout, but at least know where you're going. Some stupid hombres actually try to claim your time and attention with a rambling recital to which they don't even know the tag-line.

6. Dialects. (Gad, this is getting painful.) Well, it shouldn't be necessary to warn people that they shouldn't try to talk like dusky Alabama citizens if they have never seen a dusky Alabama citizen—that they should not make Lord Leddingham-Montmorency sound like the Mattoon, Illinois, version of a Cockney—that they should *NEVER* try dialects unless they're proven to be good at dialects by a rousing vote of the populace. But I guess it is.

7. Study tenderly, refurbish when required—not in the Cerf manner!—and alter when necessary. For instance, Artist Jerry Farnsworth told me about the town incompetent who was given a job polishing the cannon in the square. I liked this story and tried to tell it straight, as Jerry did, with only meager success. Suddenly I got the idea of turning it into a hare-lip, and right away agents started calling up on the telephone.

8. Don't be in such a rush to tell your own stories that you don't give anyone else a chance. Water will find its own level, and if you're better at D.S. than the rest, pretty soon they'll be working you to death. But how are you going to learn any new stories unless you listen for them? Furthermore, many a vague dud can be turned into a real live bomb in your own bomb-

dump if you are agile about ordnance. Watch, wait, listen. If it's good or has possibilities, grab it and put it in your pocket.

That's about all the rules and regulations I can think of right now, but maybe I will have some more tomorrow. In the meantime, have you heard the one about—?

Not Built with
Mortal Hands
1952

Eternal house, not built with mortal hands! . . .
—DRYDEN.

When I was a boy in Webster City, Iowa, I would go out of my way to watch Mr. Ed Snow drinking a glass of milk, signing a receipt, or tipping his hat to the ladies. So would any other boy in town.

Ed Snow was our County Superintendent of Schools, which title we children considered an accolade bestowed upon him not so much for executive proficiency in educational matters, as for his remarkable facilty at gardening, penmanship, and automobiling.

By the way, I neglected to mention that Ed Snow had no hands.

He never had had any hands, insofar as little folks knew.

Certain older people could remember when the Snows lived in a house out on the prairie where the old-fashioned Illinois Central trains trumpeted their way to Fort Dodge and Sioux City. It seemed, according to an anecdote with which we became familiar in time, that Ed Snow had indeed possessed hands, up until the age when he could first toddle away from the door-stoop through prairie flowers native to the railroad right-of-way.

He had wandered onto the tracks, and there he had encountered a passenger train—no matter with what urgency the engineer applied his brakes. Little Eddie was conveyed to town for such repairs as might be managed, while weeping passengers aboard the train shook their heads and declared that the infant would be better off dead.

Scraps of the upper arms left to him seemed inadequate for the struggle ahead. Surgeons did the best they could; but when the wounds were finally healed, Eddie was missing one arm close to the shoulder, and the other just above the elbow.

A modest sum of money was paid the parent Snows for damages to Eddie, and the world forgot him until he grew up. Then the world observed him again: a resolute blond-haired stripling intent on earning a college education, and taking orders as a book salesman in order to do it.

"It was too easy," he chuckled, long afterward. "So I had to quit selling books. I was a phenomenal success—too phenomenal."

"But why did you quit, if—?"

"Oh," he said, "I know why I was selling so many books. The books weren't the greatest books in the world, nor the most necessary ones, nor the most inviting; and few of the people who were buying from me could be called well off. They were just sorry for me. I didn't like that."

The active brain of the maimed young student soon hit upon a better plan. He got hold of a horse and wagon, hired a boy for the driving and harnessing, and spent the next summer trekking from farm to farm through the more remote countryside of that region, collecting abandoned iron, copper, and other fragments of cast-off metals.

An old engine axle here, a flywheel there, a set of cogs from some abandoned mill—things like those were not worth the time and labor of busy farmers, if they tried to transport them across the long miles to the junk yards themselves.

Ed Snow used his imagination and his knowledge of rural geography and equipment, and his energies paid a handsome profit. I don't think he was ever really worried about how to get along in the world from that time forth.

His education was adequate when he started his life's work in earnest. He taught school and did a few other jobs so well that it was no surprise to anyone when he achieved practically a lifetime tenure on the office of County Superintendent.

Other people have gotten by without hands before and since Ed Snow, and some have done it brilliantly. But I always experience a severe attack of rapid eye-winking when I witness their jaunty courage.

There is Harold Russell, the handless veteran who played the handless veteran in *The Best Years of Our Lives,* the movie made from my novel, *Glory for Me.* I remember our first meeting on a Hollywood set.

"Rus," I asked, "what are you planning to do after you finish your work in this picture?"

Harold Russell flashed his easy grin—and his prosthetic hooks —before my eyes.

"Look," he said, "I'm not worried. I can always get a job picking poison ivy."

It must be remembered that Ed Snow's injury was incurred a couple of generations or so before World War II. Artificial arms and hooks and clamps being as crude as they were in those days, it is easy to understand why Mr. Snow never bothered with them. He preferred to let the mighty stump of one arm perform the lion's share of necessary manual activity, and let his active intelligence and merry nature do the rest.

He married, because he was affectionate and home-loving and gregarious—he married a pretty little woman with bright eyes, and Alice Snow swore forever that there were only two things she had to do for Ed: (1) cut his meat at table, and (2) put the brass collar-buttons in the old-fashioned stiff collars he liked to wear.

Take the very ordinary matter of manners on the street. It disgusted Ed to note how slovenly some men were in their observance of an etiquette that offered spice and pride to his soul. It was fun to march down the street with him on a busy morning. He wore a derby in cold weather, and a stiff-brimmed straw hat in summer. It had to be a stiff-brimmed hat—that was the kind of hat he could handle.

"*Good* morning, Mrs. McAdow!" and the hardy stump of his arm would reach aloft. In some miraculous fashion the hat would be tossed from his head, caught and whirled by the stump as he bowed, and set evenly and trimly back again on top of his head, so that he might have the joy of saluting another lady, ten paces farther on. "*Good* morning, Mrs. Hunter! . . . *Good* morning, Miss Frank!" and the hat would be off and on twenty times before he reached the corner of Second Street.

Ed and his wife were members of the church which my grandmother attended, and I frequently had the pleasure of watching him eat and drink at picnics or suppers. He wore a broad leather strap buckled around the stump, and under this strap the spoon or fork or fountain pen or pencil or whatever other implement he wanted to use would be thrust, with lightning rapidity, by a brief shake of Ed Snow's head and a quick pressure of his strong white teeth. I never saw him spill a thing, and I don't think anyone else ever did, either.

I remember accompanying a friend of my mother's down Willson Avenue one day. She was a woman from out-of-town who was unfamiliar with the skills of our Ed Snow. There was a rattle of old springs and Ed passed us—buzzing by in his old Ford roadster. I waved after him, and my mother's friend stood gaping.

"That man!" she gasped. "He was driving—"

"Yes," I told her. "That's Mr. E. F. Snow, the County Superintendent of Schools."

"County Superintendent of Fiddlesticks!" the woman cried. "He hasn't got any hands. Why, he'll kill somebody! He'll—"

The whole task of explanation seemed too much for me. To explain how, on a Model-T Ford such as Ed Snow piloted, you did your braking and gear-shifting with your feet . . . how he had a strong steel ring fastened to the steering wheel, into which he could cement the sinewy wad that grew from his shoulder; how—

I do recall being able to say to the lady: "It may interest you to know that Mr. Snow has driven a hundred and fifty thousand miles without an accident. He won a certificate for his safe driving."

It was a toss-up whether we young people were more entranced when watching Ed breezily guiding his vehicle along our streets, or when estimating the wonder of the pen-and-ink marvels he could achieve. He was an avid student of what was known as "the Palmer Method" of penmanship. Besides long scrolls, loops and double-loops, he could make elegant roosters or pictures of Abraham Lincoln or Heaven knew what else, all contrived with the circular manipulation of his sharp-pointed pen.

Still I think it was in the homely phases of his life—the long, bustling years spent with Alice (there were just the two of them. A child came to them once, but there was only a tiny grave in the cemetery to show for all their hopes and longing) that Ed Snow found the supreme realization of his dream to be a man like all others.

It happened casually, but when it happened I think that Ed Snow felt a pride that rarely comes to men, even when a hundred thousand hands are applauding them, even when the medals are pinned on.

The Snows had been having the woodwork in their home newly painted, and Alice was vastly pleased with the snowy coating which lay upon old doors and banisters. But on the second day after the paint had dried, little Mrs. Snow emitted a snarl that brought her husband on the run.

"Ed Snow," she was commanding in no uncertain tone, "you come right here! See what you've done!"

He stood beside her and saw how the fresh ivory on a door-jamb had been sullied by the print of several very dirty fingers.

"We're entertaining the Sunday school class tonight," Alice

cried, "and I wanted everything to look nice, and now just look what you've done!"

Ed Snow gazed down at her. "Alice, do you really think I made those finger marks on the doorjamb?"

"Well, if you didn't, I don't know who did!"

"Alice. On your honor, now. Do you really think I made those marks?"

His wife stared up at him for a long moment, and then—as he told it a hundred times afterward—"She just sort of collapsed. . . . Laugh? I don't know when we've ever laughed like that before."

It is quite apparent, when one views the life of Ed Snow, that hands are not a necessary implement in the building of either laughter or tears. And tears did come to the Snows, as I have remarked. There was that little grave. . . .

Alice was very ill when the baby was born, and only Ed might stand in tremulous awe before the small quiet shape which had slept so soundly and permanently before it ever drew a breath of life.

He told Alice later; and in time she told my grandmother through a blur of tears as she recited what Ed Snow had said.

"Alice," he whispered. There was a wistful smile on his big shiny face. "The baby had *hands*."

She gave his smile back to him, though her cheeks were as wet as his. "Ed, did you actually think it wouldn't have hands?"

Ed Snow shrugged the powerful shoulder with which he had managed to build a better life than many people have been able to build with eight stout fingers and two thumbs. "Well," he said, "you know—I couldn't *help* wondering. . . ."

Of Course There Are
Apparitions
1965

Burl Ives said to me, "I have news for you. You've got a ghost."

"Where?"

"In your house."

I considered these astounding tidings. "A ghost in my house? Who told you so?"

"Mr. Noël Coward."

I said, "Noël Coward ought to know. It used to be his house."

This conversation took place in Burl's temporary home in Mount Street, in London. Our own house, the one which Burl was talking about, was down in Kent, not far from the village of Aldington.

The property was called Goldenhurst. It roosted comfortably, winningly, serene with ancient pink bricks and ivied tiles, beaming out across the Romney Marshes. When Irene and I first saw it we fell in love with the place, and agreed to lease it within the hour. Goldenhurst had recently passed from Noël Coward's ownership into the hands of the Kenneth Clarkes (not the *Sir* Kenneth Clarke known to the British radio and TV world, but the Kenneth Clarke who is rangy and grey-thatched; whose military background includes both the Bedford & Herts Light Infantry and the King's African Rifles; who has a lovely little blonde Norwegian wife; and who looks more like an Arizona cougar hunter than he does like a man whose hair would stand on end when ghosts came close).

Only a week or two previously, Burl and Helen Ives, with their son Alexander, had been down to Kent to spend a weekend with us. (Parenthetically let me say that our friendship goes back to Burl's first sustaining-program days; and also we've had a little business relationship along the way.)

Shortly after the Iveses left Goldenhurst, my wife and I suffered simultaneous dental calamities. A bridge and inlay came loose somewhere amid my jagged brown fangs; and Irene discovered some minor blot on the otherwise immaculate escutcheon of her own mouth. Thus was entailed a visit to London and to Cavendish Square, where dentists do most congregate. Also, happily, an overnight visit with the Iveses.

But on our arrival at Mount Street, a servant informed us that Mr. Ives hadn't gone out to Ealing to the studio that day —no indeed he hadn't, sir— "He has a perfectly frightful cold, and he's taken to his bed, he has."

I went up to find Burl looking like a bearded Buddha, propped by a dozen pillows, sniffling a bit, but still able to puff his pipe.

That was when he told me about the Goldenhurst ghost.

There was a very good reason why this information meant more to me than perhaps it might have meant to another. But my friend didn't know that, just then. . . .

"O.K., Burl. Now, about the ghost. Did you observe anything —any sort of phenomena—when you folks were down there this month?"

"Not in the slightest. Didn't know a thing about it until Coward happened to come on the set yesterday. I told him that we had been at Goldenhurst to visit you folks. Then he wanted to discuss the place in detail, since he lived there so many years himself. The ghost came along with the property. It was there when Coward first moved in."

Burl continued, "Commonly it seems to be in the shape of a man in dark clothing—antique costume, of course—who strolls across the lawn, accompanied frequently by a black dog. Often

he seemed to be carrying something in his arms. He comes in
through the window."

"Which window?"

"Dining room."

"Ever do any real harm to anyone?"

"Apparently not."

I said, "They seldom do."

Burl blinked at me. "What's that?"

"Oh, nothing."

Next afternoon, preliminary dental work concluded, Irene
and I went back to Kent. When we pulled up in front of our
door the Clarkes came from their adjacent house to greet us.

Goldenhurst in those days consisted of three houses. There
was a cottage at a distance from the main structure; and that
main structure consisted of two separate houses. Between them
there used to be a courtyard—probably a stableyard in the sixteenth century; but Noël Coward had filled up that area with
a large studio. (Irene said it wasn't much good for painting:
the light came in from the south and west.) I suppose Coward
used it for choreography, rehearsing songs, so on.

North of the studio stretched a tangle of walls and stairways
and casement windows and fireplaces and crannies and passages,
now sacred to the Kenneth Clarkes. South and east of the
studio was the same sort of tangle of rooms, roofs, stairs, grates,
mullions, scullions and what-not, temporarily occupied by Kantors.

Lord knows how many times masons and carpenters had
made with their mortar and hammers since the original place
was built. Scores of times, I reckon. Our own bedroom on the
second story had once been a hayloft (lots of cute comment
from acquaintances about *this*); and some of the huge flat stones
in our vestibule were rutted by ancient cartwheels and hoofs.

We got out of our car, and I reproved the Clarkes. "Kenneth
and Reidun—why didn't you tell us about the ghost?"

They looked at each other. Kenneth exclaimed, "The Golden-hurst ghost. But where did you hear about it? And when?"

"In London, yesterday. Burl told us what Noël Coward had told him."

Again the Clarkes exchanged looks. Reidun asked slowly, "Mack, what time were you talking about the ghost? Because even sometimes when you are just *talking* about it, something *happens*."

I stopped and thought for a moment. "It was about a quarter to four, yesterday afternoon."

They both jumped. Reidun shrieked, "I knew it, I knew it! Wasn't that at the time, Kenneth, when you were working in the rose garden, and I came dashing out and cried, 'I won't stay in this house another minute?'"

Kenneth nodded sadly.

"What do you mean—*happens?*" I asked of Reidun. "And why did you dash out, and say you weren't going to stay in the house another minute?"

. . . Oh, they told us, same old story. It had happened so frequently before: knockings, bangings, cold drafts, footsteps.

"Usually," said Kenneth, "the ghost walks across the yard on the other side of the house, out by the flower gardens. As for that window business: there used to be a door at that point. Often the specter seems to be carrying something. Could be a little child."

Reidun told us, "There are local legends concerning an illegitimate child, and a cruel grandfather who was determined to keep the secret."

I thought of Coward's famous old song, *The Stately Homes of England*. Its lines began to chase themselves through my head.

> *The baby in the guest wing,*
> *Who crouches by the grate,*
> *Was walled up in the west wing,*
> *In Fourteen-twenty-eight. . . .*

Before dark Irene and I went down a nearby lane to get fresh eggs. The farmer we sought had been there in the neighborhood a long time, and he bred flocks of the well-known Romney sheep. Hence we shall call him Farmer Lambkin.

Mrs. Lambkin fetched us our eggs, and we stood for a few minutes in neighborly conversation.

"No one," I said, "had told us about the Goldenhurst ghost to begin with. We've just learned about it, up in London."

Said Mrs. Lambkin. "Coo, you should have been here when we had the veterans' picnic last fall. *Everybody* was seeing ghosts."

"No," I said, "I'm not referring to that sort of ghost at all. Why, Mr. Noël Coward says that several of his guests fainted dead away, on seeing the Goldenhurst ghost enter through the dining-room window."

Farmer Lambkin had a poor opinion of actors and theatre people in general. "Aye," he said. "They would—that lot."

I've been breezing on gaily about Ives and Coward and Goldenhurst, and the Clarkes, and Farmer Lambkin. But let me tell you that I was a little more concerned—seriously so—when we went to bed that night.

Because I knew that apparitions do exist.

How come? Because I'd seen one. Just as simple as that. . . . Wise old Kantor, you understand. With him, seeing was believing. Oh yes, as a young reporter in the nineteen-twenties he'd gone around ghost-breaking, and laughing to scorn any serious attempts made by anyone in the field of psychical exploration. To the keen perceptive brain of this younger Kantor, anyone who haltingly described any sort of phenomena whatsoever, which he claimed had befallen him or had come within his observation— That man was a *Spiritualist*. Or else he was one with those crooked mediums who prey upon the forlorn and the gullible and the poverty-stricken.

There just *weren't no ghosts*, said Kantor.

Not until he came face to face with one. Then there were ghosts.

I remember once, toward the end of World War II, when I was sitting in a hotel room in Paris with a couple of friends: Colonel Mickey McGuire, then historian of the 9th Air Force; and Colonel Philip Cochran, who should need no introduction to anyone who knows that there *is* an Air Force and there *is* a Steve Canyon.

I told the story about my own very-recent-very-personal-very-special (because it was *mine*) ghost, and then sat back to await comments.

McGuire said, "Well, I hate to disagree with you. You said that you weren't drunk, that you went to bed sober. And then this all happened to you?"

"That is correct."

"I think that you *believe* these things happened to you; but actually you had more to drink than you realized. It was all a result of alcohol. It was in your imagination. *Nothing* actually happened."

" 'Tain't so, Mickey," I told him. "I've been drunk a lot of times in my life. I know that I wasn't drunk on that night. Or dreaming."

Then up spoke Phil Cochran. "I believe every word of it," he said. "I believe that it occurred just the way Mack related it."

I really jumped from my chair on that one. "Phil, did you ever have any similar experience?"

He shook his head. "No, not at all. But just because it didn't befall *me*, doesn't mean that it couldn't have happened to somebody else."

There was rebuke in this—rebuke a mile high—for all my cynicism, sneers, closed mind—my stupidity of years gone by. Cochran didn't know that the rebuke was there. But it was, and I had it coming.

Very well. Here's the story.

London, early April, 1945. . . .

The war isn't over yet but the V-2s have stopped. You need, most awfully, a place to spend the night. Where's that address the Billeting Office gave you a week or two ago, when you were last up to London?

Here it is. No. 40-42 Truxley Court. That's out in South Kensington, and a long way to go by taxi, but it's a lot better than not having any place to stay at all.

You've been there once before, and even engaged a room. But you got stranded in Hampstead that night, so you didn't use the room: just came back to Truxley Court next morning, picked up your musette bag, and hit for the train.

. . . Mrs. Effie Stuart escorts you. It's a story and a half upstairs, and the only room vacant. And it was vacant before. A vacancy is really something in a huge city where people are flocking back after all the bombings—where every inch of space is at a premium because of the thousands of public and private bedrooms which have been destroyed.

You move into quarters about ten feet long and maybe a little more than six feet wide. Apparently a hall which used to run all the way to the front of the house was walled off in order to make this chamber. There's a window down there at the south end of the tiny area; and there's a door at the north end; the rest of the north end space is taken up by the head of your bed. It's really a couch with pillows on it for daytime use. Not much other furniture. Barely room enough to turn around in.

. . . You go out for an early dinner with friends; and then the bartender cries, "Time, gentlemen! Time!" You say goodbye to your friends and come back to this tiny room in Truxley Court.

You push the door shut, hear the spring-lock click. You take the cover off the studio couch and toss the extra pillows aside. You've got a green sateen comforter with a thin blanket under that, and sheets under that. It's only eleven o'clock, and you're sleepy. So to bed.

The haunting doesn't begin until a few minutes after 3 A.M.

You know the time, because you wandered down the hall to the toilet. Then you came back, and looked at your wristwatch on the way. 3:06.

Go in, lock the door, hop back into bed. The fun begins.

First it's covers. Why someone should wish to pull the covers off of you, you don't know. But that's their intent and their attempt as well. You've turned off the light, and you've settled down comfortably. You're cold stone sober, and not expecting anything like this. But suddenly the covers start to go. Everything: sheet, blanket, sateen puff. They go rippling down across your pajamas, and end up in a pile on the floor.

. . . This isn't any way for people to behave! Who the hell got into your room while you were gone to the bathroom? What's this all about, anyway?

You get out of bed and turn on the light. There are your covers, all dumped down at the foot of the bed. You look under the bed, to see whether some mischievous soul has crept there and concealed himself while you were out of the room.

Nothing.

O.K., pull up the covers again and arrange them. Turn off the light, get back into bed. Away we go again. There go the covers.

Something or someone is pulling them with dull persistence. This time you grab tightly and hang on. You fasten your hands around all three sets of covers, and you pull, and the other entity pulls, and it's quite a tug-of-war.

Close beyond the foot of the couch or bed (it's more like a mat in a gymnasium now, with violent people exercising on it) you can see the window and dull gray light outside. The blackout curtains are slid open—you did that when you first went to bed—and you should have closed the curtains again when you turned on that light; but you didn't do it, and you could be "had up" for that. Still— No more air raids. It's been at least a fortnight since Death rained from the skies.

Is there Death in the room with you now? Death in another form? A menace whose activity you would not have admitted an hour previously? You consider it again and again, the while you're hanging onto those covers—fighting the weight, the steadiness, the inert strength which your unseen opponent musters. It's as if rocks or maybe anvils—something solid and massive—have been cemented in the lower end of the bedclothing, and every time you relax your grip and your own contending muscles— Away those covers start to go again.

You very nearly speak aloud to yourself. Indeed, maybe you do speak aloud . . . the words are shrilling in your ears. . . . "By God, it's not *true*. Things like this don't *happen*. There *aren't* any ghosts. I've always scorned the subject. But— What's happening, anyway?"

They Can't Do This To Me Department.

(In later reading on the subject of spontaneous phenomena I smile to think how many times I've come across the same inflexible attitude and assertion, as chronicled by other witnesses concerning their own prejudice. *Mr. X had always been a firm disbeliever in any psychic phenomenon. . . . Mrs. Y had never believed in the existence of paranormal occurrences. . . . Previously Professor Z had scouted any interest in the psychic field.*)

You're not terrified. You're just mad, mad, mad, and bound to resist.

Here's the system: lock the bedclothes around and under you. Make a solid cocoon of the stuff; it's pinned down under your shoulders, and in some degree under your back on both sides of your body. . . .

Warily now, you strive to alter your position. You think you are winning the battle, and can afford to yield a little, and have the bedclothes retained only by your right side. So that's the way you're lying: on your side, facing the west wall of the room where the couch is shoved against it.

After a few minutes in this position, you realize that the wall, a foot away from your eyes, is brightening. It's reflecting light from some source.

How come? Where from? Who's got a light in this room?

You twist your head. The window stares blank and dark, because now there is more light *in the room* than outside. So you twist around further, and turn your head more to the left. And then you know the story. It's a truth which is pretty hard to take (especially for one who swore eternally that nothing like this could occur).

What you've seen on the wall next to the bed was just a reflection. The source of light is the *east wall itself,* several feet away from your bed. There's no joke about it: a pale luminous glow, much like the quivering of a radium compound, is melting all over that wall.

This light is increasing in intensity as it lessens its area. Something is *taking shape.* The light oozes into central focus as if a mighty lens were being twisted. It was wide, messy, without any definite boundaries, to begin with. And yet— Again: as the area lessens, so does the intensity increase. And the suggestion of a human shape is emerging.

Now, also, does an auditory phenomenon come to detection.

It's a vague hum at first—you're not quite sure that you heard it . . . just an indefinite whistling or wail or mumble . . . faint, far distant. But still you'd swear that a great number of people were engaged in making the sound or sounds.

Then, in full accord, and in progress with the sharpening of the wall glow, so do the auditory phenomena increase, so do voices chuckle or wail louder, so do tongues clack. So much is being said! There is sadness, there is laughter in the house; yet who are the authors of the chattering? You can't possibly guess. You can't define them or pin them down.

> . . . *Sheeted dead*
> *Did squeal and gibber in the Roman streets.*

You think, "Insofar as you people are concerned, I've been inoffensive. There is no excuse for you to disturb me like this —no reason for you to be yanking at my bedclothes, no reason to cook up a storm. To press the switch of that spectral light—"

It is tightening and congealing . . . going to be either a man or a woman, you don't know which. The kernel of the filmy glow is intensifying, you see a head and shoulders, you see long hair. Could be a woman, could be someone with a periwig, could be a man with the long hair affected by cavaliers.

You've reached the limit of your endurance; you feel a strange mixture of dissolving patience and dedicated defiance. You rail against the yammer of unknown voices and that brief bright humanlike shape marking itself against the east wall. "Oh," you cry, "I know what the idea is. You really *want me* to observe you and to listen to you. Well, I won't!"

It is as if you wished physically to assault a meddlesome mass of enemies. Bed and room have become a proving ground; a military exercise is being offered, and you can stand or fall on your own merits. You declare that you're going to stand. At least you'll heave yourself around in bed and keep those covers wrapped, and turn a deaf ear to the gabble, and close your eyes against that luminous character who is emerging from the wallpaper. Just as folks say when speaking of some personified vermin, *Let him crawl back under the wallpaper again.*

Well, God damn it, you *crawl* there.

Football days are long faded, but you have a strange sense of throwing a block. You fling yourself upon your right side, so that you're looking at the west wall of the room instead of that fateful east.

Immediately you achieve results. The babble of voices diminishes, the glow lessens. In a matter of minutes there is no reflected translucence to be observed, no mumble and murmur to be heard. Soon there is . . . nothing, nothing. You maintain your iron grip, even while sleeping exhausted through the few hours until daylight. When you awaken you find the bedclothing crushed into a million squeezed wrinkles. If folks had pressed those wrinkles into sheets at the laundry, with one of their great hot mangles, they couldn't have ironed them any tighter.

. . . It's morning, and you wash and shave, and stare at yourself in the mirror. Thinking, "I'm not the same man who

went to bed here last night. There's an entire new category
with which I must now deal. There is a bewilderment which
I did not believe could be."

(You don't know it then, either, but before that day is done
you'll be sitting with Mr. K. Richmond in front of his fireplace,
and telling him about it, and begging for some explanation.
Mr. K. Richmond is top wheel in the British Society for Psychical Research.)

And along with that vital excitement which is bound to re-
solve from an experience never endured before and never believed possible, there is the gushing of inordinate curiosity.
Who was it? Why? Where did it—or they—come from? How
were the sounds and the luminescence related? What was all
this absurd business about bedcovers? Why would any force
do anything so ridiculous? What was the purpose? What did it
all point to?

This whirl of amazement and wonder will still be occupying
you when you sit down in the cozy little breakfast room. Already the elderly people—retired admirals and their ladies and
the like, who inhabit this hulk— They have assembled to
munch their toast, to spread the thin pathetic wartime marmalade, to sample with pardonable suspicion the sausages stuffed
so solidly with cereal—

And then will come our snowy-haired Mrs. Effie Stuart (not
her real name). And she will stand there, the landlady of 40-42
Truxley Court (not the real address), and she will gaze down
at you. Her pleasant old voice will be lilting.

"And did you rest comfortably?"

She knows—as well as she knows any truth of Heaven—that
you didn't rest comfortably. She knows that *no one* rests comfortably in that room. She doesn't *like* to rent the room, but
there are times— It's always the last to go. Very often it doesn't
go at all, because that final beleaguered applicant doesn't arrive to discover that the room is vacant. She knows all this.
And she knows, from one look at you, what happened up there
early this morning.

She's still polite, still very much the gentlewoman. That's why she asks the question.

You look up at her, and your eyes meet. You say, "Oh yes, very comfortably indeed," and she stares a minute, and her whole soul is yelling *liar, liar*. Then the expression changes, she becomes chalky and wooden. She goes away and doesn't look back.

So, with such experience behind me (fifteen years behind me, in fact) I knew that apparitions do exist. In the meantime I had become a life member of the American Society for Psychical Research. I had read voluminously—read everything which I could find written in English which dealt primarily with spontaneous phenomena. Millions of words: Myers, Podmore, Gurney, Carington, Harry Price, the works.

I had my own theory, too, and sustain it today. My belief is: the appearance of an apparition is not an event evidential of any surviving human entity. By that I mean that it doesn't prove there is such a thing as a disembodied ghost strolling through Eternity.

I see in the appearance of an apparition no evidence necessarily of human survival.

What I do believe is this: human beings, and animals, and events in which beings participate while living in this life— They can store up an electrical charge (call it electrical for lack of a better word). It is a charge of authoritative power. In later years, under certain circumstances, other mortals can come along and pick up the whole thing—through sight, sound, even in some cases through actual tactile demonstrations.

Not all people are sensitive enough to recognize certain charges when they are fired back at them out of walls, trees, floors, any surrounding unbreathing substance. Some may get the barest whisper of a sound, the briefest glistening or shadow of a sighting. Some may get nothing at all. And yet again some of these charges have extreme power. Thus there can be collective demonstration; a dozen people together can witness the apparition or hear the cry. It's happened again and again. And it doesn't mean that the author (originator) is alive; the author of the event has been moldering all the way from days to centuries. It matters not. He compressed himself or his moment of grief or arrogance or violence or pleasure, compressed himself into that battery—or dynamo?—to the utter limit, and it happened when he was alive, and the charge is still here, still with us. The author isn't.

This theory may not suit everyone else but it suits me very nicely, thank you.

I never encountered it anywhere until one fine day when I picked up a book by the late Harry Price (must have been the third or fourth book of his which I had read). Lo and behold, there was my own theory staring at me from the page. I couldn't resist, naturally: I wrote to Harry Price immediately and told him that I'd thought it to be my own privately managed little theory. And here he was, anticipating me all along.

The result was a rewarding correspondence. I lamented when Harry Price was no longer with us.

. . . Days and weeks went away, and Irene and I didn't witness any sort of demonstration in our own portion of Goldenhurst. When there was a moon the light lay kindly on floor and on vines outside . . . when there was rain, its music was genial as well. And when there was wind, it was robust . . . nothing ghostly about the wind blowing up from those marshes, but just a wholesome breeze.

With the Clarkes it was quite different. They were in a constant state of fret.

"It's that damnable cold spot in the hall!"

"Whereabouts?"

"Come over and you'll see. It's in the hall: the one by the rear entries, just past the studio."

. . . You could close all doors and windows, and walk into the cold spot, and feel it hit you like an icy brick. I remember one evening when we were having cocktails with the Clarkes in their wide living room (remodeled from Noël Coward's dining room). Kenneth went back yonder to get some ice, or another bottle or something or something, and suddenly he emerged from the hall with a smothered cry. I looked up to find him shivering and laughing. He set down the tray he was carrying, and used both hands to smooth his hair back into place. It was rather long hair, and all tousled.

". . . Coming along that passageway, you know. When I reached the cold spot, it was just like an electric shock. My hair stood completely on end. Annoying business. . . ."

As for little Reidun, his wife, she was always being tormented one way or another. She talked about selling out and moving away; but they couldn't bring themselves to do that—not yet. (They did eventually.)

No one has to admit these things. No one ever has to say, "I was coming along my hallway when some sort of unexplainable cold force pulled my hair on end." If you do relate something like that, you're going to be scorned by a great many people, laughed at by others, greeted with every reaction from jeers to pity. Such a situation isn't comfortable. You can well avoid it by keeping your mouth shut.

But some of us are born to talk, and some others—who aren't —think it their bounden duty to report what they have seen or heard.

In demonstration my mind goes back to 1934, when the *Mauretania* sailed into New York harbor from a Caribbean cruise. You can dig through newspaper files and read about it in the New York *Times* for February 11th, 1934. And see a picture also: an artist's sketch, drawn from descriptions given him by the ship's officers. It was a sea serpent. Quite a serpent too: sixty-five feet long. It was sighted on the 30th of January at 1:20 P.M.

Senior First Officer F. W. Moughtin and Senior Third Officer J. W. Caunce stood with solemn faces before the ship's reporters and told what they had seen. (A little later the master, Captain Reginald Peel, made a similar sighting.)

It wasn't all in the *Times* . . . I remember another report in another newspaper. Naturally these people were asked why they had put their professional reputations upon the block, so to speak. Were they deliberately asking for publicity? Were they advertising? "Come and take a cruise on the *Mauretania,* and maybe you'll see a sea serpent." Why did they have to say anything? Why didn't they just shut up? Why make a report?

One of them effected a mild response, utterly disarming and utterly heroic and utterly British. "Well, you see— We *saw* it, you see."

. . . Irene couldn't go to the Houchins's dinner party because she had a mild case of flu . . . not really sick, just a bit achey and coughy. She thought she'd be happier in bed.

The party began at Hythe and ended up in Dover, and it was quite a party. The Clarkes and I didn't come chugging home until 2 or 3 A.M.

But when we turned in through the gates of Goldenhurst we all exclaimed. The south house, the Kantor house, was blazing with lights.

. . . Irene had said, "Now, don't even give me a thought. I've had my tea, and some soup, and that's all I want. And Jill, the Clarkes' corgi, will be lying here on the bed. I've got plenty to read and—"

We all went tearing up to the bedroom, calling from the stair, "What's the trouble? Are you all right?"

"I'm all right."

Yes, she was fine. She was in bed, sitting up, wearing a black velvet gown which made her look like the dish she was and is.

"What on earth? Why all the lights?"—when we managed to make ourselves heard above Jill's barks.

"Well," said Irene, "I guess someone was playing knock-knock with me."

"Who?"

"I suppose it was the Goldenhurst ghost."

She said that knocks were really banging and busy. She

couldn't determine whether they were on the actual head of the huge four-poster bed itself, or on the wall behind the head of the bed. Anyway, the blows trembled and vibrated and thudded; sometimes they were sharp and quick, sometimes slower.

My bride said brightly, "I wasn't really afraid but— Jill and I thought we'd like to have the lights on."

. . . Before we left for Italy in the fall, Irene and I drove off on a trip to the Midlands and Yorkshire.

It seemed, when we returned to Kent, that Kenneth Clarke had something to tell me. "Let's stroll over here by the pond. . . ."

The pond was a weird and beautiful place: walled, filled with iris and rushes and lily plants, seeming almost solid with aquatic growth . . . frogs were busy there. . . .

Kenneth said, "You know, I had the workmen here tearing out that old staircase in the corner of the front room. We weren't using it any more, and— While I was gone down to my greenhouse beyond the garden, the foreman of carpenters came to report to me. He said, 'We're all through now, sir. We're taking away our tools. Oh, yes—and I got rid of those bones for you.'"

"Bones?" I asked.

"Yes," Kenneth Clarke said. "That's what I asked him. 'Bones? What kind?' 'Oh, I don't know, sir.' 'Where did you find them?' 'Well, they were behind the boards. I don't know: very small. I should say perhaps they were pig bones. A sucking pig, perhaps? Anyway I threw them in the pond.'"

We both looked at the green-stuffed water with insects dancing brightly in autumn sunshine. "In here?"

"So he said."

I mused. "Pig bones. . . ." All the time that little chant of Noël Coward's about the baby in the west wing, etc., etc., was beginning to reëcho in my mind.

"Yes," said Kenneth, "pig bones," and then we walked back to the house.

The Best Cooking of
My Life
1952

The old friend dropped by for a drink, as old friends do, and I led the way into our Florida kitchen, seeking ice. The friend halted within the door, amazed. "What on earth are you doing?"

"Making Chicago Hot."

He grunted. "I thought that was the prerogative of Shriners and American Legion conventions. Anyway, you're here—on Siesta Key, near Sarasota—and Chicago's a long way off."

I spoke to him gently, as any benevolent person might speak to an idiot child. "Chicago Hot is a relish."

The steam from scalded tomatoes rose around me.

"I propose now to remove the skins from these fresh tomatoes and chop them fine in this huge wooden bowl, and drain off the juice. I can make Chicago Hot in one hour. If you should be invited to stay to lunch—mind, I said *if* you should—you can then taste one of the most delicious substances known to man."

"But where on earth did you—"

Reverently, I lifted a green, dog-eared book from the shelf beside me. "Chicago Hot," I said, "is from a recipe contributed by Mrs. Sam Trumbaur. It comes out of the *Webster City Cook Book.*"

Beyond our windows the palms and Spanish moss began to fade. We dwelt instead amid elms and silvery maple boughs.

I guided my friend down cottonwood-shaded streets, past white

frame houses. Around us were wafted genial women in volumi-
nous blue-and-white aprons—women who knew how to deal
with a quince or whole ham if need be—women who knew that
yeast was not an alleged panacea to be munched by unfortunates
with blotches on their skin—women who baked chicken pies in
church basements, who recognized the provocation of a few
nasturtium leaves minced into a leaf-lettuce salad. I shared my
spice-flavored childhood, and found joy in the sharing.

Big awkward kitchens with linoleum tacked across sagging
boards; ranges with kettles steaming on their uneven lids; the
busy talk of Seth Thomas clocks upon the shelves; the vigorous
barking of a good-hearted dog outside; screeches of children at
play amid arching rhubarb plants: Webster City, Iowa, and all
the hints of delectation contained in that magic section of the
shabby book which was and is entitled: Pickles And Catsup.

Cucumber pickles, green-tomato pickles, watermelon pickles,
spiced beets, cucumber catsup, chili sauce, pepper hash . . . a
cinnamon tide of recollection . . . Chicago Hot!

1 peck ripe tomatoes, chop and drain, 2 cups chopped onions,
2 cups chopped celery, 2 cups sugar, 2 cups cold vinegar, ½ cup
of white mustard seed, ½ cup salt, 4 red peppers, 4 green peppers, chopped fine, mix together.

That was Mrs. Trumbaur's recipe. And soon we would savor
the breath-taking scent rising from the red-white-green melange,
the slight burn that came to the tongue, the heavenly seeping
of rich juice with which you anointed a portion of pot roast.
Chicago Hot! You didn't even have to cook it; it just made itself.
The only complaint was that, like most raw mixtures, it was
hard to keep into the winter, but it wasn't too extensive a
tragedy, at that. Chicago Hot was far too popular with sum-
mertime appetites for much of it to survive and go to waste in
the autumn.

It is currently the fashion to sneer at Midwestern cookery.
Cookbooks from Kansas, or Iowa, or Missouri, or Illinois have

never set the fashion in eatables, as have similar volumes from other regions. Things like *Memories of My Great-Aunt Abigail's Massachusetts Shore Dinners* or *Creole Gumbo as Presented at the Court of the Three Sisters* circulate widely among those whose taste in regional delights is as circumscribed as the tradition suggesting them.

Nobody puts out cute red-checked volumes about how to boil good Hamilton County sweet corn (roasting ears, the old folks used to call them—but imagine what would happen if you lingered now at a vegetable counter in New York and asked for roasting ears)! Nobody recites a recipe for squirrel stew with dumplings as Grandma Morean used to contrive it. Grandma Morean had never visited Cape Cod, Androscoggin, Meeting Street or the French Quarter, but, by golly, she—

As a matter of fact, we prairie natives who were born forty, fifty, or sixty years ago were singularly lucky. We reaped benefits derived from three distinct schools of American regional cookery. Pioneers who settled our towns and counties were generally descendant—filtered through, by one generation en route—from New England, or from the comfortable valleys of Pennsylvania German regions, or from farmhouses of Virginia or Kentucky.

Early we were taught to recognize the best in baked beans, crullers, spoon bread. We smacked our lips over scrapple and sausage, but also we knew what to do when confronted with the pot liquor seeping from stew of a Brunswick persuasion.

Apparently the *Webster City Cook Book* was not intended for circulation beyond local precincts. It was printed, I believe, at the same shop which published the weekly *Journal*. The first volume must have been issued sometime along in the '90s. Ours was dog-eared and sirup-stained; it bore loving brands of hot spoons and butter by the time I became aware of it, and that was in the earlier years of this century.

Along about 1916 the ladies seem to have got together again and produced an enlarged edition. The book's inception lay amid the prodigious bustlings of one of the Ladies' Aids. The book boasts one hundred and twenty-two pages, with a lot of blank extra sheets at the rear wherein people could write their own favorite recipes, and always did.

The assembling of the pages seems to have been done by a bemused printer. At least that is true of the copy now possessed proudly by the Kantor household, presented by my sister Virginia some Christmases ago. Page 49 follows directly after Page 32; Page 64 precedes Page 33; 48 is in direct opposition to 65. Thus the peruser drifts from a boiled-turnip recipe to one for cherry salad. Rice and Tomatoes are an immediate second course for a delicious Snow Pudding filled with stiffly beaten egg whites. Mrs. W. F. Smith's Apple Salad flirts gaily with Lemon Custard as ordered by Mrs. George S. Barner.

In my mind's eye the food means the people, the people mean the food. Miss Grace Hillock contributed Brown Bread. Miss Grace Hillock looked something like a thin, finger-size slice of brown bread herself. She taught Number Four in the South Building, and always stood aloof, tan-faced, currant-eyed, at the foot of the stairway when lines of children marched down. She was to be regarded with historical deference, if you came from a historically minded family, and most of us did. The name "Humphrey Hillock" was graven on a tablet at the courthouse less than a block away, along with the names of other sainted survivors and martyrs of the Spirit Lake Massacre Relief Expedition.

Osgood Pie is from the lore of Mrs. H. P. Mason, and she was the mother of my playmate, Charles, and whenever she tripped her way down Second Street, her little fox terrier trotted beside her, holding up her long skirts by his dainty white teeth. . . .

And who is that bowling around the corner in an old buggy-shaped electric automobile? Baked Squash is an inheritance from Mrs. George S. Neel; so we see her now, with Mr. Neel beside her. Half blind he is, lifting his bearded face high, squinting boldly out at the world behind his little black nose-glasses, and glorying in martial memories.

Mr. E. N. Lee is just crossing the street, brought back into the flesh once more by the invocation of Mrs. E. N. Lee's Berry Pie. He is bent and frail as he pauses to salute Comrade Neel with a wave of his cane. Though so frail, he will be the last to die of all those fife-led GARs. (The big roster in the public library basement will not be closed until 1938.)

Mrs. D. C. Chase, the wife of our senator, is halting beside a picket fence to peer at a catbird prowling amid lilac bushes. She was a great bird-woman, was Mrs. Chase, but she could also make such Pound Cake Patties as you never guessed. . . .

Who waddles past the corner up there at First and Prospect? Aunt Martha Cook, sure enough, who helped out the family budget with angel-food cakes, French cream pies and golden jars of mayonnaise, in those seasons when W. H. Cook's music-mastering yielded naught. Also, she played piano or organ at the Congregational Church when the need arose.

Now we are walking out of that church into the sun of a May-time noon, contemplating the meat loaf or roast chicken browning at home. Mrs. D. L. Hunter is ambling ahead. (Pickled Eggs —the book gives her secret.) She stops a moment to chat with Mrs. Ed Burgess (Butter Soup).

Mrs. Hunter has a dim view of the minister's long concern with vanished Pilgrims. "Plymouth Rock!" she is snorting. "I've heard about Plymouth Rock till I thought I'd turn to rock!" But Mrs. Burgess does not stay to hear her. Mrs. Burgess must hasten up the short block to her own house where Honey-bunch is waiting.

Honeybunch was a golden Persian cat, the only Persian in town. Mrs. Burgess made a great point of this. She had no intention of letting Honeybunch consort—she could not have employed the word "breed"—with other cats of ordinary persuasion. But one spring night it seems that there was a broken windowpane in the Burgess basement, and it seems that Honeybunch got out, and it seems that—

The resulting progeny were smuggled eventually to more free-and-easy homes. They were smuggled by night and in covered baskets. No infant delivered by any wayward girl of the community was ever put up for adoption more covertly. Years later, our landlady, Mother Letts, had a black Tommy, some generations removed from the original illicit romance, but with a tinge of Persian showing in his fur. "By the way," said the saturnine Mother Letts in conversation with Mrs. Burgess, "I guess my Tommy is a relative of your Honeybunch."

Mrs. Burgess drew in her petticoats. "Very distant!" she cried.

Ah, they are gone—the Hunters, the Burgesses, the Chases, the Cooks, the Lees, the Neels, the Masons. But they have found immortality amid us lucky survivors who possess copies of the little green book.

Certainly you are supposed to know something about cooking, to begin with; perish the thought of a Webster City bride who did not. Time of cooking, quantities of liquids or of meats, measurements of spices—these are hinted at vaguely, but the most glorious latitude is permitted.

"Cut up as for frying," says Mrs. Fred Beerman in her formula for Chicken Soup, but she doesn't tell you how much chicken. "Boil gently in three quarts of water till meat is well cooked." Any woman in her right mind should know when chicken is well cooked. "Skim carefully. Add a teacup of rice, and season to taste." That makes sense. There are tastes and tastes. There is *orégano* in the world, but also there is mace. "Some prefer," declares the chef, "to add sweet milk or cream. Pick meat carefully from bones, and serve with soup or," she advances a final suggestion, "make into salad."

Did I say something about quantities? My own grandmother, in personal annotations added with pencil directly below Shrimp And Peas on Page 12, goes so far as to suggest the prices which reigned in local markets when she scribbled her favorite recipe for Heavenly Hash. "15¢ hamburg," she begins, "10¢ sausage." The next item is "1 quart tomatoes (or less)."

There are countless injunctions to "simmer until very tender" or "bake until well done." Thermometers, range clocks, automatic warning devices, thermostats and the like—thunderation! Those were tiresome gadgets of the future, never to be bothered with by serene Hamilton County folk who simply built up a soft-coal fire in the Great Majestic until the oven was good and hot, and cooked the roast until it was good and done.

There is a satisfaction in this easygoing approach. If people don't know how to cook at all, they should be taught in person by someone who does know how. I don't think it possible to learn competence second-hand from a book. You have to learn while sniffing hot steam over a hot stove, while Grandma or Auntie stands beside you and says, "See? Now don't put in too much flour—just enough to take up all the grease in the pan. See? Now keep stirring while you add the milk, slowly, just a little bit at a time. That's right. Put it back farther where it won't cook so fast. See?"

That's how I learned to make gravy—wholesome flour-and-milk gravy, to go along with pork chops and mashed potatoes. I would rather eat my gravy than any esoteric *sauce supreme* contrived by some third-generation hireling of the original Escoffier, who may be able to enchant sophisticates with his *Foie de Veau Poêlé à la Bourgeoise,* but who wouldn't know how to cook a meat loaf with browned potatoes if the entire fate of the Thursday-night church supper of the Berean Guild depended on it.

Certainly the French know what to do with cherries—I remember well enough. I have munched dangerous little sodden bulbs retrieved from alcoholic bath amid Montmartre midnights when the *chansons* shrilled within stony half-forbidden cellars. But I would defy the French to make non-alcoholic salted cherries—the kind that can be doled out by the handful to small boys when they come sniffing like puppies at the back door.

1 pint white wine vinegar, 1 pint cold water, 2 tablespoons salt, to ½ gallon cherries. Crowd cherries down well. Do not stem. Fill jar half full vinegar, rest with cold water. Put salt on top cherries. Seal.

And be sure you put the seal back on firmly after the hand-out, or the boys will eat them all.

The book is by way of being a record of the town's marriages and relationships. One recognizes that Mrs. Francis E. Whitley, whose Spiced Veal Loaf "should be baked nearly three hours," is one and the same as the Cora Call Whitley whose Chocolate Hermits "may be frosted if desired," and whose chicken, if it seems to be getting too dry in baking, should receive the addition of "a little more milk."

Any survivor of that Webster City in the days before-the-shoe-factory-burned-down-and-when-the-Chase-Lister-tent-show-used-to-come-every-summer would know also that Grandma Whitley's daughter, Gladys Whitley Crosley, could make Oatmeal Cookies the like of which never dwelt within the confines of a package at the grocery store.

1 cup sugar, ½ cup butter, ½ cup lard, 1 cup chopped raisins, 2 eggs, ¾ teaspoon soda, 4 big tablespoons sweet milk, 2 cups flour, 1 cup oatmeal, 1 teaspoon cinnamon. Drop from a teaspoon on buttered tins.

And that, dear children, is that. Any idiot ought to know how to mix the stuff and how long to bake it on the buttered tins. Gladys knew. She was as plump and warm as a cooky herself, and so was her mother.

Some of the ladies were given to the bizarre. Mrs. C. E. Atkinson advocated something which she called Fricatelli. Raw fresh pork and small onions were chopped together with bread crumbs and eggs to be mixed well, to be made into patties and fried like oysters.

Mrs. Atkinson also advanced something she called Prawline— a recipe which on examination suggests the pralines of New Orleans, whither indeed Mr. and Mrs. Atkinson, being well-to-do, had ventured on their travels. But she might have spared her energy and the space in the book. Young Webster City, to the last gangly-necked boy and freckle-faced girl, ate chocolate fudge. It bubbled on half the stoves, come Friday night.

Here is my own recipe scrawled with blunt pencil inside the back cover:

1½ cups sugar, ⅔ cup water, 2 squares chocolate, large lump butter, 7 marshmallows. Boil until it forms soft ball in cold water. Add vanilla. Cool and beat.

I haven't found the time or the weight-margin-for-error to allow me such dalliance in recent years, but I remember where I got the recipe. It was from a redhead named Mildred Wetkavski. Boy, could she cook!

So could the Hoots. That was their name: Mrs. A. C. Hoot and her daughter Blanche. Blanche offers Bran Muffins, and her mother counters with the somewhat disquieting title, Laxative Biscuits. It was fitting that the Hoots should be concerned vitally with cereals: Mr. Hoot was the town miller.

Away over beyond the I.C. tracks, Mrs. Elva Howard—prim slim, and gray-haired—is baking a prune cake; her sons Lowell and Merritt are waiting anxiously outside the screen door. And back across town again on South Willson Avenue, Mrs. Howard's sister, Mrs. C. D. Carpenter, equally prim and slim, is making mock duck. And what delicious odors are stealing from a small house not far from the Hoot mill? Mrs. Clara Comley is hard at work fabricating chicken croquettes and nut-potato salad.

Through most years the Comleys were the only colored family in town. Charley himself was an excellent chef, and used to go along and cook at our summer camp during the infancy of the Boy Scout troop; and Clara Comley could be depended on, in final analysis, to utter the last soft word on any matter concerning salads or chickens.

These good-natured people held the respect and affection of the community. The presence of the Comleys became awkward only when people sought to regard them as servants. A thunderous postnuptial reception was planned by one of our richer families . . . to the amazement of all, Charley Comley greeted guests at the door, accepting the gentlemen's hats, and wearing a white coat.

"We didn't know what to do," ran my mother's perplexed report. "We didn't know whether to say, 'How are you, Charley?' or whether to ignore him, or whether to say 'Good evening, Mr. Comley,' or just shake hands."

Apple Pickles— Grandma Wicks's formula appears on Page 110. She specified that Whitney No. 20 apples be used, and who today has got a Whitney No. 20 for sale, or loan, or gift? I was in Webster City, right through the apple season in 1947, and nary a Whitney No. 20 did I see.

The Wickses owned a Whitney No. 20, but it yielded to the corrosion of time, just as Grandpa Wicks did. Not, however, before he distinguished himself at the circus.

He trotted off one hot summer day to the circus tent— empty sleeve, little pointed beard, bronze lapel button and all. As crowds filed into the shade of the hot canvas they were diverted by the antics of two clowns, one made up as an ancient rustic, the other as his wife.

These mimes gravitated among high benches on opposite sides of the tent. They had been separated, they squalled—the wife had lost her husband, the husband his wife. The wailing plea for strangers to please help locate Hezekiah, or Emmy Lou, made for glee with most of the crowd, but for concern on the part of Grandpa Wicks. He was a little hard of hearing, and a little slow on the uptake generally.

"There was a pitiful thing happened up at the circus today," he told his daughter. "Pitiful, pitiful! There was some poor woman from the country who had lost her husband, and she was just a-crying in the crowd. Well, I looked around most everywhere, but I couldn't find him. Then later on I come across *him,* and then I couldn't find *her.* It was pitiful."

Somewhere amid the dusty avenues down which he has trudged, Grandpa Wicks may still be stalking the clowns, endeavoring to bring them into tranquillity. As for Grandma

Wicks, she was forever tranquil. Doubtless she is sitting on a green painted stool by an old sink, serenely preparing apple pickles. Whitney No. 20s, of course.

Time was not of the essence when a Webster City cook prepared to take off on any great adventure. Mrs. E. F. King was the mother of my chum Bob. We boys testified that her rolls were of a delicate consistency comparable to those same marshmallows which I advocated mixing into my fudge.

One pint scalded milk, 2 tablespoons butter, 2 tablespoons sugar, 1 teaspoon salt, 1 yeast cake dissolved in warm water, 3 cups flour. Make sponge and let rise overnight; add flour for stiff dough in morning and knead. Let rise again 1 to 1½ hours. Pinch off little pieces of dough about as big as a walnut, roll in melted butter and put 3 of these in each gem iron and let rise again until very light. Compressed yeast may be used and start rolls in morning to bake for six o'clock.

Most modern housewives would scorn a recipe which took so long for its fruition. Still, these are the same cute little characters who think nothing of going through the most complicated gyrations with damp bread, wine, shallots, caviar, Cheddar cheese, and the like, in order to produce flimsy hors d'oeuvres which will be gobbled heedlessly by folks who have had far too many martinis.

The trouble seems to be that the emphasis has been put in the wrong place. If this civilization were ready to spend more effort in attaining the ultimate in clover-leaf rolls instead of the ultimate in cocktail titbits, we might be able to face our enemies with more purpose than we now achieve.

I can't help thinking also that Flint Pickles, as promulgated by Mrs. M. Beaucheine, would cause us to praise the Lord a little louder and pass the ammunition a little more successfully. Mrs. Beaucheine was serious about her pickles . . . time,

time, time. The flavor of humming-bird days and four-o'clock-frilled afternoons and nicotiana-scented nights would be in every warty lump, if we could stay our headlong rush to disaster and dally by the big pickle keg for a while.

One gallon soft water, 1 cup salt, boil and pour over pickles while hot, for nine mornings; skimming each morning before pouring on pickles. The tenth morning throw away salt water and take 1 gallon soft water and boil with alum the size of an egg, pour this over pickles while hot. The eleventh morning throw alum water away, boil 1 gallon cider vinegar, 6 cups sugar and 5 cents' worth mixed spices and pour over pickles.

Someday I am going to cook an entire bill of fare and for every meal, out of that *Webster City Cook Book*. I shall have to imagine the purple morning-glories climbing on cotton strings, the melodious barking of a dog named Trix, and the squeak of buggy wheels in the road outside. These external emoluments will be present, however, in such hearty illusion as to flavor each dish with a spice undreamed in all the exotic plantations of the Orient.

For breakfast I shall have slow-fried crumbly slices of pink and tan bacon, the like of which used to come from Mr. Lillegard's prize hogs, and crisp apple fritters as only Mrs. Minnie Arthur could make them. I will have dinner at noon and supper at night. My own mother's recipe for vegetable soup will be observed with genuflection, and once again there will be plenty of time for everything.

Cover 1 good-sized veal shank with cold water in large pot or kettle and simmer for 3 hours. When the veal begins to boil add: salt, 3 peppercorns, 3 or 4 bay leaves, 3 cloves and 1 good-sized onion sliced. Skim soup from time to time, and one hour before serving add: 2 carrots diced, 1 sliced turnip, 1 cup cooked tomatoes and 4 potatoes sliced. Strain through sieve before serving.

The evening supper baffles me each time I try to plot it.
I wander from contemplation of Mrs. Joe Richard's Honon
Steak to Spanish Steak as suggested by Mrs. J. C. Lasher.
Still there must be an opportunity for Mrs. David Eyer's Hot
Slaw, and what should go with it?

One-half head cabbage, ⅔ cup sour or sweet cream, ⅔ cup
vinegar, butter size of egg, yolks of 2 eggs, 1 heaping tablespoon
sugar. Mix cream, sugar and eggs together, then add vinegar,
salt and pepper to taste. Put cabbage in earthen vessel, sprinkle
heaping tablespoon flour over it, then add dressing and boil ten
minutes.

Homemade sausage, perhaps? Mrs. McMurchy knew how to
make it, and there is her recipe, gleaming on Page 15, suggesting in its imagined odor and sharpness the meaty attributes
of her husband, Captain James McMurchy.

Or should I try Baked Ham, as Dot Kamrar suggests? Or
should I indeed go back to Grandma Wicks's Pressed Beef?
There is no nonsense about timing here, either. Grandma
Wicks directs you: "Boil a shank of beef until meat drops from
bone." Again that makes sense. There is no fooling around
with time-saving gadgets which could easily lead you astray if
they became radioactive.

Jellies, sauces, conserves—the spiced pears and beets to accompany my feast. . . . I'll take time and more time. I'll measure my sugar with glory, and sing *Oh, Be Ye Reconciled* at the
top of my lungs as I do it. I'll stir with the wooden spoon
which my own great-great-grandfather carved from applewood
some generations before this now moss-covered *Webster City
Cook Book* was even thought of.

If, after I have sat in orgy, absorbing the fruit of devoted
toil, I rise from a midnight couch with beating pulse and clammy
skin and anguished interior—the victim of unwise if passionate
devotion to the gentilities of another age—if Mrs. Comley's
Chicken Salad has fought with Mrs. Burgess's Cheese Soufflé,

and Mrs. James Hoyt's Hickory Nut Drops are quarreling with Mrs. Samuel Baxter's Chili Sauce, I shall remain in the end unalarmed. The *Webster City Cook Book* contains a choice array of recipes for invalid dishes too.

Lobo
1956

When first we encountered him, he was disguised as a *fiesta*.

If ever I did know what particular Spanish historical occasion is celebrated on the night of February 15th, I have forgotten. It was on such a night.

The unique enterprise which Lobo had decided to grace with his presence is deemed the Montemar-El Remo complex. It is directed by the Marqués de Nájera, whose exploits on the golf courses of Andalucía vie with his hold on fame as a cavalry officer during the Rif campaigns. Angel, as he is called by intimates, is seconded in command by the lovely María Luisa Rein. From these people I learned eventually such details of Lobo's past as might have escaped the attention of ordinary biographers.

The Montemar Hotel is a sprawling white plaster building rambling along the shoulder of a hill, with the Mediterranean turning choicely blue or bitterly gray a quarter of a mile beneath. Down on those shores is the gayer portion of the concern: El Remo, a busy little restaurant by day, and by night a club where the light fantastic is tripped, and where on occasion a few of the light-minded fantastic individuals of the Gay International Set have indulged in earnest hair-pullings.

The cuisine, presided over by one Cristóbal, is above reproach if some of the guests occasionally aren't. Grouped near El

Remo are cottages and a row of modern glass-fronted apartments, all a part of the same brave social scheme.

. . . A *fiesta* was in progress, and what with serpentine and confetti and noisemakers and champagne and brandy, everything was moving right well at 2 A.M.

By nature an abstemious man, I was not at all polluted. But my senses shivered as I watched a portion of the carnival scenery detach itself and move calmly toward us.

I murmured to my wife, "Do you see what I see?"

Irene said limply, "I guess we've had too many drinks. We ought to go home."

"Let's go—I'm with you. Serpentine doesn't just get up and walk around."

That is what the serpentine was doing. A huge parti-colored mound of the gay paper streamers progressed ominously across the dance floor.

"Serpentine's got a tail," we observed. Sure enough, the paper mountain did have a tail, a stubby sickle-shaped appendage with a white tip.

Cristóbal approached our table.

"Please, what is *that?*" We indicated the ambulatory hummock which now had turned majestically on another course.

"Ah, that. That is Lobo."

Thus began an acquaintance which ripened into friendship, which in turn ripened into obsession, which in turn ripened into madness. In the direction of Lobo (in Spanish, *wolf*) lay madness.

If you chose to introduce a Doberman, a German shepherd, and an old red-bone hound and have them somehow intermingle and beget, they might have produced something like Lobo. He had yellow eyes and droopy ears. His legs and feet were fawn-colored; and they were slim legs and tiny feet, although made of piano wire. Also tan was the mask across his face, which he wore flagrantly in a land where the wearing of masks is a felony. He had a white necktie; from this formal white decoration a pale zipper extended backward under his belly.

Often I was possessed of the insane impulse to unzip that zipper but was too appalled at the notion of what I might find inside.

Lobo weighed an even fifty pounds on the dot. He could run about twice as fast as any greyhound at the Sarasota Kennel Club, at least any that I ever bet on. His teeth had been hand-forged in Seville by some master swordsmith; his tongue was a slice of palest *Serrano* ham; most of his body had been well blacked and rubbed by the best *limpiabotas* in Spain. (That is foreign talk for bootblack.)

According to Angel and María Luisa, Lobo's mother belonged to a shepherd in the hills behind the Montemar. This unhappy country matron presented the not-too-proud shepherd with a litter of puppies one cold day. The Spaniards are a philosophical race—also practical, if at times uncertain according to our standards in their moral motives. The practical and benevolent shepherd turned the puppies out to die. He said that he could feed no more dogs than the one. I suppose that most of them did die. Perhaps up there amid flint and boulders of the coastal range are lying the long-picked bones of Lobo's kin. No bones of Lobo are there.

Lobo betook himself shoreward. I can understand how his reasoning went, and so can anyone else who knew him.

"Let's see," Lobo meditated. "Shelter, of course—I don't like being rained on. . . . Food . . . yes, yes, but not ordinary food. Something exotic would be more to the point. . . . Companionship? For a certainty. And I do like a place with an open fire and red leather cushions."

So he showed up at the most expensive café on the southern coast of Spain, and moved in as manager, a grade or two above the rank held later by Cristóbal.

How long since all this had taken place?

Time means very little to the Spanish.

You would say, "How long has Lobo been here?"

"Oh, for years."

"How many years?"

"Oh, for some years, *Señor*."

"Well, two years, three years?"

"Oh, yes."

"Four years, five years?"

The shrug. "Perhaps."

"Six years?"

"I don't know, *Señor*. He has been here for years."

Actually he had a few gray hairs when first we knew him. But a vet who looked at his teeth later said they were the teeth of a young dog. . . . *No lo sé, Señoras y Señores.*

Far from being the playboy type, he was a man of serious purpose, definitely community-minded. A native of the United States, he would have belonged—congenially, productively— to the Elks, the Masons or K of C, the Rotary Club, and probably the American Legion or the Veterans of Foreign Wars. (If a war had been going on, you wouldn't have been able to keep Lobo out of it.) A native of Spain, however, he belonged to no organization; although on good rumor he attended sessions of the Friends of New Torremolinos, the village booster organization—most especially if the meeting had a banquet attached.

He was known in every shop. All cooks and gardeners and maids knew him. The children knew him. The Civil Guards treated him with respect. "Good morning, Lobo," they would say. He would bow and continue on his course, which usually had something to eat at the end of it.

Most of the *turistas* who came to El Remo thought naturally that this beast belonged to Fermín or Antonio or Miguel or Cristóbal or Pedro or someone of the staff. At times the staff thought he belonged to the Devil. He was not in those days a cross dog. Neither was he a dirty dog, he was not a smelly dog; he did not jump up on the tables. Still the mere ubiquity of the creature was something to be contended with.

His comforts were eminently provided for at the café; the huge golden eyes did the trick. He was catholic as to his tastes. Often we saw him leisurely munching chicken bones contributed by some tot. He ate every variety of hors d'oeuvre in the place, although he was most partial to caviar.

His procedure consisted of approaching a table and putting his stony head on a knee or a lap. When you looked down to see what was this weight you were bearing, the weight was Lobo. You fed him, you had to, you couldn't *not* feed Lobo. This is, nineteen out of twenty people couldn't. The twentieth person (often a Swede or a German, with strict ideas as to the table deportment of dogs) would fly into a rage and flail with his napkin. Lobo sought neither to resist nor retaliate. He simply shrugged and strolled on to another table.

This is not champagne or brandy talk, Spanish or otherwise; but it does seem that I have seen him eat at least twice his weight in anchovy olives, cold sausage, almonds, tuna fish, white bread, omelette, ice cream, pickled shrimp, candied cherries, and vegetable soup in a single evening. When even his rubber belly could hold no more, he would saunter toward a cushion on the built-in bench near the fireplace. If some interloper happened to be there, he would fling himself across the interloper's feet as a hint that the spot should be vacated.

Generally he was very even as to temper—again, in those days. From time to time he traveled with a troop of native dogs ambling about the neighborhood. He was larger than most, he seemed to rule by influence rather than by brawn. I never saw him in but one fight—in those days—and then it was with a snobbish French poodle who swished into the place and apparently whispered some slighting reference to Lobo's ancestry or background.

Being seated closest to the scene of strife, and having achieved by that time a working knowledge of Lobo, I managed to save the visiting poodle from complete dismemberment. . . .

"How *dare* you!" the poodle's mistress was shrieking in five languages. "How dare you retain such a wicked beast? You should keep your dog on leash!"

"Madam," I said, "he is not my dog." Suddenly my heart was a little heavy at the thought that this was true.

If Lobo had no family of his own it was not his fault. He was willing to have a family, he courted families. Did the mighty General Carlos Martínez Amadeo Silva y Serrano appear for a quiet holiday on the seashore, complete with *la señora*, nine children, and eleven maids? Lobo moved in with them. Invariably he was welcomed as a combination court jester, tutor, night watchman, and scullion. Then, the fortnight of seaside bliss being duly expended, the Silva tribe would return to Madrid minus Lobo.

The following week one of those same cottages might be occupied by an elderly countess, with whom Lobo would promptly effect a liaison. Next month it might be an ailing English couple, or an American painter, a Swiss professor, a Copenhagen merchant, a French opera singer. Lobo must have distributed more international affections than a Hollywood playboy on his first trip to the Riviera.

Thus he developed his allergy to suitcases. Lobo dissolved at the mere sight of a suitcase being dragged from its lair. His reaction was to depart into the nearest dark closet and lie with his face turned against his tail. When the suitcase was packed and closed, and a departure grew imminent, he froze even colder—he would not lift his head. He would not come out and say Goodbye, he would not display a brave heart in the face of separation. He would simply congeal until the *camareras* shoveled him out of the way when they came to prepare the abode for new tenants.

Later, when Lobo's life was identified with my own, other people used to come proudly and declare that they too had dwelt in such intimacy. "You know, Lobo lived with *us* once. For three weeks." They seemed confident of securing prestige by the statement.

The night we returned to Spain in the early spring of 1954 for our second period of residence, we entered El Remo. Lobo greeted us with open paws. We had planned to take a house that year, probably down the coast a little farther. Angel arranged temporary quarters for us in one of the glassy apartments on the shore; without invitation, Lobo accompanied us thither when we withdrew from the table.

This apartment had been occupied until the previous week by the John Steinbecks, and I do not think that Lobo lived with them. Lobo did not like gypsies, or sadly enough, beggar children, since the latter element had been unkind to him in his infancy, and he had reason to remember cuffs, kicks, and hurtful stones. Beggar children gave him a wide berth. They would not have approached the Steinbeck establishment had Lobo been in occupancy. Mr. Steinbeck, however, is a resourceful man. He proceeded to get rid of the beggars whenever they came hissing outside the window with that persistence known only to Andalucian mendicants. Mr. Steinbeck would erupt from his dwelling suddenly, screaming in English, "Buttered toast!" This had become a part of neighborhood tradition. It served well. Promptly the landscape would be overwhelmed with fast-fleeing brats. . . .

Lobo did exude an air of having been there before, when he trotted into the apartment. Carefully he selected the best portion of the upholstered couch, curled up, winked at us, went to sleep. He was still there in the morning, motionless, and did not even deign to stretch—until breakfast was brought and there was some reason for getting up. He took his usual continental breakfast of buttered roll and marmalade, then asked me to open the door for him. He disappeared. We did not see him again until ten o'clock at night, when the very earliest-dining Spaniards begin to gather. Then he consumed dinner along with us, and moved in again for the night.

On the third day we were invited to a party. It was to be a large assemblage, and common sense and a certain degree of sophistication suggested that we should decline. The hostess was a member of the Gay International Set—by no means one of the hair-pullers—but still there were bound to be the usual Hollywood types, Left Bank types, Monaco types, Costa Brava types, with a good prospect of several people plunging fully clad into the swimming pool before the night was over.

Few diners were present when we walked into El Remo

about ten or a little later, and certainly there was no Lobo in sight.

"Where is Lobo?" I asked.

"*Don* MacKinlay, he has gone to the party. Were you not invited to the party? Everyone has gone to the party."

We chattered out something about still being weary from our trip.

"Oh, yes," said Cristóbal. "I know that Lobo is there, because he saw them fetching in the food very early, and preparing tables in the Contessa's patio. He went up there immediately."

This night Lobo had decided to cast discretion to the winds, to become in name and deed one of the G.I.S. It was 4 A.M., and we were sound asleep, when the most horrible caterwauling burst forth outside our door, punctuated by a scratching assault on the panel. I arose and opened the door. Lobo staggered in. He had had too much to drink as well as too much to eat. He barely made it to the couch, and didn't get up until noon.

We started explaining suitcases to him a couple of days later.

"You see, Lobo, we have taken a house about five *kilómetros* down the beach, and of course that is too far from El Remo for your comfort. So—"

But we were talking to thin air, because he had gone into the closet. There was just that shiny black rear with its four-leaf-clover design of tan at a strategic place; that was all we could see.

He didn't move, not even after we crowded our bags into the car.

Irene bent over him tenderly. "Lobo, aren't you even going to say goodbye?"

He did follow us into the yard, but after one look at the loaded car he lay down and turned his face away.

"I almost hate to leave him," Irene mourned as we drove off.

"Why, heavens. He wouldn't be happy anywhere else. El

Remo is his *home,* the only place he knows," and I had almost convinced myself of this by the time we reached our new quarters on the precipice at La Verdad.

Following a few meals cooked over charcoal, we felt that since we were the proud possessors of a regular kitchen and a regular stove, we would try a little roasting or baking. Most Spanish stoves might be good for fogging up an Air Force Base to conceal it from visual attack by the enemy; ours was no exception. A storm of smoke drove us out. We left the windows open and fled to El Remo.

Promptly a solid head was dumped on each of our four knees in turn, and Lobo expressed his pleasure by gobbling most of our dinners. Then he disappeared; we presumed that he had gone among other tables to beg for further sustenance—as if he needed it!—and after a postprandial visit to the bar, we went out to our car. The windows had been left open; this was still the off season, with very few cars parked beside the café, and no such fripperies as parking-lot attendants and the like.

Lobo was seated in the car. He had no license, but he was in the driver's seat.

I shoved him over between us. "Let's take him home for a visit. Might be fun."

"Now, don't you start that," said Irene.

"Oh, what's the harm? He can visit us for a couple of days, and then we'll bring him back and dump him down here the next time we come. He'd much rather be *here* than *there.* Anyone knows that."

Anyone didn't know that. We dumped him in due course a few nights later. I was rather sick of having him under foot all the time, and I was busy working on *Andersonville,* and I didn't see how Lobo could help me very much. Accordingly we came back for a Sunday evening snack; once we had seen him retreat toward the patio to join dancers and diners there, we tiptoed quietly to the car and drove away.

All he did was to go up to the big coastal highway, the main artery which bisects the hillside area between El Remo and the Montemar Hotel. He lay beside the road for two days and two nights. The *Guardia Civil* told me so later, for they saw him and wondered about it.

We started to drive in to Málaga. Our car stood out more or less in that land of few automobiles, most of them of darker hue. We were driving a sedan with a cream-colored body and rust-colored top; it could be spotted far away.

As we whirred past the intersection I saw a shape beside the road.

"Is that Lobo back there?"

Irene turned for a look through the rear window. "It is indeed Lobo back there. He is coming at exactly ninety miles per hour."

There were some trucks around, there was a flock of sheep to be circled. I didn't want to see Lobo mashed before our very eyes, so hastily I pulled over to the side of the road and slowed down. He overtook the car like Mr. John Landy passing somebody in a wheel chair. He took off in a running dive when he was about fifteen feet away. Fortunately the window by the driver's seat was open, because that was his target.

When a fifty-pound plummet of solid dog lands smack on your stomach and chest, you know that you have been hit.

He said to us, "I couldn't imagine where you'd gone! You weren't down at El Remo; but I decided that you'd be driving along the highway one of these times, so I just waited there. Thanks a lot for stopping."

We went groaning to Málaga, where I left Lobo incarcerated in the car under the watchful eyes of the little crippled public-parking-attendant, and found a store where I could buy a collar and a leash. I bought Lobo a fine red collar. He had never worn a collar; I thought the red would be gay. No, he had never worn a collar in his life, nor had he been on leash either, as far as we knew; but delicately he trod the crowded sidewalks, overseeing our shopping, as if he had a half-dozen diplomas from obedience schools. There was nothing to do now but to take him back to La Verdad, where he'd remain in residence until our departure.

During an interlude he visited the local veterinarian in Torremolinos, whose quarters and talents were more suited to the drenching of oxen than the conducting of a boarding kennel. We had promised to move over to Mallorca for some sixteen days, homework and all, and we just couldn't see lugging Lobo to Madrid and thence by air to the Balearic Islands.

"He'll be perfectly all right up there at that so-called vet's." I assured Irene and my conscience. "Anyway, I know he needs to be wormed, and he ought to have a rabies shot, and he should have a good scrubbing, because probably he's never had a good scrubbing. I know that he plunges into the sea now and then; but that's not like soap and elbow grease."

I left Lobo in the car outside the vet's, while I went in to explain. . . . A poor dog, I said. . . . A beggar dog who has adopted us temporarily. . . . I would like to leave him for a while, until our return. He needs to be wormed, bathed, etc. . . .

El veterinario listened sympathetically and suggested that I bring the dog inside. We appeared, at opposite ends of the leash. The vet's eyes widened with delight.

"Why, mercy sakes," he said, or the Andalucian equivalent thereof. "I thought you said this was a *poor* dog—an unknown! Why, this is *El Lobo!*"

. . . Our friend brooded a good deal while we were gone, according to later report. The vet said that he was *muy desconsolado*. Lobo awarded us a flattering reception on our return.

. . . We found that he was given to mysterious illnesses. He had a couple of them that summer—times when he would lie in a chair or on the floor and not move of his own volition for several days; and he would not eat a bite, and would drink nothing. Once I took him up to the vet's for examination; after his temperature was taken and found to be normal, the vet only shook his head and gave Lobo a *laxante*. The animal perked out of it in a couple of days, and went bounding about the cliffs again.

During this season Lobo began to realize that he was become a man of substance. His disposition underwent a slight if corrosive change. For the first time he growled at the Civil Guard.

In Spain, quite sensibly, many of the guards dwell in family barracks, complete with wives and children. One of these establishments was on a hilltop directly across the road from our place at La Verdad. Hence it was customary for the guards, who at a later hour would have to report for duty at the central office in Torremolinos, to take up stations outside our gateway, and there await the American who might drive toward the village on morning errands. Sometimes there was one man, sometimes two or three, all very handsome in neat green uniforms, with Tommy guns slung amiably over their shoulders and black hats shining. It was Standing Operating Procedure for them to wait there, and Standing Operating Procedure for me to stop, ask if they should like a lift, and fling open the door. The first time I did this, Lobo nearly flung himself out of it. He had decided that the car was his, and he saw no reason why the *policia* should take over. I counseled him severely and he remained quiet, but with ears up. A rumbling growl moved in the caverns of his body as the trim military figures climbed into the rear seat.

"Why, here is *El Lobo,*" they said. "Lobo, how are you today?"

Grrrrr.

They forgave him the slight without resentment; probably they thought it was quite natural. One guard said, "Lobo is now very rich."

I told him firmly, "Lobo is not rich. He is the same dog he always was."

"Ah, yes. But, *Señor,* he is rich by comparison. You see, Lobo had nothing before; now he has a beautiful home, and of course a handsome large American car. Yes," he said contentedly, "Lobo is rich. *Es verdad.*"

Grrrrr, said Lobo.

Also in this same month romance lifted her pretty head. Romance appeared for shy and tentative calls, which increased to daily frequency as the summer season—and the lady's own season—advanced. We didn't know her name, we called her Perrita; she belonged to some one of the guards across the way. She was yaller-dog as to color, and owned somewhat the proportions of a mule deer, and stood nearly as tall as one. The net result of this disparity in stature was complete frustration on the part of Lobo, no matter how willing he was to achieve wedded bliss. Finally Perrita gave up in disgust and married a taller dog down the road. . . . Sometimes I've seen the same thing happen in the human species: generally speaking, it seems unwise for shorter men to fall in love with much taller women.

We began to hear rumors. "Is it true? Are you taking Lobo back to the United States when you return?"

"Nothing could be further from the truth."

"You should take him. He loves to be with you."

We felt that it would take more than a merely expressed preference on Lobo's part to compel us to submit to such an ordeal. An ordeal also would it be for him. We planned not to proceed directly to the United States, but to drive to Madrid, thence through the Pyrenees into France, all the way up through France; and we would leave the car at a seaport while we went—by boat, air, and train—to look after some business in England, Denmark, Germany.

"You think that would be a kindness to the dog?" I demanded witheringly of these self-appointed advisors. "Why, the poor thing would have to be shut up in a kennel, week after week."

. . . I had made a few tentative queries, and had even secretly consulted a book of rules and regulations at the consulate in Málaga. . . . Not much trick about getting him into the United States, in case we really wanted to do so. All he had to have was a rabies certificate, and a deposition of good health, signed by a doctor shortly before embarkation. Then, if he stood up under scrutiny of the Public Health Officer in New York (and didn't take a piece out of him) he could be admitted at once. It was entirely discretionary with the officer.

But in the meantime—

France he could get into: no trouble about that. In England, dogs must be quarantined for six months. No exceptions; not if you are Prince Philip himself.

"Just think of Lobo, accustomed to all this freedom, bounding about the stone staircases and cliffs, scampering along the shore, jumping like an ibex from rock to rock. Think of his languishing in a French kennel! It's too hideous to contemplate. We certainly shall *not* take Lobo. He is very happy at El Remo; he has his friends; he has plenty to eat." Etc., etc.

Men and women propose, Lobos dispose.

Community opinion seemed to be about equally divided. Some people asserted staunchly that we were right—imprisonment would be a cruelty of the worst kind. Others said, wasn't it terrible for those Kantors to go away and abandon their dog?

Our dog, indeed. I scowled at Lobo and felt almost that he needed to be abandoned. "Far as that is concerned," I said with sternness one late summer's evening, "shouldn't tonight be the night?" We had just returned from a dinner party, and Irene was yawning.

I said, "I thought I'd go by El Remo, have a drink or two, and say goodbye to the staff. We've got dates every night until we leave, so we shan't be going back there for dinner. This is as good a night as any other to leave Lobo. Pack your bags, Lobo." Which feat Lobo performed by bounding into the car again and sitting up expectantly.

Irene reached in, put her arms around him, hugged and petted him, and then went quickly down the steps toward our house, going rapidly because she wanted neither Lobo nor me to see her cry.

During the few minutes it took us to drive along the highway I expatiated on the comforts and glories of that café which was in fact Lobo's hostelry. . . . The season was in full swing, the parking lot was filled with little cars, attendants darted here and there with flashlights. There was a uniformed boy outside the door, another cheerful greeter inside. The joint was certainly jumping.

Lobo made his usual recognition grunts. These were a series of piglike sounds which he had originated. They meant, "Oh yes, we're back *here*. I know this place. Yes, yes. Well, well." I used to ask him whether he thought he was dog or pig; but he would only give a lopsided glance and keep on grunting.

Lobo set a course for the patio where people were still dining, and I found the Marqués de Nájera at the bar. I told him of my plan. On this very night I would abandon Lobo; or, not liking the word *abandon* under the circumstances, I should say that I would *return* Lobo to his own domicile.

"Yes, yes, I quite agree with you," said the host. "A very good idea. He might cry around for a day or two after you depart, but he will be much happier here than in a kennel."

Angel is not a drinking man, but I believe he recognized desperation in my attitude. We lingered for a time at the bar. The marques's pink face shone even pinker under his neatly clipped gray locks, he stabbed the air with his finger for emphasis. I tried to convince the marques, the marques tried to convince me, I tried to convince myself, that this thing was right. Best make a clean break. Deeds, not words, were needed to affirm and underline the process of getting rid of Lobo.

Cristóbal came by. His unoccupied moments are few, but I managed to grab him during one of them. I took him aside and folded into his palm—not exactly a king's ransom in *pesetas,* but at least a duke's.

"Lobo must lack for nothing this winter."

"*Don* MacKinlay," said Cristóbal. "Lobo has never lacked for anything."

"Nevertheless, he might get sick and need to go to the doctor. He might— Oh well, you will take good care of him, won't you?"

"We do not take care of Lobo," said Cristóbal with dignity. "Lobo takes care of us."

I peered out on the pretty little lawn below the orchestra's platform. All the regular Saturday night celebrants were gathered, and as usual there were newcomers and transients. I saw familiar faces, familiar bald heads or patent leather ones. I saw María Luisa, her dark eyes flashing as she danced; I saw the lawyer from Málaga, the motion-picture director from Barcelona.

Also I saw a black tail with a white tip, a tail shaped like a sickle, moving casually among farther tables. I turned away.

The marqués had to join people at dinner. We shook hands, embraced, parted. Antonio the musician took a break and came to the bar. We shook hands, embraced, parted.

Well, I thought, you won't get anywhere this way. Come on, get moving. . . .

Quietly I went toward the outer door which opened upon a graveled driveway in the opposite direction from the patio. The inner doorman sprang forward. There was a frown between his brows.

"Señor, where is Lobo?"

"Lobo," I said, "is among the tables in the patio, and there he will remain. Shhhh."

Shhhh, repeated the inner doorman.

I descended the steps. The outer doorman, or doorboy (Botones, we call him there, since he wears many buttons on his uniform) came up, also frowning.

"But, Señor, have you not forgotten El Lobo?"

"I have not forgotten El Lobo," I said. "I can never forget him. Shhhh."

Shhhh, said Botones.

I went around through the dark driveway, past innumerable

little cars. The parking-lot attendant came up through the
gloom, his light flashed.

"Ah, *Señor!* But where is the dog?"

"Shhhh," I said. "The dog is among the dancers and tables
of food on the patio. Shhhh."

Shhhh, said the parking-lot attendant.

We moved upon my car through darkness. Now, with so
many strangers about, so many transients at this height of
season, it behooved anyone to keep his car locked.

The attendant flashed his light . . . *and who should be waiting there?* A beautiful line from Alfred Noyes. I remember
that Noyes said it was Bess, the landlord's daughter, plaiting
a dark red love-knot into her long black hair. . . . Who should
be waiting there, indeed?

He had black hair but he was plaiting no love-knot into
it. He stood, red collar ashine, amber eyes gleaming, tail swaying
with assurance.

I unlocked the door and he swarmed into the interior.
"Hombre," I said huskily, "let's go to America."

We were overly optimistic in assuming that because Lobo
had been informed verbally of his projected adventure, he
would shrug off promptly all allergy to suitcases, traveling bags,
and the like. In fact he never did lose the allergy. Any object
which looked as if it might contain clothing or possessions
packed for a journey meant just one thing to Lobo: it meant
that people were going to go away and leave him. The fear
was too deeply rooted, it had flourished too long, it could not
be changed. Sometimes I even caught him regarding my briefcase with gravest suspicion.

. . . Felipe carried the last of our bags up the forty-nine
steps to where I was struggling to force all our European-
Continental possessions into and upon the top of one sedan.
It was more or less like the clowns in Ringlings' circus—those
several dozen figures who rushed cheering out of one small

coupe after it was driven into the ring; except in this case
I was trying to get clowns into the car, not take them out.

. . . Irene peered into the depths of the closet where Lobo
had been monkishly entombed for the past forty-eight hours.
"Come along, Lobo."

Naturally we always addressed him in Spanish.

"You will accompany us in the car."

The creature bounced into a sitting position and regarded
her, eyes rolling, jaws agape. She started to repeat the reassurance, when he made a dive past her, nearly upsetting her;
he plunged through the patio and soared up the several
flights of stairs. He emerged from the pink-geranium-smothered
hill (again a circus comparison: he reminded me of that character who used to be shot out of a cannon). In mid-trajectory,
however, he halted, then flopped to the ground. He had seen
all those suitcases. This must mean the end after all. It was
not until Irene herself had labored up the steps, opened the
car door, and pointed, that he really knew. Jet-propelled by the
inexhaustible fuel of his desire, he annihilated gravity and
space, and lay gasping atop the highest piled wardrobe con-
tainer in the rear seat. There was just room for him between
the roof and the layers of baggage.

Felipe and Anita came to say their *adiós* but Lobo heeded
not. As we drove through the gate and down the highway, I
could see him in the mirror. His was also a rear vision, his
face turned toward the back window, his ears sagging, as in
coma he regarded the Andalucian home existence which he was
leaving. He did not even growl at the *Guardia Civil* when
they gave us a rifle salute in farewell.

Like all sisters of her sex, Irene had been tempted into
a wonderful bargain which in this case consisted of a pair of
green shoes, burnished with nailheads, which a local cobbler
was going to fashion for her at a price so ridiculously small
that she would have insulted her femininity had she not yielded
to the temptation. (The fact that she was never able to wear
the shoes after she got them is beside the point.) Delivery

had been promised for lo these many weeks. She reminded the cobbler forcefully that we were to depart on this day, and that the shoes must be ready: she herself would stop to pick them up.

Thus we drove into Torremolinos for a repeat farewell, since already we had done our duty by grocer, butcher, druggist, and the rest. We parked in a narrow street which, though crowded and dirty, is dignified by the name of Generalisimo Franco, when someone spied Lobo.

"You are about to depart," we were told shrilly. "But look—do you not see? Lobo is in the car."

"Yes, we know."

"But—Lobo?" The voices rose higher. "Do you mean to say—? Is it true? *Madre de Dios!* Is Lobo to accompany you?"

"It is true."

Yells arose on every side. People began to flock from the stores. "María! Pepe! Antonio! Matílde! Observe! Lobo! In the car! Lobo is to travel in the *coche!* Lobo is going to other nations! . . . Is it true, *Señor?* Is Lobo to go to North America?"

"It is true."

Children pressed in the first rank, adults squeezed behind them, mules came to observe. Not a one of them drew as much as the courtesy of a direct glance from Lobo, who lay collapsed, brassy eyes brooding.

"Enrique! Pablo! Bepa! Lobo—in the car! He goes to many countries! He goes to *los Estados Unidos!"*

. . . We were halfway to Jaén before Lobo emerged from his state of shock sufficiently to threaten two herdsmen who shambled past in the dusk when we were having Sevenses.

Now ensued an interesting series of events both for ourselves, for the black-and-tan beast who ordered our lives, and for sundry hotelkeepers, bartenders, waiters, chambermaids. By custom or legality there was nothing wrong in Lobo's sharing our intimacy. Of course everyone knows that Spain is a backward nation. To my notion the nation is nothing like so backward as those States of our Country which prohibit the appearance of dogs in public restaurants. I should much prefer to enjoy my meal with certain dogs under table than with certain people sitting across from me. But little matter now. . . . No eyebrows were raised at Lobo in any café or hostelry throughout Spain or France. (Not until we reached Le Havre, where it seems they are somewhat satiated with American tourists who purchase cute poodle puppies in Paris, transport them to Le Havre to await the sailing of their vessels, and in the past have attempted with futility to housebreak their newly acquired pets upon the best carpeting. I think the refusal of the Le Havre hotel authorities to admit Lobo was rather solidly founded.)

The leash had become an essential in Lobo's traveling equipment, since to his mind all tables were meant to be begged at, and all kitchens to be explored. He accepted his restraint philosophically; and since we were more or less fed up with Spanish cookery (and longed for nothing so much as home-made Spanish rice according to an Iowa recipe, and not at all like the Spanish rice of Spain), Lobo was deeded larger portions of our own fare than had previously come his way.

I shall never forget the fabulous evening in Roquefort, where we deviated from main routes and traveled on back roads, drawn by the mysterious scent of cheese caverns. A certain restaurant there is heavily starred in the guide books. In this place we sat down for the evening meal. Baked Roquefort cheese in light piecrust—I forget what they call it—was out of this world; and so the steak would have been, the first decent-looking steak I'd seen in many a month. In Andalucía steaks are carved from the very bravest of bulls by means of electric saws and diamond drills.

However, I have neglected to state that I am just as allergic to grilled garlic as was Lobo to steamer trunks. It was my own fault I had not told the waiter. I should have known that they would saturate my sirloin with minute insertions of garlic, drench it with a marinade of garlic, serve it in a garlic sauce.

Muttering curses at my own stupidity, I set to work to carve the steak for you-guess-whom.

He was under the table, and put his head up between my knees with the scarf of cloth concealing his eyes and draping his brown mask like a nun's cowl. Promptly at intervals a pink cavern opened, a chunk of beef was dropped in; then, at the stated interval, the pink cavern reopened. It was one of the most interesting disappearing acts I ever saw. That steak was at least three inches thick, and proportionately wide. . . . Lobo seemed fretful when we took him for his evening walk. I think he thought he had had his *canapé* but when did the dinner begin?

His compulsion in the direction of food was something like that endured by Mr. Burl Ives. Mr. Ives spent a lean infancy and childhood amid fellow sharecroppers in southern Illinois, where the butter was spread very thinly—when indeed there was any butter to spread—and where sometimes even the bread was cut much too thinly. In his modern existence as an internationally admired minstrel and actor, Mr. Ives tries vigorously to compensate for the fact that forty years ago there were not enough beans in the pot, and sometimes no bacon at all.

When you are dwelling with Burl, often you are awakened in the middle of the night by a slow thunderous tread in the hall, a squeak and opening and closing of the front door, which is repeated in reverse process some time later. Then comes the rustle of innumerable midnight delicatessen paper bags in the kitchen. In the morning when you go out you find empty cartons with the marks of potato salad and pickled herring still apparent—sausage rinds, seeds, peelings, empty cream containers, soggy receptacles in which various pasties and Boston cream pies have previously been housed. It looks rather as if Henry the Eighth has been entertaining the Yeomen of the Guard in one small kitchen. A few walls away, some three hundred and thirty-three pounds of Ives lie in deep and contented repose.

Lobo also may have had nagging recollection of the sharp-ribbed puppy which was himself, trailing down harsh hillsides above the Mediterranean, and sniffing drearily into ditches which bore not a single morsel of garbage . . . all before his guardian angels conducted him to El Remo.

Carennac is a picturesque village on the Dordogne River in France. There we were ensconced for some time in an ancient abbey turned into hotel, where I worked on my novel even harder than ever, where Irene painted, and Lobo lay on our two old B-10 jackets with a wary eye turned toward the antique Gothic doorway—just in case one of the tourists who sometimes visited the flagged courtyard might intrude.

It was at this place that I requested of Lobo a written report for the Society for Psychical Research.

In sunset afterglow, weary from toil, the three of us would prowl among shrubbery and walls behind the old chapel. On the first occasion my eye was caught by a coal-black aperture—some sort of tunnel extending down into a dank and mossy area beneath the structure. I was unaccompanied this first time; I went to the car, got a flashlight, and proceeded to examine the chamber. There was nothing in there except a few garden tools, but somehow a storied sepulchral quality was present.

Later that same evening, chaperoned by my two domestic pets, I essayed further investigation. Irene went in boldly enough; Lobo balked at the entrance. He could not be budged. He spread his muscular legs, his deer's feet might have been set in concrete. No matter how I pulled or tugged or persuaded, he was rigid. The hair was up on his back, his ears were raised, and all he said was, "If you want to get me into that place, you'll have to kill me first." Twice at later date I attempted to meet this challenge, and was vanquished. It was not merely darkness that he feared—he had pranced gaily into far blacker holes than this. He had been with me in caves and cellars of various kinds, but into this particular spot he would not venture.

It piqued my curiosity. I sought out the proprietor and asked him the original nature of that room.

"Well," he said. "It was a— The whole place is quite old, you know."

"But what was that subterranean room you now use to put the garden tools in?"

"Oh, it's very difficult to say, *Monsieur*. You see, during the centuries that have elapsed, the room has undoubtedly been used for various purposes." He wriggled uncomfortably.

"O.K.," I said. "Was it the crypt?"

He ducked his head, nodded, fled away. I did not attempt to escort Lobo into any more crypts.

We worked our way up through central and western France toward the inevitable, if temporary, parting in Le Havre. There, in the hotel originally befouled by poodles, our companion was relegated to a dungeon in the basement for one sorry night. Recognizing belatedly that the air was damp and that the place was too uncomfortable for even a toughened veteran like Lobo, I had a bright idea, and bedded him down in the car itself, parked in front of the hotel.

This to Lobo was the height of luxury and satisfaction. That car represented assurance to him; it represented us, it represented his new life. I saw that in the future it would be unnecessary to remove visible bags against the incursion of car thieves. In wildest flight of fancy I could not envision the bold prowler who might attempt to force one of those doors, when inside there existed an arsenal of gleaming teeth and a snarl which would have frightened *El Cid* himself.

Lobo was so entranced with his new lodgings that he refused to budge each morning, and had to be hauled out bodily. The old jackets were fleecy, security was here, he doted on security. He knew always that we would come to the car again. He had a pan of water on the floor in the front seat; seldom did it seem to be touched. All night long he dreamed his dreams and, I firmly believe, wrote his poems and offered his quiet invocation to the Goddess of Security.

The eve of our sailing for England was arrived, and we felt that we were leaving our friend in good hands. There was a genial veterinarian who, on viewing Lobo, asserted that he was far too fine an animal to languish in one of the small pens adjacent to the doctor's city office. He explained that in cases like this he always took the dogs to his mother's place in the country. With light hearts we accepted this plan. Lobo wagged and danced, not knowing that we would soon disappear.

Our actual leave-taking occurred abruptly and without planning on my part, since the veterinarian-kennel-keeper had told me that he must have Lobo's rabies-shot certificate. I fetched it over to him, with Lobo along, of course; then we were stricken simultaneously with the same idea. It was only a few hours until I should have to bring him anyway—why not leave him now? Accordingly he cavorted off with the kennel-keeper, confident that *entremeses* were about to be served in the rear.

I returned to the hotel and found Irene come back from shopping. She was grieved. "I didn't get to say goodbye to Lobo."

"Oh, Lobo's fine. The last I saw him the doctor had him on a leash—"

Irene considered for a time. "Just give him a couple of days," she said. "Lobo will have the doctor on a leash."

In fact we did not believe that we were leaving him marooned on a linguistic desert island. He had shown a remarkable aptitude for languages. I don't know what all he spoke before we came along. . . . Andaluz was his native tongue. I am sure that he spoke considerable Castilian and perhaps Catalan, gained from other contacts on the beach. He could not have dwelt long in the polyglot Montemar-El Remo surroundings without at least a smattering of German, Dutch, and French, with a few Scandinavian words thrown in. I think also that he knew some Arabic; he looked as if he did.

Already he had given us a striking demonstration of his ability to absorb English. The month before, in Pau, we endured a

rainy afternoon during which all Irene wanted to do was put
a new canvas on a stretcher-frame, and all Lobo wanted to do
was sleep. We were domiciled in a remodeled chateau on the
edge of town, and garages were not far off.

"I think," I called across the living room and into the bedroom where Irene sat on the floor with a mouth full of tacks,
"I think that this is a good afternoon for me to take the car
down to the garage and have that little matter fixed"—whatever
it was—"so I think I'll go now."

I addressed my wife in Midwestern United States, which is
our mutual native tongue. Now, mind you, Lobo was sound
asleep on the bed; furthermore, neither of us could recall ever
having addressed him before in any language except Spanish.
In a split second a black-and-tan projectile was fired off the bed
and exploded into the target area beside the front door. He
stood quivering, bright-eyed, ears up, tail aloft. He said, "Actually I had been intending to sleep the rest of the afternoon,
but of course if you're going to the garage—"

We looked at each other helplessly.

"You'd better take him," said Irene. "Perhaps he can help
you, when you have trouble with the garage people with your
French."

We had not expected to find any other than that which we
found on our return after three or four weeks in London,
Copenhagen, and West Germany: Lobo was speaking French
fluently. We had sent him two or three postcards along the way,
and obviously he forgave us for our desertion. ("Why should
they send postcards to Lobo?" cried veterinarian and staff. "He
cannot read!")

But he could speak French. When the girl assistant brought
him out to me at a special rendezvous arranged by telegram
from Paris, and which reunion took place within half an hour
after our arrival in Le Havre, Lobo was busy in conversation
with her. She was talking of the country house, of *Grand'mère*,
of the other dogs; and Lobo was joining in, obviously understanding every word she uttered.

We came together. I was assaulted with tongue and claws. I paid my bill and stumbled out. "Let's go right over to the garage," I said, hailing a taxi. "So we can get the car out, and you can have a decent place to sleep tonight."

Like the greater part of Le Havre, the garage area has been rebuilt from scratch since World War II, and this particular garage is a handsome edifice with ramps leading from floor to floor, and room for scores of automobiles on every story.

An old man took us up in an elevator, and we got off at floor Number Five. I unsnapped the leash from Lobo's collar. He raced up and down the aisles of silent parked vehicles.

He found the car quicker than I could have found it—far quicker, I know, than could the old attendant, for he was one of those people who go by card and number. He was still squinting at the ticket and trying to decide in which row the car might be, when Lobo notified us that the car *had* been found, with grunts amplified out of all natural proportion by the peculiar acoustics of the place. I unlocked the door, Lobo flew into the rear seat. The attendant regarded him with something akin to fear, all the way down, as we poked around the short hairpin curves.

Two days later British soil, in the shape of the S. S. *Mauretania*, was treated to its most singular Spanish invasion since the unsuccessful attempt in 1588. . . . Out at sea, I had a little difficulty with the good-looking young assistant-ship's-butcher who was detailed to the care and feeding of canine passengers. I remonstrated about the vast masses of food which were pushed into Lobo's cell.

"But he wants it, sir! He keeps asking for more, he does. I don't know what he does with it all, to be sure. He seems quite hungry. I *did* cut down his rations—"

Even then, there was a certain complication because of Lobo's very strictly conceived toilet habits. The only place allotted to the exercise of dogs was the aft end of the tourist deck; there Lobo and I repaired six or eight times a day. Definitely there was a rule against keeping dogs in one's stateroom—not on the

French Line, but on this one. I saw an elderly woman sneaking
a suspicious-looking bundle back and forth—something wrapped
up in an old raincoat—but even then I didn't protest. A real
live Lobo, domiciled in our cabin until we reached New York,
would have been just too much.

. . . Trouble was, he had the idea that the deck was a room.
It was a room that was not a room. We would go all the way
aft, and Lobo would brace himself and stare down at the wake
and give grunts as if he recognized the wake of some small
vessel in which, many incarnations agone, he had moved through
the war-tossed Mediterranean. For several days he simply
would not Do Anything. One did not Do Things in rooms, and
certainly the deck was a room, because it had a floor. It was a
great relief to me when outraged Nature finally threw up her
hands, and the deck needed special treatment. Undoubtedly
it was a great relief to Lobo as well.

The chief difficulty which I encountered on the voyage was
clerical. Not long before we reached New York, I received a
message from the old baggagemaster, who insisted that I must
come to see him about my dog. Baggagemasters take care of
the business of booking dogs aboard steamships. Mr. MacWilliams was a Scotsman with well-established ideas of protocol
when it came to filling out papers.

"I am sorry, sir," he said. "Your papers on your dog are no
complete."

"But what's wrong?" We spread the papers out. "Look here,
you've got everything: you've got my home address, date of
shipment, certificate of good health signed by the French veterinarian within ten days of embarkation. You've got the rabies
certificate, you've got—"

His finger indicated one blank square. "You have no put
down the *breed* of the dog. Now, will you please to give me
the *breed* of the dog?"

I said, "That would be very interesting."

He regarded me disapprovingly through his spectacles. "I can
no put *that* down on the paper."

I took a deep breath. Irene and I had discussed Lobo's possible lineage; we knew that he came from the Montemar region, and also that he was prone to worry. "Very well," I said. "If the truth must be known, he is a Montemar Worrier."

The baggagemaster gripped his pencil. "How do you spell it?" Letter by letter, I spelled it out. There is no doubt that Lobo was the first Montemar Worrier—and probably the last —ever to be admitted to the United States.

I was apprehensive about New York. What would happen? Would officials come aboard, would they attempt to take specimens of Lobo's blood? I shuddered to think of what might occur if this came about. Would they pull his eyelids apart? Would they stick things down his throat, and up—elsewhere? I wished that I had some compendium of law through which I might search to gain an idea of exactly what penalty befell the avowed owner of a dog who undertook to carry out a one-dog *pogrom* among Public Health officials.

"But what do I do?" I asked, on that last morning. "Do I wait in the lounge for the officials? Does Lobo ride off on a pile of freight, or does he walk off with me, or what?"

"Just take him along with you," said Mr. MacWilliams. "If yon official wants to see you, he'll find you with no trouble on the quay." Thus Lobo marched on clicking toenails down the gangplank and became an immigrant.

As for the Public Health officials, we saw not hide nor hair of them. The customs officer studied the item on our declaration: *One Lobo. Acquired through self-adoption in Spain. Weight: fifty pounds. Color: black-tan-and-white. Intrinsic value: uncertain,* and then tried to strike up a conversation with Lobo in Gaelic. . . . I still have the papers. Maybe he was never officially admitted after all.

It wasn't until I walked Lobo through the streets of New York that I began to realize how like a carefully bred dog he did look. He was all of a pattern, he didn't look like a mongrel. His doe-colored stockings were all of the same size, his tan mask well-balanced; there was the set and feeling of a breed about

him. No mere ascribing of possible parentage through the process of free love among German shepherds, Dobermans, and
hounds seemed to suffice. It wasn't until quite a time afterward,
when—Lobo-less—Irene and I ventured on back roads of the
Basque country, that we came to know what he was in fact,
although it had been suggested a time or two.

He was a Basque shepherd. If we saw one we saw forty Lobos
in the Basque country. We saw two or three that could have
been his litter-mates; but I fear that I shall never own another
Basque shepherd. . . .

How Lobo's father ever found his way down the long rugged
Iberian Peninsula to Mediterranean shores, I leave to be decided by the canine archaeologists, ethnologists, genealogists,
and historians who should deal with this fascinating subject in
the future. As it was, in New York people kept coming up to
me on the street and wanting to know what kind of dog that
was. I always said that he was a Montemar Worrier, which
satisfied in every case. One old lady informed me that indeed
that's what he was—a Montemar Worrier—she remembered
now; her sister used to have one of those.

Lobo and I left Irene surrounded by doting grandchildren in
Westchester, and sought Florida quickly. Again we had the ton
of baggage to be transported; but this time Lobo could share the
front seat with me; although now, on alien shores, he had a
propensity for putting his head in my lap. This I regarded as
a safety hazard. We had a few words and cuffs on the subject;
after that he behaved properly—thrusting his head out of the
right window, and observing critically the Howard Johnson edi-
fices along the Jersey Turnpike.

In Maryland an interesting experience befell when—perforce,
of necessity, as is the habit of motorists—I decided suddenly to
stop by the wayside and take a stroll into a thicketed area. Lobo
tumbled out along with me, and went around through the woodland like a runaway jeep, except that he made more noise about
it. I discovered that his grunts were not all recognition grunts
(or maybe they were: this reincarnation idea, you see, although

he had never heard of Bridey Murphy). They were also inquisitive grunts.

"Goodness sake, what is this—what are all these trees? What are all these bushes? What are all these smells? Ah-ha, above all, the smells! Well, what is this, anyway?"

The idea struck me full force. It is a strange experience to proceed into the mild forests of Maryland, with a dog of obvious maturity, and realize that the dog has never been in *woods* before.

There are no woods in the locality from which Lobo sprang. There are a few trees bordering gardens, a very few bordering the roads; there are olive groves, and some tiny groves of poplars grown as a crop. Nothing more. The rest is rocks, wasteland, low tough herbage. No thickets, no bushes, no wild brakes.

There was something touching about all this . . . I wondered how he would go plunging through the bit of Florida jungle which has not been Yankeeized, and which we own. (He went plunging, all right. He came home twice without his collar.)

Few bridegrooms ever lugged their brides across fabled thresholds with more excitement than that with which I escorted Lobo to our beach, once we were safe on Siesta Key. His hard racing feet tore the white packed sand.

. . . Birds, birds! He was after them full pelt. Of course I knew that he could never catch one; but he did not know that, and never learned the fact. Water would smash as he struck it, the birds would go squawking. . . .

Coconuts were more vulnerable to his attack. A green coconut, shell and all, washed up on the beach, is a heavisome thing, God wot. To me they weighed just as much as so many atomic bombs, but to Lobo they were peanuts. How he got his jaws around them I'll never know, but he did. Not only did he get his jaws around them, but he would bear them off at full gallop. I have seen him do this with coconuts which weighed roughly a quarter of Lobo's own weight. If you are a man of ordinary size, try clamping a forty-pound burden in your jaws, and dashing off with it.

Lobo had several private coconut hoards: one under pines on the beach, a couple among palms out in the yard. These treasured toys were doled out to him in frolicsome moments. But unfortunately coconuts were not the only objects against which he now directed his threat.

The old parable of rags to riches had come true again. In Spain a penniless beggar, Lobo was tolerant as to disposition. He drew no property lines around El Remo or the Montemar. Let who would come and go, was his philosophy.

Not so after he had acquired a seaside home in Florida, with a couple of cars thrown in. He was more avaricious than Hetty Green, more savage than Simon Girty, less charitable than Ebenezer Scrooge.

"Good grief!" he would roar at the top of his lungs, dashing through the gallery and across the living room and out to the porch, slashing the rugs as he came. "Look out there on the beach! There's an old man walking on *my beach*. I can't *stand* this. He needs to be torn limb from limb! Please open the door and let me out! I want to go down there and *assassinate* him—"

I thought of the smug but discerning Civil Guard, far back in the Province of Málaga, who observed, "Lobo is very rich now." In vain did I explain, cajole, and set examples of hospitality and benevolence. He was far gone into a most predatory sort of snobbery. If people didn't belong on his property, they didn't belong on it. That went for practically all humans.

As for dogs, he would pay ardent court to those females who were in a courting mood; would calmly ignore other females or the especial type of spinsters with which the canine world is so frequently blessed. But—a *male* dog— I was kept busy snatching at Lobo's collar, and explaining to the world that he was not truly vicious—he was just savage, and had an exaggerated sense of property rights and controls.

Our two small grandsons came with their parents to spend

the Christmas holidays, and we watched Lobo narrowly. I heard him growl just once. He had an ear infection and Mike, the elder, pulled his sore ear. I explained to Mike, and he did not do this again. On the other hand, I came in one day to find the smaller boy in his play pen with Lobo lying just outside the wooden bars. Tommy had fastened his grubby mitts on Lobo's muzzle, and was kneading flesh and nostrils energetically. Lobo was not uttering a sound, nor was he trying to move away; he was just taking it from the baby. We breathed more easily after that.

As if to compensate for whatever inconvenience his high-handed defense of the home caused us, Lobo now offered assistance of an acceptable kind. Heart and soul he became dedicated to helping me in my work.

In Spain he had paid but little heed: I went out each day in the car with my portable typewriter installed on a folding chair which served as table. I took a basket of lunch, bottle of wine, my briefcase and whatever reference books had been selected for the day's activity. That was all right with Lobo; most of the time he was content to remain at home, lying on cool tiles, leisurely inspecting Irene's painting as it progressed.

But *Andersonville* had grown from an originally promised one-hundred-and-fifty-thousand-word novel into a novel of a projected three-hundred-and-fifty-thousand words. . . . There are such things as deadlines in the publishing business; mechanical details of manufacturing have to be set up in advance; thus they were starting to put the book into type long before I had finished it. Uneasy lies the head of an author under such circumstances. . . .

I dared not let a day pass without a substantial amount accomplished, and sometimes I was very near the breaking point. Friends and relatives urged me to slow down, take a trip, go away somewhere—but I knew I'd be working every day I was gone, so what could be gained in going?

I began to find Lobo in the car each morning when I went

to the garage. He sensed that I needed help and was willing to offer such as he could give. The house was unendurable as a work-place most of the time, even with the telephones shut off, because of people who came to the door, and my vulnerability to such interruptions. I had to drive afield, usually into the Myakka wilderness east of Sarasota, or to a lonely spot down the Tamiami Trail where I could not be reached or interfered with.

I took to fetching along Lobo's lunch as well as my own. He never interfered with my typing; I left the rear door open when parked in the shade, and Lobo could hop in and out as the spirit moved him. There was only one difficulty: forever he was coming back hobbling from the effects of sandspurs. I would have to extract myself from behind the typewriter and succor the needy—always rewarded by a slobbery tongue well applied.

He did feel that we should sleep together when we took our naps. It was disconcerting to be aroused from stupor by the crushing blow of his compact body as he flung himself over the seat on top of me.

There came a day when I thought I could work no more. My head ached, my eyes hurt, my finger tips were filmy. I had been at it daily, without exception, for over fifteen months. *You can't finish*, evil voices were crying. *You can't. You can't. Don't try. It's too much. It's too big. It's too long. It's too tiring. You can't do it. You're no stronger than anyone else. Flesh and brain can endure only so much. Emotions break, and discipline vanishes, and you're tired, tired, tired.*

I managed to back the car out of the garage, but couldn't turn it away toward the driveway from the live-oak shade. Lobo was in the rear seat. Over on the right-hand side of the front seat, the typewriter waited on its stand—grimly, implacably, presenting that threatening countenance which typewriters have forever turned toward exhausted writers. I put my head back on the seat and was close to tears.

Then there came a heavy breathing in my ear. A nose was thrust close.

"Lobo, what shall I do?" My own voice sounded far away and flogged. "I can't go on. What shall I do—quit? Quit for a while, try later, put the book off? What shall I do?"

With a single bound he was over the ridge. He was in the front seat, sitting bolt upright behind the typewriter, staring ahead. Then he swung his head to the left, grinned, rolled his eyes.

"You mean," I faltered, "that I've got to go to work anyway? That I've got to go out in the car and at least try to do *something?*"

He bent down, put his head on the seat, pushed with his hind legs, stood on his head, and smashed over across my lap.

"O.K.," I groaned. Away we drove. I wrote twenty-seven hundred words in the next two hours or so. They were pretty good words—or so at least some of the critics thought who quoted them later.

. . . The Pulitzer Prize seemed a long way off in those days; so did the films, so did the critical response, so did the fortune which would be earned for booksellers, publishers, the Federal Government, the book clubs, editors, agents, and even myself. But Lobo knew. Assuredly he knew.

It was pretty tough on Irene, managing him when I was away. I had to go back to the Andersonville region several times; there was a research trip to Mississippi, and so on. During each of these periods Lobo appointed himself High Sheriff of Siesta Key, and lay most of the time either at Irene's feet or upon her bed. The mildest step of dry cleaner, spring-water man, or mere casual caller was sufficient to bring him into a defensive attitude similar to that of the Iberian women who tore out their hair to braid it for bowstrings. Not the most thorny commando in the world could have entered the house without first riddling Lobo with his burp gun.

Once Irene had flu while I was gone, and our friend and family doctor, Tom Garrett, came to attend her. Tom went out of that bedroom faster than he came in. This was not even reasonable, because Lobo knew Tom, and tolerated him socially. But I was gone, and he was *pro tem* guardian of bed, board, and belfry.

There was nothing sensible in his attitude, and I am not apologizing for him. In short, he was a damn nuisance about this sort of thing. No dog should behave in such wise. But I had come to the terrifying opinion that Lobo was not actually a dog.

I asked him about it one day, when we were coming home from work.

"Is it true," I inquired in my most carefully constructed Spanish, which I fear isn't very carefully constructed, but was always understandable to Lobo, "is it true that you are not in fact a dog, but are actually a king of the Moors?"

He had the answer to that one too. He stood on his head, to show me that he was a veritable emperor of the Moors.

He had spent all his years, uncertain though they were as to number, in trying to find a home of his own and people of his own. He had found them, and now nothing in the world must interfere with his possession of them.

. . . Did he ever dream of the whitewashed farmhouses, the noisy village street, the mules, the creaking carts, the green-uniformed constabulary he had left thousands of miles behind? An echo was there one night for him to hear; he heard it and responded.

We were sitting in the living room with friends, and Lobo was flat on his back, sound asleep on our bed at the other end of the house, all four paws dangling in the air. I knew this because I had seen him so a few minutes before. . . . People were asking about the Holy Week processions current throughout Spain, and we were trying to give a description—trying to make them see the images with their jewels, the flare of ten thousand candles, the robed figures walking, the drums and bugles and weird Moorish pipes coming on ahead.

"Why," I said, "I have an album, a recording made over

there. The Girl with the Combs—a fat gypsy woman who is one of the finest *saeta* singers in Spain. It sounds like the real stuff. Let me play it for you—"

I put on the record. First there came the throb and shuffle of feet. You could imagine the heavy *paso* being lifted onto thirty or forty shoulders, the striving bodies, the ragged cord-soled sandals scraping uneven pavement stones. You could hear bugles beginning to talk, the pound of drums as slatternly fif-teen-year-old musicians in their baggy khaki uniforms rolled and marched. *La niña* started in with her chant. Her voice swept on high, the traditional arrow of song above the sound of marchers, the military hullabaloo, the religious illusion.

Then another sound intermingled with this, and it did not come from the hi-fi. It was a series of grunts, approaching steadily up the long hall which led from our bedrooms. *Unh, unh, unh, unh, unh?* Here he came, recognition sounds floating ahead.

Unh, unh, unh, unh?

He was in the middle of the living room, ears lifted, body tensed, face turned toward the corner where the instrument lived. The gypsy's voice soared on; she wailed about the agony of Our Dear Lord; bugles blatted, drums throbbed.

Unh, unh, unh, unh? He was gone into the corner to stand close to the amplifier, and he was still sniffing, but his nose told him nothing, *nada*.

He was not home, he was not back in Spain. Oh, yes, this was home, but . . . there was a memory, he had heard sounds . . . where did they come from? Because there was no actu-ality here. No smell. Only the sounds which he had learned in puppyhood. . . . Finally he collapsed, flopped on the floor, went to sleep, paid no more heed.

Once I knew and loved a man who was a notorious tightwad. He was often inconsiderate of others—he was not even very good in his profession, nor very dependable, although he man-aged to make quite a lot of money. He did not ever do little thoughtful things for other people, he seldom repaid favors to friends, he did not always sacrifice himself too sublimely on community projects. Yet when he died the whole town wept. Everybody adored him, no one knew quite why. Everyone missed him; they miss him still.

Thus it was with Lobo. He was a gourmand; he set a high record for selfishness; he was far too savage for comfort; he was always wanting to go in and out of doors just because he wanted to go in and out of doors. He was a thief: he stole a roast in New York, a steak in Sarasota, two pounds of ground beef at La Verdad. He lay on beds, he begged at table, he left a cloud of shed hairs wherever he moved—cars and furniture were coated with them. (Months after he left us, I was still picking black white-tipped hairs off the ceiling of one automobile—and how they ever got there is more than I know. I suppose it was when he stood on his head and waved his tail in the air.)

Lobo gave no alarms of fire. So far as I know he never saved a child from drowning, or a traveler from freezing to death in the snow. He bit inoffensive Other Dogs. He lay right in the middle of all the main avenues, and you were forever falling over him.

By ordinary standards of polite conduct, Lobo was a mess. Yet the majesty and mystery which he exuded reached far. People were mad for him, even the ones he growled at.

Friends would call up with informal invitations to dinner, and were always careful to state that Lobo was especially included. Once established in the kitchen—say, at Ed Beattie's —he got in the maid's way every minute, and Mardelle loved it. . . . He went along with me to Newtown areas where most of the Sarasota servants live, to help take the laundry to Hattie May. Immediately soft dusky voices would speak lovingly from neighboring porches. "Why, there's Lobo. Hello, Lobo. Don't you remember me, Lobo?" His ears would sprout, nostrils sniff in awareness, his saffron eyes would be polished and sharp.

He knew far too much for his own good and for my own. He knew, on that last morning, the eighth of August, when I left him at the vet's in Scarsdale, New York. We were up there temporarily; we had to be in order to attend to the preliminaries of publishing *Andersonville*.

This was just a routine thing: he seemed to need worming attention again, I would leave him to be wormed. But the vet heard a suspicious cough, and asked a few questions, and said he should like to make some tests. The next day we heard the verdict: heartworms—the parasites which dwell in subtropical regions, but now I hear are making their wicked way North.

"It won't be much," the doctor said. "I'll start his series of shots . . . he'll have to be here all of this week, and next week you can bring him in every other day."

. . . He didn't want to be left there. Lobo said, "Please do not leave me. There is something I fear," and he twisted in circles at the end of his leash, and kept thrusting his head between my legs, and quivering. It hurts like hell to remember that now. . . . They gave him the first shot that evening, and it killed him *pronto*.

Nobody could understand. The doctor got another doctor out of bed in the dead of night. They worked hard, they called the laboratory from which the serum had come. Nothing was wrong with it. They got chemists out of bed and talked to them. But nothing could be done, although they tried to do everything.

The next day there was an autopsy, and we thought of the weird illnesses which had seemed to possess Lobo at La Verdad. Still that wasn't all the answer, and we have never found some of the answers yet.

Other veterinary physicians must have cried in the past; but it so happens that that was the first time I ever saw one do so.

We took Lobo up to the Hartsdale Canine Cemetery and put him into the hillside. There he lies, the eight-thousand-eight-hundred-and-ninety-first pet to sleep there. He has his stone—in Spanish, of course. It says: *Adiós, Amigo*.

The people at the place have been catering to bereaved humans for a long time, and so they know just what to do. They put flowers on his grave in summer and evergreens in winter. There he rests in the clutch of his adopted land—adopted through choice, no one can gainsay that.

So we left him on that tenth of August, and I took Irene home. Then I did what a good many other men would have done: I headed for the nearest bar.

It happened to be Buddy Kennedy's bar on Central Avenue. When Buddy saw my face he knew there was very bad news. Lobo used to go in there with me, and everyone knew him. Buddy is sentimental, like most ex-vaudevillians; we had our tears together.

An amiable Irishwoman was sipping a beer down the bar. She said, "You know, I'd like to tell you something. I dearly loved a mutt one time; he came to my door in the snow, half-starved, and I took him in, and he brought sunshine into my life. When he died I couldn't take it. Our priest was an old family friend, and I said to the priest, 'But why did my Paddy have to be run over? I loved him so—I wanted him with me always.' And the priest said, 'Daughter, you never really *had* your Paddy dog. You never *owned* him. He was loaned to you by God, as are all good people and beasts. And God needed him somewhere else, perhaps, to help some other people as he helped you. So He took him back.'"

I could barely thank the woman, but the comfort of her little story stayed with me. That is the way I began to think of Lobo then; that is the way I think of him now, and always shall. A strange and endearing form of Spanish Lend-Lease. . . . Paws across the sea, and all that sort of thing.

Pretty Pictures
for Tooey
1946

The very first evening I came back to Chelveston all the folks were talking about Bogie and his pictures. I didn't know who Bogie was, and I had never seen his pictures. Such references suggested a movie actor who was rather hot in the news just then because it was expected that he would soon be wedding Lauren Bacall (watch that w in wedding, Mr. Linotype Operator, please, and don't make it a b).

But the 305th people were talking about pictures of an entirely different sort, and also about an entirely different Bogie. This one really should be spelled "Beaugy" and therefore we will spell it that way. His name is Captain Francis H. Beaugureau; he hails from Chicago, Illinois, and at the time I met him he had just finished a tour of duty as a pilot.

One wearying thing about being a war correspondent is that you get pretty worn out saying nice words about the soldiers' attempts to interpret their experiences through the various media of art. It is natural for a man—perhaps even one previously inarticulate—to attempt to tell the world what he has seen and feared and felt. Firmly I believe that the American arts will be enriched for generations to come by the product of people who served in the war. There was bound to be a Mark Twain at Salerno, a Herman Melville off Okinawa, a Bellows and a Ryder and a Winslow Homer dodging flak and mortar fire here and there. But they were few in number. Most of the veterans have no capacity for interpreting war or for interpreting anything else. They cannot write moving poems or compose impressive music or paint effective pictures. But they are hellbent on trying.

Steve Benét said once, "A poet with a new poem will read it to a child, a wall or a tree, if necessary." Well, the GIs with poems or pencil sketches showed them to anyone or anything within reach, too; but usually there were a lot of people within reach. They seemed to think also that a mere war correspondent could, by some magic, put their wares into the eager hands of editors, agents, and movie producers.

There was no escape from this. You were on the spot the moment they happened to see your green-and-gold shoulder patch. And if you didn't witness these artistic attempts with apparent enthusiasm, and voice immediate praise, you were not a good Joe in anybody's language.

I have invariably praised everything thus presented to me by soldiers. My conscience has not bothered me either; because plenty of those fellows were going to be killed, and I thought it would be a lot nicer to be killed after having heard your daubs or your doggerel praised, than it would be to be killed after hearing them condemned.

Sooner or later, I was going to have to look at Beaugy's watercolors. His acquaintances said that the paintings were damn good; but I had heard other acquaintances of other people say that other things were damn good when really they were awful. For five days I ducked and dodged and parried, but finally on Sunday afternoon, April 8th, 1945, I really had it. Captain B. L. Thompson, who bossed the photo lab at the 305th, nailed me to the cross. He took me into his office and displayed photographs which he had taken of five of Beaugy's watercolors. The back of my head hit the concrete, and they had to burn feathers under my nose to wake me up.

Beaugy arrived a little later via jeep, with the originals done up in a homemade canvas folder which he had lined with dural metal to keep the watercolors from becoming bent or dog-eared. The paintings were large—two or three feet wide. The artist himself is a handsome, stocky man with blondish hair which is always sedately combed. He has a pleasant, drawling voice and acid blue eyes. On top of his accomplishments with the brush, he knows certain answers when it comes to dials and switches and trim-tabs. He had been checked out for Group lead; and that on a field where in 1945 we were putting up as many Forts as our whole combat wing used to put up two years before.

He had painted in watercolors because he didn't have any oils. I think that if he had only possessed Crayolas or a chewed-up dime store pencil, he would have gone to work just as intently. He had studied at the Chicago Art Institute and had considerable experience in portraiture. (Also he is a grand-nephew, or great-grandnephew, of the Adolphe William Bouguereau who painted his way to sugary fame in France in the nineteenth century. Beaugureau, descendant, does not think that Bouguereau, collateral ancestor, was so hot; and he scorns those archaic relics as insipidity best forgot.)

There were B-17s in every painting; in some there were a lot of B-17s. One he called his flak picture and another his fighter picture. There were others of lone Forts beating their exhausted stubborn way homeward across the North Sea, firing out the colors of the day and looking frightened and raunchy, just as you feel frightened and raunchy when you are in an airplane like that.

I do not know how many other pilots have seriously set to work to paint high altitude bombardment warfare; but I have never seen any more attractive and effective delineation of a very complex and terrifying subject, than these paintings of Beaugureau's.

His B-17s didn't much resemble the majestic polished juggernauts that have bedizened the well-groomed advertisements in magazines these past several years. They looked instead like Forts flying combat and having trouble with their Number Two engines, dragging their contrails through the sky, and

ready to smack to their doom "in some bloody hole up by
Wick."

I don't know a lot about art; I was rather past my first youth
before I became really aware of the plastic arts as a medium of
expression. I think that a lot of modern artists might better be
painting box-cars. But Grant Wood was one of my closest
friends for years. I know Thomas Hart Benton intimately, and
observe his work with respect. I think I know something about
the attitude of a good painter—the necessary discipline and nobility of conception which he must offer to his work.

I went away from the photo lab thinking that something
should be done about Beaugureau. . . . Paintings don't win
wars. Machine-guns and armored divisions and five-hundred-
pound GP bombs do win wars—and had very nearly won this
war in Europe. But Beaugy had served his stint, had played out
his hand successfully; the fates were kind to him. Thirty times
he had driven his freight through the overcast amidst every opposition the enemy could bring.

It seemed fitting to have him telling what our boys had done
to Kassel and Magdeburg, or what a future enemy might do
to us if we didn't watch our step . . . it seemed more profitable
for our Nation if Beaugy kept on constructing his strato-cumulus
clouds, or trailing his long limp tracer-streams through the air.
His bullets didn't cut with ruled sharpness across the body of
the Messerschmitt (once more, the reassuring ads in the magazines!) but trailed haphazardly behind; and thus the Messerschmitt got the Fort instead of the Fort getting the Messerschmitt.

Things like that were war the way she is. I don't know exactly how they would impress the Boeing stockholders; I don't
care exactly, either.

Colonel Henry MacDonald, latest commander of the Group,
was very much of the same mind. I tried to catch Mac in a
free-and-easy mood, but that is hard to do with any CO. Still, we
had the tie of the early 305th between us—the old Group that
was, in 1943—when MacDonald lay in a hospital while they

worked on his face—when we lost thirteen out of fifteen Forts at Second Schweinfurt: the largest percentage of loss suffered by any Group of heavy bombers anywhere, any time, unless I am more mistaken than I think I am.

Mac stood in his little living room and looked out at the chilly dusk coming up across the meadows. "I wish we could do something about this. I've kept Beaugy around here almost as long as I dare, just so that he could keep on painting airplanes. He's been finished up some time, now, and it's SOP for him to go back to the States. But, as he told you, he's not very eager to go. He wants to paint airplanes in combat."

"How about Eighth Air Force HQ?"

"Well, we recommended him at Pinetree, and that's the reason Tommy Thompson took those pictures of Beaugureau's paintings—so that they would know about him, down there at Bomber Command. We just haven't reached the right guys. Probably the photographs are all filed in neat envelopes somewhere."

I played awhile with my drink; then I made a Rank suggestion. . . .

Mac said, "It's always all right if it works. Who would you take him to?"

I told the colonel that I would tackle Major General Fred L. Anderson, who was at that time Deputy Commander for Operations under General Spaatz, at USSTAF. Anderson and I were old friends; he was the kind of general you couldn't put anything over on, but I didn't think we were trying to put anything over in this case.

I thought it highly important for the future of the Army Air Forces that they be apprised of a talent which could be employed advantageously in their behalf. Anderson would not resent it if I came wagging in, dragging Beaugy in my jaws and hoping to be patted on the head. If he didn't like the paintings, he would not order my accreditation rescinded and have Beaugy racked back to second lieutenant. He would dispose of us both, quickly and courteously. He would find something very pressing commanding his immediate attention.

He might have Pittenger or Casey or somebody buy us a drink; and Beaugy at least would not be any worse off than he was before. And the next time I encountered the general he would squeeze down his rust-colored eyebrows and say, "Why did you come around wasting the Army's time over a lot of lousy, would-be paintings? They need people like your captain down in Dalhart, Texas, and Grand Island, Nebraska. Let him wait until after the war and then he can paint all he pleases."

If, on the other hand, General Anderson did like the paintings and did think that this man should be painting combat now that he had finished his active participation in it— Well—

Colonel MacDonald said that he would give Beaugy a week's leave, and heaven protect us. I still had one more mission to fly from that field, so we left the date up in the air. The weather was terrible that week. Get called at 0100 hours, Briefing at 0230, start engines at 0510, then get a delay of one hour, two hours, three hours. We were scrubbed twice in a row; and then my squadron of the moment, the 364th, was stood down for two days. Finally we bombed a railway yard in Holstein, and I was through with this very small tour of duty; I left the base and went to France. Beaugy was to follow me after two days.

He banged on my door at the Scribe Hotel in Paris, on Monday forenoon. His take-off from England had been delayed because of fog; and I hoped we wouldn't be late for the appointment already made with General Anderson. Beaugureau clutched the portfolio containing his paintings, and we got into the car I had wangled, and whizzed along the straight highway past the Etoile.

Beaugy was scared; he didn't think his shave looked very well. I was getting a little scared myself. The war seemed to be going all right, but suppose that some things in General Anderson's portion of the war had gone very wrong indeed?

"Gee," said Beaugy. "What if he doesn't like my stuff? Are you sure that you know the general *well?*"

"Oh, very well," and I kept calling attention to the blue-clad nuns in the road, and old scars of dried-up war along the way, and blossoming peach and apple trees. It was funny, the way our nervousness communicated itself between us. It piled up, adding like cube root. By the time we got to the Ecole Normale we were in an advanced state of jitters.

No, said a pretty Wac, the general was not in, not yet; and we sat around in the outer office, and then finally decided to go and eat lunch just about ten minutes after the mess closed. Food would have been a welcome diversion; we were both starved and frightened, the way you are at the end of a ten-hour operation.

We went prowling all over that end of St. Germain, hunting for something to eat, and finally barged into a little canteen conducted by the Red Cross for GIs, and we wheedled some coffee and two doughnuts from a buxom blonde who pitied us. Americans were prohibited from buying food in French restaurants but we could buy anything alcoholic that was available. We found a little *estaminet* and then we were afraid to drink calvados because we did not want to be tight when we faced the general. We sipped some dreadful lukewarm beer and admired the doorsill and the landlady's cat. We did things like this, and then hastened back to the Ecole Normale. Still no General Anderson. He had been delayed by matters more portentous and exacting than the problem which we shared.

That afternoon lasted exactly fifty-six hours—or so it seemed to me—and by six o'clock Beaugy swore that we had been there a week and his leave was up. We did everything we could think of to pass time and divert ourselves. We walked down the road and watched a lot of French boys and girls stealing lilacs that hung over the gray wall of a British headquarters on the highway.

Back at our own headquarters, about six-thirty, Colonel Snyder called me into the hall. "The general is back," he said. "He is out at his house. I have just been speaking with him on the phone. Here, come in my office. . . ."

I took up the phone and squawked a feeble hello to the general. I started to tell him that I had an artist with me whose pictures I wished he would look at; but in another second he was talking to me instead, and it is not Standing Operating Procedure to interrupt a major general.

There was something he wanted to talk to me about—and would I please grab some transportation and come over to his house immediately, alone. I returned to Beaugy and mumbled that I had to go to see the general, alone.

Beaugy turned a few shades paler, if that was possible, and his palsied lips said something about "Sure, go ahead," and then I went out to find a jeep. It was Colonel Snyder's own jeep, a very rattly one. I drove over to Marley-le-Roi, and found Fred Anderson freshly combed and shaved, out on his terrace, enjoying a momentary spot of refreshment.

"Sorry to be so peremptory," he said, "but I have to go to dinner over at Tooey's." Tooey, in case you are not informed, is the affectionate designation which his associates confer on General Carl A. Spaatz, who has four stars as white as milk, and was at that moment bossing the entire American Air Force deployed against Germany.

"Now," said Anderson, "here is what I want to talk to you about. . . ." and he went on for half an hour, and nothing of what he said may be recounted by me at this time.

But when he was finished, and while the general's car was driven up before the door, and other guests headed Tooey-wards were assembling, I managed to shoot out something about an artist I had fetched from the 305th, a fellow who painted B-17s and—

An officer appeared with some papers for the general to sign. "An artist?" Fred asked over his shoulder. "Is he good?"

"Yes."

"Maybe Tooey would like to see the pictures," said Fred Anderson.

"Maybe he would," I said, "but, sir, don't you think, Fred,

my God, listen, I don't know General Spaatz, or don't you think you had better see them first, and—"

"I'm in a hurry," said Fred, soaring out of the door while I stumbled after him. "Tell Snyder to give me a ring at Park House about ten o'clock; he can drive you and this artist over there."

"But what," I squealed, "if the paintings actually aren't any good? What if—?"

The general said, in a tone calculated to reassure me, "Oh, I'll take your word for it that they *are* good," and he taxied out beyond the flower beds in his gray roadster and then, as nearly as I could tell, he took off and vanished.

I banged my way back through St. Germain, and dined with Colonel Snyder, a visiting Raf Wing Commander, General Anderson's pilot, and an abject Beaugy whose complexion was turning slowly from saffron to chartreuse. When finally I drew him aside and whispered the glad tidings about the evening visit to General Spaatz's house, he became patently grass-green.

Zero hour was ten o'clock. We sat in Colonel Snyder's office, communicating our fright to Colonel Snyder by degrees. The colonel didn't know much of what this was all about but before we got through with our forebodings I think he decided that he would soon be peeling potatoes along with Beaugy and me. The fatal call was made, the telephone clacked, the receiver went back on its hook, and Snyder regarded us as he might have regarded one of his own crews about to visit Essen without any fighter protection there or back.

"This is it," he said.

Everything happened with the horrid rapidity of a newsreel which we observed but were powerless to alter. The staff car hummed through brown French streets; we dipped into the valleys and hurtled up the hill toward Marley-le-Roi. We turned in at an old stone gate and the MP stepped forward, recognized the colonel, stepped back, saluted . . . we were being deposited in front of the main door now, the colonel called goodbye, and the gravel jumped beneath our feet. All of Park House, a

beautiful vine-draped wide-windowed château, was drenched
with lights and laughter.

(There was a sprightliness in the air in those days, be it at
Park House or out at some miserable beat-up ex-Jerry barracks
on a Belgian flying field. The war was almost over. People
laughed readily, nervously. They made colossal jokes about seeing each other next time on Iwo Jima or in New Guinea. The
coffee and the liquor flowed generously on social evenings,
whenever one could find coffee and liquor, and whenever one
had a social evening.)

For a moment we halted like medieval waifs hoping for a
hand-out, and gazed through the windows. We saw everything
from RAF Air Commodores to VIPs in civilian clothes—men
wafted importantly from Washington five hours before. We saw
French uniforms, we even saw a few pretty girls and a handsome old countess and more stars than Jess Willard ever saw
at Toledo. Beaugy clutched his home-made portfolio in a grasp
of iron and sweat, with perhaps a few dashes of blood and
tears thrown in.

As for me, I kept contemplating the rupture of my beautiful
friendship with the Army Air Forces . . . I could hear unborn
grandchildren prattling, "What did you do in the Second World
War?" and hear my own mothy accents in reply: "Well, that
reminds me about the night I was flung out of General Spaatz's
quarters. I was a mere stripling of forty-one—"

Somehow we got the door open.

The first person we saw was Fred Anderson. He was bending over, digging a cigar case out of a coat folded on a chair.
I had time only to wonder vaguely about whether those were
his own cigars and whether he had any extras, before I was
muttering, "Sir, may I present . . ." and then Beaugy had
saluted, the general had returned his salute, and they were
shaking hands.

Fred was saying pleasant things but they meant nothing to
our ears. He was leading us on and on across a hall, away from
the brass and chatter and coffee and brandy of the after-dinner

throng. He pushed open some double doors and then we were in the billiard room. He closed the doors behind us and there we were, trapped.

It was the biggest billiard room I ever saw. I think it was slightly larger than the floor space of the Number One hangar back at our base. There was a green billiard table, the continental kind that makes an American billiard table look like a cribbage board. We walked about fifteen minutes and then we were past the billiard table and could pick up the target, dead ahead perhaps 3000 yards. The target was General Spaatz. He sat at the farther side of a circular poker table in an alcove of the room, all alone, one menacing figure in an Eisenhower jacket.

Yesterday I read an article about General Spaatz in a Sunday newspaper. It had things to say about a leonine head and deeply-etched lines, and so on. For my money, General Spaatz didn't look like that at all. Instead, he looked like a shorter, slimmer General Pershing, and he had the neat gray hair, the glasses, the close-clipped silvery mustache, and the bearing of all heaven and hell in his body.

General Anderson introduced me to General Spaatz. I in turn introduced Captain Beaugureau to General Spaatz. We stood and gulped; and the sweat pouring off Beaugy's jaundiced forehead seemed to flow down and make a pool around our feet.

"Sir," I heard myself stammering, "Captain Beaugureau has painted some pictures of B-17s in combat. I felt that perhaps you would like to see them."

General Spaatz replied that he would like to see them. Certainly there was nothing else he could have said under the circumstances. Beaugy lifted the grimy, oil-stained portfolio with shaking hands.

"Here," said General Spaatz, "let's put them over here on the billiard table."

He took the receptacle from Beaugy's jellied paw.

"Sir," whispered Beaugy, "that canvas thing is awful dirty and—"

"On the billiard table," repeated General Spaatz firmly. "Turn on the light, Fred."

Fred turned on the light. One by one the watercolors were drawn out of the folder and placed in order on the pure green cloth. It seemed to me suddenly that there was a pathetically small number of paintings. Furthermore, it seemed that the paintings were pathetically bad. Was it possible that I had ever decided to recommend such atrocious smudges to anyone? The clouds were all wrong, the Forts looked like broken-down chicken crates, the flak looked like bunches of purple grapes. There was no blue like that anywhere in the air above, no flame so orange, no bombs so evenly spaced in their fall. In short, they all looked lousy to me and, as private confidence revealed later, they looked even more lousy to Captain Beaugureau.

General Anderson stood staring at them with his hands on his hips. General Spaatz bent coolly forward, adjusted his glasses, and lowered his face until it was about six inches above one of the paintings.

"Sir," came Beaugy's unhappy whimper, "maybe you can get a better idea of them—uh—from a distance—sir."

The stars on General Spaatz's jacket gave me a sudden, acute conjunctivitis so I turned away.

"Got him in the gas tank," said Spaatz, glaring at a particularly accurate burst of flak.

"Yes, sir," whispered Beaugy.

"What target was this one, Captain?" The brown finger tapped another painting.

"Not any target in particular, sir. I guess maybe it could have been Hannover. There's that lake over there. . . ."

Anderson nodded. "It does look like Hannover."

General Spaatz seemed to take a deep breath, then he seemed to sigh, then he seemed to say nothing. Beaugy was weaving on his feet, and I would have tried to sustain him by holding his arm but I couldn't even lift my own arm. General Spaatz turned toward the captain, bending his head slightly, compressing his brows, and peering past, rather than through, his glasses.

"What are you doing here now, Captain?"

"Sir, I am just over from Britain on leave. . . ." Beaugy's voice trailed off into space again.

"Still flying missions?"

"No, sir. I've finished up."

Spaatz turned back to the paintings again. He began to discuss them in an even voice. He criticized them, not artistically, but technically. He said that he would like to see flak and fighters mixed together more the way it actually happens in the air; and Beaugy stuttered out that he had thought of that but, after all, it might be confusing to the uninitiated.

"Go ahead," said General Spaatz. "Paint some that way, anyway. Show them what it's really like."

"Yes, sir."

There was another long pause. We could hear a C-47 muttering along, high above Park House. Maybe it was lost in the fog, maybe it was hunting for Villacoublay, maybe it was hunting—

General Spaatz straightened up and took off his glasses. "Well, Fred, I guess we might use this fellow here at USSTAF, mightn't we?"

"I think we could, sir."

"Take care of it."

"Very well, I'll have Colonel Bowman arrange it."

About this time General Ted Curtis opened the doors of the billiard room; and then a lot of other people came in with him, and they all stopped to examine the pictures. . . . Five minutes later I drifted off in search of Beaugureau. I was afraid that he had died in a corner somewhere.

I found him in the living room. General Anderson had introduced him to Colonel Bowman, and Colonel Bowman was already talking on the phone. Someone had put a drink into

Beaugy's hand, but he wasn't touching it. He was standing with docility beside the colonel, and his eyes were perfectly glazed.

Fred Anderson passed, and pinched me on the rear. "Tooey liked the pictures," he whispered.

Flight and Murder of the Multitudes 1964

"Out in the Cincinnati aviary, a shabby bird with an iridescent neck and a breast the color of apricots, drew farther and farther into the corner of her cage. There were times, it was said, when she rolled her red-rimmed eye upward, as if roused by spectral couriers who warned her to overtake the multitudes which had clipped the atmosphere so long before. She was the last. She was eighteen years old, and her plumage would be handsomer when the taxidermists had their way with it."

It is more than a quarter of a century since I wrote those lines for a book about the passenger pigeons, a novel called *The Noise of Their Wings.*

It is fifty years on September 1st of this year since the last passenger pigeon died, as recounted above. Her name was Martha. If you should wish to see her, she is "perched in singular beauty" in the National Museum at the Smithsonian Institution in Washington. There are thousands of other birds in that natural history treasure-house but she is one of the prettiest.

Her ornithological name was *Ectopistes Migratorius.*

There is no specimen of *Ectopistes Migratorius* alive today.

A century and a century and a half ago, and two and three centuries ago, they were the most numerous birds in North America, probably in the entire world. Many of the pioneers called them "passage pigeons." Why formerly they were termed "passenger pigeons" I don't know. Nor did I ever encounter anyone who could explain for sure.

Nor do I know how many birds are alive today in the entire world, nor does anyone else know. But as far as *people* are concerned, it is reliably estimated, according to current almanacs, that in the year 1960 there were two billion, nine hundred and seventy-one million, eight hundred thousand people alive in the world.

There used to be alive in our United States a tough young Scotsman named Alexander Wilson, the father of American ornithology. He preceded Audubon by some years. He stood one time in Kentucky, in the early eighteen-hundreds, and watched a single flock of passenger pigeons roaring overhead.

He stood for many hours, watching, counting, measuring, estimating with the keen naturalist's eye which was his. He said that the number of birds which he saw at that time in a single flock, horizon to horizon, and passing with the almost incredible speed which these pigeons attained— He estimated that their number was two billion, two hundred and thirty million, two hundred and seventy-two thousand.

In a single formation.

At that same moment there were other flocks crushing down the forests in Carolina, Pennsylvania, the Northwest Territory, Ontario. There is no reason to suppose that, of these other flocks, some might not have been larger than the one witnessed by Wilson.

It doesn't seem that we would be sticking our necks out to say that, of the estimated three billion persons alive on this planet today, the passenger pigeons didn't outnumber us a dozen times. There were more passenger pigeons during the years of their numbers and substance, slicing the air and weighting the trees of America, than there have been human beings born since the dawn of time.

To carry numbers into something more readily recognizable, I've looked up the amount of square acreage in the land surface of Ohio. I selected Ohio because that's where Martha went to her quiet old-age death.

Land surface of Ohio measures about twenty-six million,

seventy-three thousand, six hundred acres. The flock which made the howl of its passing above Alexander Wilson's head could have put down eighty-five birds on every acre in Ohio.

The passenger pigeon was not only a big bird, he was a gorgeous bird. In length he was half again the size of the largest mourning dove seen today—about three times the size of the little ground dove of our southernmost states. That made him nearly as lengthy as a crow; but all resemblance stopped there.

If you fancy pastels instead of the sharper colors, the passenger pigeon was the most gorgeous thing we ever had around. His back was slatish blue, his breast like ripening pale fruit. The iridescence of his neck remains alive on the old skins today . . . tarnish of a hundred years cannot remove its brilliance.

I remember examining a study collection at the Smithsonian, holding in my hands the stiff skins of many passenger pigeons. These had been put away carefully in drawers, locked in darkness with the odor of preservatives about them. They had been treasured well. But their shimmer was alive: an oily beauty, purple and green, the changeable satin allure of women's rustling taffeta.

. . . And then out into the street again, and standing there on Constitution Avenue, wondering about the long-dead birds I had been studying; and looking down at my feet and seeing the live pigeons of modern Washington waddling about the steps and over the curbstone. Iridescence of the live birds was not so persuasive as that of their dried cousins in the halls behind me.

When they were not high in the air and bulleting at sixty mph (that's John James Audubon's guess: some other people reckoned as much as one hundred mph) the pigeons fed across the surface of the earth. They churned through fields, pastures, swamps, forests. They disordered the growth like a monstrous colorful wheel. They trotted cooing and burbling, seizing anything edible in their beaks, leaving the planet whitened behind them.

In every minute there was bound to become a new rear rank as multiple masses grazed their way forward. The best beech mast, tastiest acorns, fattest nuts and seeds—all these lay ahead and in profusion . . . the flock wallowed toward them. Birds in the rear rank did not wish to remain there, they did not desire to eat at second table. The instant they found themselves in the rear they leaped into the air, whirled their way over tree-tops and among branches, and settled ahead of the voracious throngs.

But, stay . . . there was now another rear rank—those individuals who had been next to the rear before. . . . *What? Remain here? Waddle in the wake of the herd? There'll be nothing to eat—the ones ahead will have eaten it all! Let us take to the air at once. Let us be the first rank!*

So it happened with the next clan, the next layer, the next files. Always and always there were slate-blue-and-peach bodies rising as if sucked by winds, billowing forward, easing down. First they were the first rank, then they were the middle rank, then they were at the rear again. They flew once more.

A British naturalist named John Bradbury roved up the Missouri River in 1811. He recalled that near the mouth of the Nodaway River he personally shot two hundred and seventy-one pigeons, as fast as he could load and fire. "The birds," he wrote, "are so close to each other that the ground can scarcely be seen. . . . It is evident that the foremost ranks must be the most successful, and nothing will remain for the hindermost. . . . They succeed each other with so much rapidity that . . . a side view of them exhibits the appearance of the segment of a large circle, moving through the woods."

The whirl of that forward-moving feathered wheel served an extra purpose. Pigeons flying overhead would, by sheer weight and force of numbers, loosen quantities of the trees' fruit: nuts and seeds tumbled in a persistent shower. This worked an advantage for young birds who were running with the flock but could not yet fly.

Constantly it was observed that the youthful doves, when in good feeding ground, looked like two-headed monsters—their crops so stuffed, their long bodies so distorted.

They ate everything, everything. Every acorn of the oak, every nut of the beech and other smaller nut trees; every nut of the hazel bush which they could find. Wingéd seeds of the elm and maple, wild grain, wild fruit, hackberries, elderberries, mulberries; hips of the wild rose; huckleberries, gooseberries, anything, anything. If denied other food, they would gobble young green shoots of any sort of vegetation. Not entirely herbivorous, they were found (when dissected and examined by scientifically minded folk) to have also eaten all the grasshoppers, worms, grubs, and caterpillars which they came across.

Aubudon observed an enormous flock, and then speculated on how much food they might require. His estimate: eight million, seven hundred and twelve thousand *bushels per day*.

They were a curse to any advance of agrarian civilization. Plodding through native forests they had left a mark of temporary destruction in the way of excreta: pungent burning of their manure made a blight on the growth. Still, this was repaired easily by rains and time.

But farmers were beginning to claim land all over the eastern and central United States. A farmer could go into his field and spend days sowing wheat or oats, either by hand or with the crude drills of the period; and then he might see every kernel plucked from the earth by a quick incursion of pigeon swarms. Often the pioneers had to plant their ground three or four times in a spring. Many were wiped out, they could no longer buy seed even on credit.

Was young corn sprouting when the birds came? Tender sprouts vanished under tapping beaks, and in minutes. Swelling cotyledons were pulled up and swallowed; soon the earth lay unimpregnated again. There was nothing to be seen or smelled

except acrid manure of the beautiful bubbling scourge which
had destroyed man's labor and man's hope.

. . . And other farmers far ahead had just planted. Then
they heard the clamor of the "passage pigeons'" approach;
they ran for their shotguns. They sent children dancing around
the fields with cow bells, sent them banging on dishpans.
Frantic wives shrieked, they flagged with their aprons. Birds
settled down, a thousand, maybe a hundred thousand, with
their awful fluid sound. They ignored this clownish intrusion
upon their perpetual lunch. Guns banged, the threnody of
hoots and hollering kept up. Then the rear rank rose, flew
ahead; the second rank became the rear rank. They rose, flew.
All harvest was gone, months before ever it was a harvest.
The year's crop was gone when it had scarcely become a
planting.

The passenger pigeons were unpredictable, there was nothing
like them in the ornithological realm. They flew when and
where they would, often they disregarded the seasons, sometimes they were seen going north at the approach of cold
weather, going south at the approach of warm. But as a general
rule they appeared to observe a seasonal migration.

". . . They would fly like greased lightning." I told about
this long ago. "And then a hawk would descend upon them,
to wrench his meal from somewhere in the delicate pack. And
then the pack would dive. They would go down like a wide
blue streamer, and up again when they were safe once more—
and on and on, into the north. The hawk would be gone one
mile, or two; he would be gone to his dead limb among the
pines, and perhaps he would feast on other birds; but all day
long the wide, racing torrent would plunge downward at that
identical point—down until they were all quite safe—and up
again and toward the north. A million birds would dive. . . ."

They bred and nested quickly, sporadically. Commonly the
females laid two eggs, but sometimes one, sometimes three.

There were several nestings, several broods during the course of a year.

Nests were crude, much like the nests of other doves surviving today: rough thatched saucers, shallow, seeming to fall apart even as they were built. Male and female shared the labor of brooding, down to the split second. Weather caused a variance in the period of incubation. Eggs were never cold; but they hatched as early as the eleventh or twelfth day, and as late as the twenty-fourth.

"Passage pigeons" were messy, voracious, destructive, overwhelming. Beautiful they were, but dumb. Observers are unanimous in declaring them the most witless birds ever encountered.

A man might ride on horseback through the woods for forty miles, and all in the same attenuated nesting . . . same burbling cries around him, same slobbery squabs tumbling from the nests to be crushed beneath hoofs on the ground . . . same stench of droppings, same masses of adult birds floundering home at dusk to populate branches of the trees with a weight almost past belief. Pioneer families were awakened again and again in the night by the cannon stroke of oak limbs broken under the impress of pigeons.

Audubon remarked that he saw trees over two feet in diameter broken off close to the ground, all by the birds. E. D. Nauman, writing of his boyhood in Iowa, describes a red oak tree adjacent to his father's farmhouse: a towering majestic plant which when its stump was examined eventually was found to be over four hundred years old. Many of the largest limbs of this tree were shattered under tonnages of roosting pigeons.

Approach of the flocks, whether in whirling feeding fashion upon the ground, or five hundred feet in the air, racing in horizon-to-horizon waves which took away the sunlight— The sound of their coming was likened to almost every great orchestral sound in Creation. They were the howl of a gale whipping through torn rigging of a ship at sea; they were bells, they were artillery, they were a groan that came as if from below the circular sky, and frightened the babies who heard it.

Edward Howe Forbush, eminent ornithologist, quotes one Simon Pokagon, a Pottawattomie:

". . . I was camping on the head waters of the Manistee River in Michigan. One morning on leaving my wigwam I was startled by hearing a gurgling rumbling sound, as though an army of horses laden with sleigh bells was advancing through the deep forest toward me. As I listened more intently, I concluded that instead of the tramping of horses it was distant thunder. . . . Nearer and nearer came the strange commingling sounds of sleigh bells, mixed with the rumbling of an approaching storm . . . in wonder and astonishment I beheld moving toward me in an unbroken front, millions of pigeons."

Their rushing wings moaned and whistled, they were a howl fit to wake the dead. They were the clapping of hands of an audience Nationwide . . . the roll of drums, the sound of horns blown lustily.

They were fireworks. . . .

"I positively brought myself so much among the Pigeons," says Audubon, "and in the woods of America that my ears were as if really filled with the noise of their wings."

They were good to eat. So everyone ate them. When explorers began to move among Indian villages of Canada and the eastern seaboard and, later, the old Northwest Territory, they were stricken with wonder at quantities of pigeon fat and pigeon oil which the Indians had rendered. There might be a gallon of such grease ready at hand for every inhabitant of a village. The stuff served as lard and butter (lucky Indians!— no one had heard about cholesterol in those days).

Boiled, baked, fried, put into pies, stewed, broiled, minced, and poached: they were dainty fare any way you chose. All contemporary accounts speak of the delicious flavor and substance, so much more palatable than that of domestic pigeons.

Squabs were the real prize and they were easily come by.

Stuffed in initial stages with pigeon milk secreted by their parents, and later with predigested food forced into their craws, they grew and swelled like bird-cream-puffs, immense and flavorable.

No wonder that hordes of hunters specialized in squabs, and that thousands of families scorned the adult birds as meat. . . . You couldn't possibly waste the passenger pigeons, you see. If you saved only the breasts you could feed the rest to the hogs: whole counties-full of people did just that. And family dogs had to eat as well, they doted on pigeons.

It wasn't hard to take the critters. Children scarce able to walk could catch them, and often did. Children were dragged from their beds at night to accompany parents when they went raiding the pigeon roosts. Birds were terrified by sight of torches and bonfires, their stupid brains were addled. They fluttered helplessly, hopelessly. They were battered to the ground with clubs and then had their necks wrung.

They were dragged about in nets, and that wasn't on roosts alone: that was in daytime, in open fields which had been baited to attract them. A single operation of a large net could bring in as many as two-hundred-and-fifty *dozen* at a time. (Three thousand birds at one swoop—that's good going.)

"The settlers got them out of the groves," my grandmother told me. "They put up high boards on the sides of their lumber wagons—the big bang-boards that they used when picking corn. Then they'd have those wagon-boxes filled right up to the top with pigeons. They'd drive across prairie to the railroad station, to try to ship the birds to market."

She said, "If they couldn't sell them all, and there was danger of the birds' spoiling, folks said they were real good for fertilizer."

Obviously the extension of rail lines and other forms of transportation throughout the Middle West and lower Canada was a contributing factor to the pigeons' doom. Big city markets were screaming for their flesh throughout the sixth, seventh, and eighth decades of the nineteenth century. City dwellers didn't get to see much of the birds in their wild state (oh yes, there was that flight which went over Washington, D.C., in 1858, so immense as to darken the sun. And one time a flock settled down on the roof of the New York Customs House. But usually city dwellers only saw the pigeons after they were ready to be eaten).

Eaten they were. Forbush says that the New York market alone could absorb a hundred barrels a day without change in price. But still there was often a glut. A man counted forty boats rubbing their gunwales in the North River, and each of those boats—sloops or whatever they were—was loaded with a buff-and-blue cargo of pigeons. The birds were offered at one cent apiece; sometimes they went begging even at that price. Then . . . the hogs again. Or rich bodies going into the earth to make it richer.

Margaret H. Mitchell, accomplished Canadian ornithologist, published a magnificent work in 1936: a contribution of the Royal Ontario Museum of Zoology. It was called *The Passenger Pigeon in Ontario,* and could be said to rank in importance above the excellent works by W. B. Mershon and John C. French, who were, as described by themselves, but "interested and enthusiastic laymen."

The charm, the mystery and puzzle of *Ectopistes Migratorius* is discussed revealingly in Miss Mitchell's book.

She says: "At one time there were said to be five thousand professional pigeoners operating in the United States, and it was possible for the individual to make from $10.00 to $40.00 a day in the height of the season which was during breeding."

Imagine that, in 1850, 1860, or 1870: ten to forty dollars *a day.* Ordinary farmhands were often glad to get five dollars a week and found. Forty dollars per *month* was a wage paid to men with excellent technical skill. . . .

For several generations people have tried to make a complex riddle out of the disappearance and extinction of the passenger pigeons. It is really not necessary to do that.

There was talk of whole flights whirled into the Great Lakes by violent storms, or lost in the ocean as they sped along the Atlantic Coast. Indeed, a French sea captain arrived in Philadelphia in March, 1740, and told of observing a sea covered with dead pigeons for miles on end.

But, mind you, that was a hundred years and more before huge nestings were counted in Kentucky, Ohio, Michigan. No calamity of Nature did away with the pigeons; the great calamity which they had to face was Man. Man killed the young and, before long, there ceased to be any young. There were no young left to grow up and breed and carry on the race.

Forever it is the fashion to blame the sports gunner for a reduction in numbers of any wild creature sought popularly as game.

Sportsmen had little or nothing to do with the extermination of our great wild doves. To be sure, every old muzzle-loader was primed for pigeons whenever they came into a neighborhood. One man reports dropping seventy-one birds with one double-barreled blast; undoubtedly this slaughter was exceeded on many occasions, when firing into thick-packed flocks.

Also the birds were live-trapped, and then parcelled out to marksmen's clubs for use as live targets. . . . "Messers. Parrish and Williams, of the Seneca Gun Club, Seneca Falls, have contracted with Frank Chaffey for the immediate delivery of 12,000 wild pigeons to be used at the coming tournament." So reports *Forest and Stream,* under date of April 15th, 1880.

According to Margaret Mitchell (*not* the Gone-With-the-Wind lady) the destruction of Mr. Chaffey's birds by gay gunners of Seneca Falls "created a storm of protest." Seriously the shooting of live-trapped birds was never regarded, in the United States, with the light-hearted jollity prevailing in certain European countries. Somehow the spectacle of releasing a frightened pretty prisoner and then banging it to Kingdom Come "in its first ecstasy of freedom" went *agin the grain* with Yankees and Canadians alike.

This writer began his study of the passenger pigeon back in 1934, and since then has read about every word on the

subject which he could find. He estimates that the ordinary
sportsman, shotgun-in-hand and lunch-in-pocket and hunting-
song-in-heart, accounted for about one per cent of the pigeons'
final attrition.

The professional pigeoners, the market hunters—these were
the characters who turned the trick.

Market hunters, especially the squab hunters, used train and
telegraph. Train and telegraph were available and they were
bound to use them and thus earn their forty dollars per day.

It is a hideous story. A flock of billions nested in Missouri
in the spring—April, to be exact—and there the majority of
the squabs were killed by hunters. The flock arose, flew to
Michigan. The same executioners followed them there, and
they destroyed the next hatching of squabs. Desperately the
pigeons flew northeast, in this case to New York State. They
nested "near the upper Beaverkill in the Catskills, in the lower
part of Ulster County."

Men used fifteen tons of ice to pack the fresh shipment of
squabs sent down to New York City from Ulster County.

All of a sudden there weren't any multitudes roaring through
the skies. Half-witted Mankind wondered why, and made up
queer stories about it. Hurricanes, lightning, natural catas-
trophies. . . .

(One wonders idly what the progeny of the squab hunters
are doing now—those intrepid professional slayers who followed
the flocks from nesting to nesting, and did away with the fat
helpless young by the million. I think I saw such a lineal
descendant the other day. He had bulldozers, draglines and
hydraulic barges. He was filling in one of our mangrove bays
here in Florida, in order to make land where he could put up
a shopping center complete with supermarkets.)

. . . A little flock here, a little flock there. Someone saw
two hundred birds up in the Michigan woods in 1898. In
that same year other stragglers were shot near Detroit and in
New York State. A female was killed at Bar Harbor in 1904,
and a man named Hamilton thought that he had seen pas-

senger pigeons circling above the Econfina River in 1907. A man named Anderson told of twenty-five passenger pigeons hunting forlornly across northern Florida in 1912. Ornithologists have thought that perhaps he made a mistake; those might have been doves of another variety . . . *Leucocephala* . . . *Carolinensis.* . . .

A few attempts were made to breed the creatures in captivity, none crowned with success.

My novel, published in 1938, told of a man who offered a fortune for a pair of passenger pigeons and finally acquired them. He wished to restore the race.

I remember discussing this with Dr. E. N. Bressman of the United States Department of Agriculture; with Joseph H. Riley, associate curator of birds at the Smithsonian; and with Dr. Harry C. Oberholser of the U. S. Bureau of Biological Survey. Also there was the contribution of an old friend of my Des Moines days, the Hon. Henry A. Wallace, then Secretary of Agriculture. Mr. Wallace knows his genetics.

The concensus of opinion was that the original passenger pigeon race could never be restored, even if you came into possession of a healthy male and female of the species. They needed space, they needed vast numbers. Some creatures find it impossible to exist in numbers below a certain level. Either they refuse to breed or else they grow sterile.

Artificially, perhaps, it might have been managed. That would have been by crossing the native passenger pigeon with birds of allied species—say mourning doves or the common domestic pigeon—restoring thus their fecundity; and then slowly breeding out all acquired characteristics, until one had left seemingly a new race of passenger pigeons identical with the old. . . .

But such is an exercise of theory and speculation, even on the part of natural scientists. Likely there would have been a gimmick to interfere, somewhere along the line.

Man stands red-handed when his relations with birds and beasts are reviewed. Especially does the native American stand with blood dripping. But we never made another slaughter like this. We could not have done so had we wished and tried, for there were never any other birds like these.

... We look up at the empty air above those scraps of forest which remain to us now, and we wonder how it was when the skies were full and booming.

He Found Life Good and
Left It Better
1966

One spring day I was driving along a woodland road in
New Jersey, when an elderly and somewhat dwarfish Robin
Hood stepped out of a path at the side of the lane.

He wore a green felt hat, cocked and pointed in medieval
style and adorned with pheasant feathers. A bow hung over one
shoulder and a quiver of arrows over the other. Robin sported
also a fringed hunting shirt . . . he was gray and tousled as to
hair and mustache . . . maybe he wasn't Robin Hood or Locks-
ley after all. Maybe he was the ghost of Kit Carson.

In any event he exerted the combined compulsion of a will-
o'-the-wisp and a Pied Piper. Without further consideration
I parked my car, and followed this shaggy sprite into whatever
mysteries lay ahead.

Eleven years of a vital and abounding friendship awaited
me.

That happened in April, 1933, but Will Crawford had deserted New York City for the Watchung woodlands away
back in the post-World-War-One days.

As the New York *Herald Tribune* said of him, "He became
one of the leading illustrators of Americana by combining artistic whimsicality with accuracy of detail."

Somewhere in this stuffed and crowded country of ours
there must still exist attics. Somewhere there are piles of
ancient magazines drying in gabled corners. Imagine that we

enjoy the richness of exploration amid such surroundings. We sit cross-legged, and delve into the stack, and find the treasure of Will Crawford.

These magazines have names unfamiliar to the readers of today: *Munsey's, St. Nicholas, Everybody's, Collier's, Puck.* Certainly *Life* is familiar enough, but the *Life* of the early 1900s was a different breed of cat, not even owned by the same firm which flourishes nowadays. The present *New Yorker* might approximate it more closely than any other: jests, anecdotes, humorous or cynical essays, cartoons. In the old *Life* there were loads of illustrations by Uncle Bill Crawford. (The Bill and Will were interchangeable—folks used them both.)

A Crawford picture was the epitome of intended representation. When his dogs wagged their tails they really wagged. His Comanches didn't look like any Zulus or South Sea cannibals—gad, no. They were wild American redskins, down to the last moccasin and eagle quill.

His Santa Clauses were never merely fat standardized bulgy old men with beards. Nay. Their bellies were full of cider and fruit cake, they were perfumed with candles and pinecones and reindeer smells. They said *Ho, ho, ho,* before you even looked at them.

When Crawford's Halloween cats arched their backs and spat, you could hear them clear across the room.

His Daniel Boones had real black powder in their powderhorns. His Old King Coles knew exactly what to do with a pipe and a bowl.

His fairies were composed by Mendelssohn.

. . . There are newspapers piled beyond our elderly magazines . . . the New York *Journal,* Sunday Magazine of the old New York *Tribune,* New York *World.* In turn Crawford was staff artist for each of these publications. He lived into his eighth decade as a bachelor, beloved by author and janitor, curator and philosopher and newsboy. Beloved by Art Young and Charles M. Russell, by Frederic Remington and Will Rogers. . . .

Will Crawford was by way of being a prodigy, and began work for the Newark *Call* in the 1880s at an age when his contemporaries were interested chiefly in dime novels, marbles, shinny sticks. But Fate awarded him a full-fledged family to support later on: his sister Lotta Ricalton, and her two children.

People who knew him in his thirties and forties said that Will was always a gnome, had always been shaggy. . . .

As the demand for his work grew, and as his prices increased and income flowed more readily, he maintained his sister and niece and nephew in Newark; but he himself moved to New York City and the *World*.

Uncle Bill acquired a barn-like studio near Union Square, and soon the place became a combination museum, junk-shop, bar-room, and senate or forum. Socialists and Republicans alike, among editorial writers of the day: they came. And actors came, and wistful ingenues, and the lieutenant from the nearby police station. There was a streetcar conductor who composed cowboy ballads, and a poetess who smoked Brazilian cigarettes. And there were prize-fighters, and baritones, and an under-sized boy of fifteen who had a pair of mutilated hands, but wished most desperately to paint and draw; and so Will Crawford helped him, with oil and crayons and brushes and elastic bands, and a blessing.

Here came a new acquaintance—a fellow who already possessed an encyclopedic knowledge of the Algonquian tribes, and (Crawford hoped) the ability to transmute wax and color into a powerful reality.

Dwight Franklin didn't have any studio, but— "Plenty room in my tipi," said Seldom-Writes, which was the Plains Injun name conferred upon Will by his friend Charles M. Russell.

Will beamed throughout his later life, relishing the fame achieved by the wax groups which Dwight Franklin made for the Museum of the American Indian, and nautical groups which he executed for the U. S. Naval Academy at Annapolis. When, in the 1930s, it was learned that President F.D.R. insisted on keeping a Franklin sculpture in his office alcove at the White House (John Paul Jones on his quarter-deck, if I remember correctly) Uncle Bill was tickled pink.

"He used to drink a lot," Dwight said. "But invariably it only made him mellower, and more affectionate toward humanity. Rarely did his conviviality lead him into danger. I do remember one night, however, when a bunch of us were sitting around in the old Grapevine Inn. Will was up against a dead-line—cowboy stuff for an Owen Wister book, I think—and no one was especially surprised when he disappeared. He'd gone back to the studio to work, we believed.

"But when some of us approached the studio a little later, we were greeted with a volley of revolver shots, and a chorus of neighbors yelling for the police. We found Bill bucking away on the wooden horse which he used for a model. The horse was saddled and bridled with orthodox Western paraphernalia, and Uncle Bill had donned a pair of chaps and hung a couple of six-guns on his belt, and he was really riding the range.

"He explained to the cops later, 'Oh, I got to thinking about Charlie Russell, and grew homesick for Montana.'"

In 1919 Crawford retreated to a bizarre little single-tax colony in the Watchung Mountains, not far above Scotch Plains, New Jersey. Like so many transcendental communities, Free Acres never established itself as a political or economic landmark, but it was fun living there.

The citizenry included several genial self-deprecating Marxists of the elder school. There were mechanics and novelists, and a placid lady poet who cultivated a personal institution called "Friendship's Garden" with herself designated as Chief Gardener. And a remuda of perpetually poverty-stricken printers, etchers and the like. Everybody swam merrily together in a home-scooped pool, and almost everybody indulged in archery.

Soon Will Crawford reigned supreme and tyrannical as Town Forester. He wouldn't let anyone cut down a tree, period.

"But, Mr. Crawford, that elm's got to come down. I must build my kitchen out on this side, and the tree's in the way."

Uncle Bill would limp around the elm, study it, shake his head. Then on an instant his seamed face would light up in the bliss of a sublime solution.

"Of course, of course! Here's what we can do. You build your kitchen out the *other* way. Then that tree won't have to come down."

Perhaps as an ironical gift, someone deeded to this benevolent despot a whole caboodle of logs which had already been cut and seasoned. Will accepted the bounty with a philosophical shrug, and decided to build himself a cabin.

He had a little money remaining from more munificent Manhattan days and, with his sister installed comfortably in a house on a wooded slope, he decided to build his own castle farther down the hill. He procured sledge-hammers and crowbars, and toiled like all seven of the traditional Dwarfs, exerting his round shoulders and stringy muscles in prying rocks out of the ridge.

One day he became aware that a red-haired stranger was sitting solemnly on a boulder, watching him. "Hello," Will said to the youth who, like himself, was not a giant, being about five-feet-six. "What's your name?"

"Jim."

"Where you from?"

"New York." The stranger spoke in a hushed rapid whisper. "We're out here visiting friends. But it's such a nice place— If we could find a little shack that wouldn't cost too much, maybe we could live here a while."

He explained that he was a hoofer. "That's what they call dancers in show business." His wife was a dancer too; but they were resting at the moment. "Resting? It means being Out Of Work." There just weren't any jobs in sight.

Mr. Crawford reviewed the situation, and mentally counted his own coins. "I could use some help on this cabin every

now and then. I couldn't offer a fortune, but how does fifty
cents an hour sound?"

Fifty cents an hour sounded like the household hymn of
the Rockefellers. Jim the hoofer and his pretty wife moved into
temporary Free Acres shelter, and Jim plunged vigorously into
any task to which Will Crawford summoned him. He exhibited
an enthusiasm so intense that it almost worked ruination.

After the logs were going up, the red-headed assistant was
directed by Uncle Bill to cut an aperture; then Uncle Bill went
away on an errand. He returned to find Jim applying a furious
saw to the key-log of the cabin.

". . . The key-log, mind you!" Will mused in reminiscence.
"If he'd cut through that thing, it would have brought the whole
structure tumbling about our ears. I named James Cagney as
an Absent-Minded Public Enemy, right then and there—long
before he ever played the part of a Public Enemy in the movies."

But Crawford's own absent-mindedness was proverbial. Once
during the Newark era his sister gave him a grocery list and
headed him for the store. "Oh, yes," Mrs. Ricalton called as he
was departing. "There's one other thing, Will, and be sure you
get that." She told him what it was.

At the store the order was filled completely, except that
Will couldn't remember what it was that his sister had called
in reminder as he was leaving . . . yes, yes, something else . . .
he couldn't think what.

The grocer tried to oblige. He named every sort of canned
goods, fruit, meat, cereals. . . . No, that wasn't it.

Crawford said, "I'll take these groceries home, and find out
what it was that Sis wanted; then come back and get it."

He walked the few blocks, chuckling at his own eccentricity.
"Lotta, what was that other thing I was supposed to get?"

"Cheese, you simpleton. Your supper wouldn't be complete
without *cheese.*"

"Cheese!" repeated Will with delight. "Of course!"

Back to the grocery again. "It was cheese."

"Why, Mr. Crawford, how could you have forgotten your

cheese?" The grocer cut and wrapped a fine yellow wedge. Will lingered a while, discoursing with friends in the shop, relating other anecdotes of his own forgetfulness. Finally he went home.

His sister said, "Supper has been waiting for I don't know how long. Will, where *is* the cheese?"

It was back on that grocery store counter.

He was eager to embrace Nature in the raw—anything from the swift attack of a chicken-hawk to the life cycle of a butterfly.

Often he suffered the interference of his own gentle heart. For instance, he caught a blacksnake and put the snake into a box covered with screening. Uncle Bill rejoiced that now he would be able to dwell intimately with this creature . . . observe its feeding habits, its sleep, its recreational activities, if any . . . perhaps in due time he might be able to secure a mate for it.

He had heard that snakes doted on milk, so he proferred a bowl of condensed milk. Blackie would have nothing to do with the stuff; he crawled into a corner of the cage and seemed to be sulking. Will grew alarmed, he didn't want his friend to starve. Will himself fed principally upon corn flakes, condensed milk, cheese, and apples. All these items he tendered to the new pet. All were scorned.

The dedicated researcher delved into books, hunting through the fabulous litter of his cabin until he could find some authoritative words on the dietary habits of serpents.

Mice!

He hunted up an old live-trap which hadn't rusted completely apart, baited it with cheese— "I even toasted the cheese," he sighed. By evening he had succeeded in the capture of a palatable-looking mouse. He introduced the mouse into the cage and turned his head away. A very dejected naturalist went to bed under the Navajo blankets on his built-in sofa.

"But," he said, "I couldn't sleep a wink. I kept hearing noises from that box. I'd think, 'Surely the snake must have eaten the mouse by now. Why doesn't he stop thrashing around?' Then maybe I'd hear the mouse squeak. It was awful."

In the middle of the night he nerved himself, arose, and—candle in hand—approached the box. There was awe in his tone as he described what he had witnessed.

The snake was cowering in the most remote corner, and the mouse was striding up and down, fairly beating its breast.

"What did you do, Uncle Bill?"

"Only one thing to do. I let them both go."

In his cabin there grew a windrow of Things which started high on one wall and sloped down across the room. Anything and everything was in that pile: Dakota war bonnets, breakfast food cartons, original drawings for books by Wister or Cyrus Townsend Brady— Helmets, lumps of quartz, pressed flowers, overshoes, *The Illustrated London News.*

After we Kantors came to live in the hills, for six months in 1933, I used to amuse myself by burrowing into the midden, closing my hand upon whatever object I touched, and dragging it out. Once it was a child's doll of Pawnee manufacture; another time, a French infantryman's *cartouche;* and, another, a rosy goblet of Bohemian glass (secretly I passed this on to Uncle Bill's sister . . . she put it up in her window for the light to shine through).

Will had some beautiful stumps and butt-ends of log left over from the building of the cabin, which he trained into use as tables and chairs. One favorite stump was his work-seat, and there he penned or brushed or wood-carved.

He would draw on anything which came to hand: wrapping paper, advertising envelopes, a torn label off a vegetable can. Some of the illustrations for my own *The Romance of Rosy Ridge,* which he did in 1937, are grainy and crosshatched. This was because of the surface against which Will happened to work—a shingle, most likely.

I got him other jobs to do for New York publishers: jackets or head-and-tail pieces, and sometimes more elaborate illustrations. Trouble was, printers and binders wait for no man, and thus editors grew reluctant to consider Crawford at all. He showed an increasing oblivion to professional demands.

Once he had a March 15th deadline. (By that time our fortunes had improved—Irene and the children and I moved away from Free Acres and were ensconced in Westfield.) I drove up to the Watchung hills and said, "Uncle Bill, it's the 12th of March. You've got that deadline three days from now. What about it?"

Well, he said, he'd planned to start the work just the day before; but some boys and girls came by with a .22 and some boxes of ammunition, and they all went down to the dump to shoot. "I did miss the target consistently," he admitted. "But barely, barely. If it had been an Indian it would have been dead."

I telephoned New York and wheedled an extra two weeks. April 1st became the new deadline for delivery. About the 25th of March I drove to Free Acres again, and discovered that Will had forgotten all about the job for the book. He was carving away on a birthday gift, a lovely hair-ribbon box.

"It's for little June Immelman, who lives just down the road. I don't know whether little girls like hair-ribbon boxes any more, but I know that she *does* like toads. See, I've created a whole family of toads, right here on the cover. June can have all the toads she wants."

He peered intently over his glasses. "And of course I should provide some hair-ribbons to go in the box, although I'm not sure that she wears hair-ribbons."

I stole away and called the publishers and told them No Soap. I lied, and said that Uncle Bill was sick abed, and they would have to commission their illustrations elsewhere.

Such lapses on Crawford's part were not intended to offend. Oh, no, he could never be offensive—not even abrupt, except to some misguided soul who sought to convert him out of his serenely embraced atheism or his disbelief in ghosts. Not for all the world would he even have implied curtness to a child.

There was an occasion when I transported Will to New York City for what it was hoped would be a rewarding meeting with a certain new art editor, and we stopped at my Westfield house to let me change into a fresh shirt. As I came down from upstairs I could hear Uncle Bill in the living room, where our son Tim was entertaining him.

"Where did you say you went yesterday, little man?"

"Went to zoo," said Tim, who had been mightily impressed by the zebras, but who was not yet very adept at conveying his impressions through the medium of speech.

"Ah, yes. So you went to the zoo. And what did you see there?"

"Saw eezbray," said Timmy.

"I beg your pardon? You saw— Saw what, little man?"

"Saw eezbray."

Uncle Bill finally got the drift. "Well," he said, judiciously, "I suppose some people do call them eezbrays."

His nephew and niece and nephew-in-law were devoted to him; but some of the rest of us were enabled to help chase the wolf, during Uncle Bill's terminal years. I am thinking now of Dwight Franklin, and that splendid actor named Victor Kilian.

There were two old-age winters in California, where James Cagney hosted him in a little hotel. Will Crawford deplored all the clanking hammer-and-tongs activities which are the mechanical and electrical backbone of studio existence. But he did wish very much to watch Jim working in front of the cameras.

Cagney arranged matters, and Mr. Crawford was conveyed to the lot one morning and escorted to a chair especially reserved for him near the director's. The set was that of a frontier saloon in old Oklahoma days. All sorts of animals' heads and stuffed birds up there on the wall. . . .

The director made Take after Take—different angles, but generally shooting with bar and trophies as background. Finally there was a moment of recess, and Jim emerged from the glare of those 750-Watt lights . . . people came from Make-Up to powder the perspiration off his face, and rearrange his hair and costume.

He looked over at the cameras. There was Will, gesticulating wildly. "I tried to get them to stop it, Jimmy! But they wouldn't."

"Will, what on earth's the matter?"

"A terrible thing has happened. All that film wasted! All those scenes will have to be made again!"

Cagney says that Will Crawford was as disturbed as the Minutemen must have been when they learned that the British were coming. He was so alarmed that Jim could scarcely get any explanation out of him.

"Jimmy, it's that deer."

"What deer?"

"That one—over there, just above the bar! It was in every scene. The whole business will need to be done over again!"

"Will, what's wrong with that deer?"

"It's the head of an *English fallow deer!*"

Cagney adds, "I couldn't laugh it off when I told him, 'Oh, maybe the guy bought that deer's head at an auction or something.' No, indeed. English fallow deer simply didn't belong in Oklahoma saloons, and that was that. Will's day was ruined. I had to send him home in a studio car."

Will Crawford was the kind of man about whom folks try to write epitaphs while the subject is still alive.

"He loved every living thing except a few carefully selected people."

"He found life good, and left it better."

"The only cruel thing he ever did to the world was to leave it."

Those are a few. And also there was the tribute paid, during one of Uncle Bill's last illnesses, by a young doctor whom I brought over to Free Acres from the town of Summit. One day, after we had left the bedside, I told the doctor that he should send his bill to me whenever it was ready. There was honest rebuke in his response.

"You mean to suggest that I would submit a *bill*, for exercising my privilege to serve *a man like that?*"

But die Will needs must do, in time. The night he went, the owls must have wept in their trees, and there was mourning among even the most sophisticated chipmunks.

As to Will Crawford's Eternal future, none of us survivors had any real worries. No one ever expressed more annoyed objection to the illusion of the Christian religion than he; and no one ever practiced its virtuous tenets more assiduously.

The Babe and the Boy
1945

This happened on an evening when the World went hilarious
as it never went hilarious before, so there is no sense in reciting
the date. Everybody will know what date I mean. I wish I had
seen this thing happen, but I didn't; it was one of those things
which happened and which you always wish you had seen . . .
but you didn't. So you have to take somebody else's word for
it.

It was Donald Friede's word which I am taking, in this
case. He was the one who saw it. It began up at 59th and
Fifth Avenue. There was still full daylight, and the sun, if
you happened to notice the sun that evening, was a blaze of
brass behind gray clouds. It was still full daylight and people
were milling all around in the street and on the sidewalks, and
a hundred boats were making their hoarse whistles resound
in the distant rivers, and people were still dumping paper out
of the high windows.

Donald said that he was just standing there watching the
crazy crowd whirling around the fountain where Mr. Pulitzer's
unclad metal lady preens herself daintily above the gush of
taxicabs.

It was a case of boy meets girl, and yet—meeting as they
did, amid the howl and hustle of a town gone mad—there
was something simple and tender about it; and Donald said
that he wanted to cry when he saw them meet that way.

The boy was an ensign—one of those gangling, sun-burned

kids we have seen by the hundreds in the years just gone—
trim and sure of himself when it came to doing his job . . . and
yet a little uncertain now, walking slowly into the scream of
an unfamiliar New York.

He had on three ribbons—theater ribbons. He hadn't done
anything particularly outstanding or heroic, or if he had, no
one else was around to recommend him for the star or the cross
which he might have received. His theater ribbons were dotted
with spots of metal to show that he knew what danger and
battles were all about; and thus he walked shyly and with a
half-smile of dazed, victorious disbelief on his smooth bony
face.

Donald said that the girl was cute and shapely, though
perhaps no more cute and shapely than a lot of babes you're
apt to encounter up there in the Fifties. She wore a pretty
dress—a flowered print. She had black gloves and a black hat.
She walked on shoes with six-inch heels and she carried her
handbag as she might have carried her virtue—not gripping it
too tightly, but unwilling to yield it up to the first person who
snatched for it.

Well, they met. They passed each other, jostling among the
demons who waved and ranted in the Avenue. They passed,
going in opposite directions. They halted, five feet past each
other. They looked back simultaneously, and then both of
them smiled.

They liked each other—you could tell that they met and
liked and loved in the first glance; and immediately, no doubt,
the ensign wanted to smother the girl in his arms and immediately she wished to be smothered. (There is no use in invoking
mention of Mars and Venus. Donald is too wearily sophisticated
to quote anything like that, and I shan't offend him by lugging
the gods into this, his anecdote.)

So they stood there laughing. The ensign turned back a step
or two. He said something. The little girl in the print dress said
something, and laughed with her rose-madder lips, and pretended
to start on. But she wasn't really starting on.

Then the ensign had taken another step and he grasped her arm. They spoke. They laughed again. The girl let him keep his clutch upon her. He hugged her arm up tight against his body and so they moved away. One last flash of gold bar and star on the boy's shoulder-board, one last scanty ripple of the girl's dress, the tap of her high heels, the tapering of her ankles, and they were gone away together. The Fifth Avenue crowd, the victory jubilee, had eaten them up. And they, thought Donald, would find the relief and the jollity they sought.

Briefly he thought they would fight their way into a bar, they would have a drink or two, they would join in the singing, they might have another drink, they might settle down to eat if they could find table space in one of the crowded restaurants of the upper East Side or over by Broadway.

He said he thought about them like this as he moved on, shouldering his way slowly through the noise of the Avenue, wandering here and there, thinking of the time he had spent in the Army, remembering the guys he knew at Camp Ritchie or up in the snow of those wintry Dakota months . . . boys sent overseas, and maybe some of them were dead by now.

If he thought about the ensign and the girl again, he tells me, he thought of them in the hesitant, appropriate rapture that these hours would bring: the voices that spoke more lowly and slowly while they played with their coffee and their after-dinner drink; the walk along distorted streets where people danced and screamed in the celebrating dusk; the trip up in the elevator—the place where he stayed or the place where she stayed; and they would snuggle together as young people do in time of war—indeed as young people do in time of peace, also, but more urgently and readily when the guns are still echoing in their ears.

There would be the insistence, the pleading, the denial, the eventual acquiescence . . . a small passion that seems so important at the moment, and is frittered away on the raucous

victory air—forgotten soon enough, mixed up with other loves
to be in turn forgotten.

So that was how he thought about them: they had their
drinks and their palpitating sin. He dismissed them from his
mind.

Donald said that he walked and walked, and thought about
the war and the people who had died in it, and those who
wouldn't have to die now. So after an hour or two (though
born a Jew) he turned toward the great gray shadow of St.
Patrick's. He was one of the figures oozing toward the Gothic
grandeur of its doors. He was climbing the steps. The candles
burned before shrines inside; the people prayed; the water that
was Holy trickled forth.

And then, there on the cathedral steps (he swears it—he
may have lied to other people but I have never known him to
lie to me) he says that he saw it: he turned and looked back
at the throngs on the Avenue and the wild laughing faces—
the tears and squawking that came so readily.

He saw them step out of the crowd: the Navy kid with his
row of ribbons, the girl with the high heels and the flowered
dress. They turned, they looked at each other; they emerged
from the crowd. And they made their way into St. Patrick's
and they got down on their knees, side by side in the church;
and Donald saw them praying there.

It Couldn't Be Pedro
1962

Some folks may remember, and many others don't know—or care—that I spent a couple of the Best Years of My Life with the New York City Police Department. First in the 16th Precinct; then a year and a half of concentrated activity working at a patrolman's job in the 23rd Precinct. That's on the upper East Side. In those days our precinct ran from 86th to 116th Street, and from the Fifth Avenue wall of Central Park to the East River.

One night in 1948 I was on the Late Tour with my partners Bill Klepper and Eddie Jackson (both still in the cops today; but with retirement waiting just around the corner, whenever they wish to take advantage of it). Along about two o'clock in the morning, when we called in at our regular time (didn't have two-way radios in the Radio Motor Patrol cars in those days) we were told to be on the lookout for a certain hoodlum.

Let's call him Pedro Sanchez: that name is as good as any other. We had one-quarter million PRs (Puerto Ricans) in the 23rd Precinct, and to my firm belief that explains why we were the busiest House in town.

The Narcotics Squad wanted to talk to Pedro Sanchez. Age, thirty-nine years; height, five-feet-eight; weight, one hundred and sixty-five pounds; swarthy complexion; curly black hair; believed to be wearing a bright-colored sports shirt, gray slacks, and moccasin-type shoes. That description might have been applicable to at least a hundred people in the 23rd, but it gave us something to go on. We went about our regular duties of patrol, but kept our eyes peeled for Pedro.

Maybe it was about three o'clock in the morning when we slowed down at East 110th and Madison.

"Over there on the sidewalk—northwest corner—"

We took a good look, and there was a PR, height approximately five-feet-eight, weight approximately one hundred and sixty-five, age approximately thirty-nine; curly black hair, swarthy complexion, gaudy sports shirt.

Bill said, "That could be the guy."

"Yes, it could," said Eddie Jackson.

I said, "No," but they didn't pay much attention to me.

The fellow was talking to one of the most elegant local bawds in a doorway; we want on a couple of blocks and made a U-turn.

I said again, "No."

"Well, that could be the guy, Mack. We'd better stop and give him a toss."

I said, "According to the dope they gave us, Pedro Sanchez is a recognized hoodlum. He's done time in Elmira and Sing Sing and Auburn; but he's beat the rap on about fifty other charges. He's supposed to be a buddy-buddy of Charlie Gonsalez, Skinny Ortega, Chico Medina, all that crowd. But that ain't Pedro."

Eddie and Bill said, "Bet you."

So we pulled up against the curb, said "On your way" to the babe, and put the guy up against the wall. He was clean—no gun, I mean—and no switchblade: just the regular toad-jabber with a blade five inches long, which most of those Puerto Ricans carry, and then claim they had to carry a knife because ze boss, he insists I keep clean ze fingernails.

The character expostulated loudly, talking about Cossacks, and Is This Russia, and saying that he would call up Congressman Marcantonio, and he would have our jobs: the usual line.

But we took his wallet and went over it, and he had his registration card from the draft board, and his driver's license, and a lot of other authentic bits of identification which designated him truly as a very innocent character named, let us say, Claudio Esperanza—a chef by trade, a family man by status, and a mere honestly paroled convict by avocation.

We apologized to Claudio, and he was soon mollified, and one of us borrowed a light from him, and the babe came out of the shadows where she had been tapping her heels nervously, halfway up the block.

We started off in the car again. The boys said, "O.K., Mack. You had seen the mug shots of Pedro Sanchez, down at the House, and you were just holding out on us."

"No," said I, proudly. "I've never seen his mug shots. I just knew it couldn't be the guy."

They wanted to know the secret of my success. I said, "I'll tell you why: the guy was smoking a pipe. I knew it couldn't be Pedro Sanchez."

"Why not?"

"Because," said Uncle Mack, with pyramiding wisdom, "I have seen a lot of hoodlums, one time or another, and I never saw one who smoked a pipe."

I'll leave it up to the jury. I plan to send this clipping right along to Bill Klepper and Eddie Jackson, and when I do, I shall include hysterical comments from all those people who will claim that they knew Al Capone and Legs Diamond and John Dillinger and maybe Billy the Kid, and that all of them were inveterate pipe smokers.

The Time in Which a Person Shall Live 1957–61

(IOWA WESLEYAN COLLEGE COMMENCEMENT)

In my own youth I did not wish to attend college. Bitterly I reacted to the circumstance of our family poverty, and, as the son of a divorced woman, the son of a Jew, the son of a notorious confidence man and swindler, alternately I felt myself pilloried before the gaze of Webster City or set apart from the rest of mankind in a bog of degradation. College, I felt, was a situation acceptable and profitable to those who belonged. I did not belong.

With annoyance, yet with inevitable jealousy, through high school days I witnessed the antics and in some cases, the grotesque posturings of individuals newly—and sometimes over-bearingly—returned from Iowa U., from Drake, from Ames, or even from Northwestern University and some eastern schools. I heard their talk of KKGs, SAEs, Dekes, or Phi Kappa Taus, and to my distorted and pained imagination every college in the world was constructed solely of fraternity and sorority houses crowded round a large gymnasium or field house. This was a time of antiquity, definitely before the existence of the Charleston or the coon-skin coat; but in the notion of at least one youth, every professor cavorted to the strains of *When Francis Dances with Me* or *Stumbling,* and every Dean went dashing in a Stutz Bearcat. It is axiomatic to suppose that age brings the armor of prejudice, but actually there is no prejudice so durable as that of the young.

The teen-age years had fetched along certain triumphs as well as certain disgraces; and having written, at the age of seventeen, a story which won the Des Moines *Register*'s state-wide short story contest, and having written also many editorials for the same Des Moines *Register*, I found myself, in the belated conclusion of high school activity, to be fair game for an attempt at proselyting. It was suggested by two Iowa colleges that I might benefit from exposure to their curricula. It was hinted that certain scholarship funds might be made available; but I declined to accept. I had all the inflexibility of the very earliest Wesleyans and not one shred of the tolerance manifested by some.

It was all of twelve years later, when at the age of thirty-one I was first invited to lecture at the University of Iowa, that I came to the somewhat reluctant awareness that college might conceivably partake of elements other than Yale boys on the prowl and Vassar girls on the loose.

Eventually, middle-aged and a little toil-worn and a little war-worn, I sat in the garden at Sarah Lawrence and watched my daughter walk proudly and briskly to receive her diploma, and realized that there was a certain treasure which had never been a part of my own life, and never would be.

Tolstoy points out emphatically and with drama that there is no end and no beginning. He traces the restless activity of the current, the wave moving beneath the seas' satin, formed originally on no specific shore, whipped into being by no particular wind, its original impulse shapeless and unclassified, beyond name or identity. And thus a man who never walked a campus is guilty of the most idle and inane speculation, if he tries to consider the form, material and result or accomplishment of his unlived life wherein the classic ivy did grow, the chapel prayer was intoned, the lecture and the rule and the tradition did hold their effect. . . . Again, it is Tolstoy's wave, in the ocean of personal time which laps around each of us.

There can be no reckoning with, or evaluation of, a thing which perhaps never existed to begin with.

At least I must confess to this: a childish masculine emptiness when the football season rolls around and I have no team to cry over.

Going vicariously into the past, of course, and listening through the decades with the ears of one's friends, it is possible to be affected by many Billy Phelpses and many Copeys. Thus, through identification with others (until one learns to so identify himself, he is only half alive and not functioning truly as a part of humanity) I was one of those who sat in a certain storied classroom on a certain warm morning, and heard George Santayana speak his immortal line, "Gentlemen, it is Spring," and saw him walk across the room and take his hat and go out the door to Italy, never to return except perhaps in his rarest imaginings.

From the strictly practical point of view, there is only one reason for, and one purpose in, the process of so-called higher education; and that is a preparation for existence. Yet I am sentimental enough to believe that there should be a dream and legend along with the acquired fact.

The force expended by Man in search and study is as compelling as the magnetism of the planets themselves. By this token an elder institution distributes an influence not to be found in a younger one. Many of us believe sincerely that the power of human breathing and living and thought permeates existing, if inanimate objects, in some manner not to be destroyed by the mere passage of time, but probably enhanced. It stains beneficently into walls and buildings and books, into the very trees which tower calmly from a well-kept lawn. According to this theory, it lies there, stored as the juice of electricity would be stored, waiting, but restless and eager. Then come the fresh and the young, to meditate within a shade made sacred by other meditations before them, to bury their faces in books sainted by long and frequent perusal, to give the yell, repeat the litany, sing the song chanted in the long ago by tongues inactive today. It is unlikely that every individual could catalog, or even sense, these nobilities as they accrue during the very hour of accretion, but they do come forth, and thus enrich the sensitive.

How often have you gone into a house, and thought, *I couldn't possibly live in this house?* It is not necessarily that the floors were disordered or that the draperies hurt the eyes; but it was emanation, perhaps a contrary and malevolent one. And again, how often have you gone into a room and thought, *I feel a contentment here. Perhaps I am suddenly keenly aware of an ambition I did not recognize before.* Once more, the matter of emanation—the great good charge of the Past, put into carpets, windowpanes, the very wood—locked and stored, waiting to steal forth and wrap and aid you.

Iowa Wesleyan is, and should be, aware of its own legend—there has been time enough for that. So often the elder vines bear the best fruits. . . . Parenthetically, let me say that I have been to Oxford, and I have been to Heidelberg, and also I have seen the University of Miami. Really there is no comparison.

One looks at you now, the cleanest and newest detachment to join a parade of graduates who have come trooping from this college during the past one hundred and nineteen years, and he thinks: Why did you come here, and what did you find, and what will you do with it? It is natural to ask these questions, yet they are all imponderable. Fate, or a supposed deliberate choice (which in turn, of course, had its roots in Fate) led you to come here; and Fate affected you while you were here, and will rule with strength after you depart—a Fate which not all intended purpose or sagacity may ever controvert.

Some of you came through motives shallow or selfish, and some stepping along arm-in-arm with a firm ideal which has walked beside you since childhood. You found here, perhaps, a tonic excitement, disappointment and anguish, definition and direction. Possibly you found a wound and then the salve to put upon it, just as you will encounter all these things in some other form through years ahead. Some of you made enemies, some discovered loves, some learned, some did not learn, and never will. But it is not without reason that the symbol of scholarship has long been a torch; some of you will carry it, and again it will all be worthwhile.

In this middle twentieth century, peculiar and terrible burdens are put upon the young. I think that as a generation you and your immediate predecessors through the past sixteen years have met and are meeting your obligation with enormous fortitude, astonishing resiliency. With nuclear fission a horrifying accomplished fact for the first time in all development, I remember that the immediate reaction of the young was frantic resentment. *You can't do this to us!* every perplexed, enraged young man or girl was crying by voice or in spirit. Then life itself took over, and the adjustment came about.

I recall coming into the living room of our home in New York one evening, and finding my own young with their friends, and in some cases, mates already selected, sitting about, gloomily condemning the future and roundly cursing the past and that present which seemed to have given birth to such diabolical changes.

Well, Bill and I are agreed upon this—we are never going to bring any children into this world, was the declaration of my daughter. *Neither are we,* said Pete and Viv, and there was more of the same.

I said, What in tarnation (or maybe I said something else) is going on here? How stupid can you get?

Well enough for you, they all cried, bridling. *You didn't have to face life under such conditions. Matters were comparatively simple for all generations which preceded ours. But now—*

I said wearily, Oh, pshaw (or maybe I said something else). I'll tell you this, my pretty little pets: people are going to go on having babies until the last universal thunder-burst sends its mushroom-shaped cloud of smoke all the way to Mars and back again. You just watch.

In a very few years they were not only watching, they were working at it. They've all got scads of children today.

Personally, I should just as soon have my grandchildren blown into Kingdom Come by some new-fangled bomb or missile, as to have their little heads hacked off by the blunt sword of Tamerlane or Genghis Khan. Examine the old records and translate them into your own idiom.

And we did take that city, and there were an hundred thousand people, and all of these we put to the sword.

We must not forget that there were ugly pyramids of skulls on the Asiatic plains long before Hiroshima or Nagasaki.

And then we destroyed their city, and left not one stone upon another.

Let us not forget how the site of the vanished, eradicated Carthage was sown to salt so that nothing would grow there. Radiation, perhaps?

Oh, you bold and adjustable young, go on and have your babies!

Amidst the clicking buzz of certain riddles and robots, your lives must necessarily be spent, and your illusions tailored to the size of the world and the age. Most certainly this is not a stagnant moment in history, and I see no stagnant waters immediately ahead. You may find your time aggravating, and even extremely hazardous, but I do not think that you will find it dull.

In manner of ritual, it is customary for the elder visitor, in addressing students at the culmination of their college careers, and in the Commencement season, to offer some rule or formula, by observation of which the beginners in this *mayhemistic* sport called Life may better equip themselves. I had no magic code to offer to my own children, and I see no reason why I should pretend to speak such a message to you.

I have seen a great deal of life, and a great deal of death; and the whole tangled mess of human activity is not always a pretty business, but I find it eternally fascinating, and I hope that you will as well.

In wonder and mystery we return in thought to that gaunt
Illinois man who, one hundred years ago today, was occupying
the White House, and had already become a friend of your
own James A. Harlan. Some Fate or Force there must be
which determines the time in which a person shall live. Lincoln belonged then; he would not belong now.

Some of us may hold to the belief that we belonged in
Lincoln's time rather than our own. We can speculate readily
about which Past might have been kindest to us, which Past
we might have been kindest to . . . but we can never even
imagine about where we might belong in the future.

A language is spoken today which falls glibly from the lips
of teen-agers as well as from the lips of men in white coats
and men with white hopes—men with trifocal spectacles and
with trifocal brains—men who would be willing to sing a song
of alleviation rather than one of destruction if urgency allowed
them to do so. The *I-ya! Ma-ni ni-yan wa!* of sullen and
sinned-against Plains Indians might have been more compre-
hensible to the ears of one of Lincoln's friends than the
language he would hear now, were his body and his wisdom
tailored to our time: the speech of atomic reactors, niobrium,
Levitation melting, cermets, klystron, Fibrafax, Zirconium,
clathrates, and Waveguide tubes. We are pickled in our own
electronic fluids, though we chose to be so pickled and made
the pickle ourselves; it was the slow and increasingly intricate
compilation by cooks who came before us. But we must accept
our own responsibility in our own time.

Billy Graham constantly exhorts us to get back to God—
which is good, sound, safe, sane advice in any time or clime.
But we are just as apt to find Him in a hissing lilac-colored
bath which looks like a liquid but is actually a solid melted
into a gas, as the neighbors of Abraham Lincoln were apt to
find God in a kettle of home-made soft soap. He is forever
promising yet provocative, enduring yet elusive; and nowadays
the elusive thing seems to be the only thing that is eternal.

There was nothing permanent about the Past when it was

the Present, and it is a falsehood to suggest or believe that there was. The only possible permanency attained by the past is in the split second when it is altered from the present to the past, and thus becomes irrevocable. We and our leaders—leaders in the main appointed by us or determined by us, and thus believed to be our choice in leaders—are accused constantly of evanescence and volatile alteration of purpose, when after all evanescence and uncertainty are merely a way of life, and the most normal one which a discerning man might consider, in the light of Humanity's established behavior.

Lincoln again . . . it is customary to consider Lincoln's every word and deed as cut in stone or cast in bronze. Mankind understands his name when mankind knows little else about him. People embrace the commonly accepted legends while still unaware of the complexity of the fact. We are apt to think of Lincoln as a kind of static god, remote and pontifical, deliberating on problems of State, weeping with bereaved mothers, preserving a saintly dignity of purpose, a saintly identity of purpose throughout his entire career.

Why, he changed his opinion and his plan whenever new circumstances rose to confront him! He did not fear to pursue a course in 1862 which he had declared he would not pursue only a year and a half before. He had a fiery and encompassing imagination; even on the last day of his life Lincoln dreamed of a vast development—it would be called a GI project today, a plan never realized or put into operation seriously by his followers—whereby the ex-soldiers might be presented with an opportunity for capitalizing on the mineral riches of the West. "I am going to try to attract them to the hidden wealth of our mountain ranges, where there is room enough for all," he declared, only twelve hours before he lay bleeding. . . .

It's all still here, Mr. Lincoln. The utter silence of stark fear, the relieved gasp of victory; the clear understanding of the sleepless youth on his bed, and the bumbling confusion of the statesmen in Washington; the classic restraint of old people who have seen too much and are tired of what they have seen; the sage solemnity of the baby whose wise eyes reflect secrets unknown to us, and which cannot be told to us when the child grows older. . . . The young man is still lugging his camera to record the foibles, grotesqueries or gentilities which excite him; the young woman is still determined to write her book. There is yet a peril in the blizzard, and a promise in the peach-colored dawn. The birds dance and feed, Mr. Lincoln, the corn fattens in its season.

Our sins are many but again they are the sins of youth and not of obsolescence. We are still a Nation where the hunted come, and more of them came yesterday. They looked at the food in the markets, and they were awed.

Roadways are crowded in the city, Mr. Lincoln; and the poor are there, but there are poor in the country too. And there are the rich and the selfish, and some rich who are not at all selfish, and some poor who are mildewed with selfishness, just as you knew them, sir. There is a parable in bitter smoke above the towns, above the trucks and the ships, for him who would seek it there; but some are never able to find a parable anywhere, nor would wish to. And the mystery of the stars still makes a man a vassal, much as he hates to admit it. And the germs quarrel, and the bodies sicken and die, and the bodies are put away, just as you saw them put away in your eighteen-sixties. The man turns to look at the girl, and he follows her, and then they are together; and soon there is the pressure of a new life.

The dreams are ever around us, Mr. Lincoln. There is a medicine in the breeze and an enzyme beneath the sod; and we still have a yearning and a gallantry, sir.

Christmas Card from Jupiter 1962

Comes a Christmas card from Jupiter, Florida, and thus along with it a string of memories.

The names *Hal* and *Etta* are on the card . . . when I see *Bowman*, I think not of Jupiter Beach. Instead my ears are filled suddenly with the roar of engines. I recall a past in which the modern Brig. Gen. H. W. Bowman (Ret.) once commanded the 401st Bomb Group (H).

He nourished a grudge against the Army Air Forces, because the tour of duty was then twenty-five missions; and he had done twenty-four when he got kicked upstairs. No twenty-fifth mission for him—he was never able to finish up. They wouldn't let him fly combat after he went over from England to France and to USSTAF, to serve as Deputy Chief of Staff for Tooey Spaatz.

. . . He had an unusual background: before he went into the Service he had been a schoolmaster. One day he was walking home from school, and he looked up and saw an Army airplane buzzing by. "That's what I'd really like to do," he thought. From then on that was It.

Bowman was in my own age bracket, which meant that he was twenty years older than a lot of the people he flew with. But he had acquired a vast fund of patience, sympathy, human understanding, and a staunch if gentle philosophy.

So they knew just what they were doing when they engaged him as General Ted Curtis's deputy. In later months of the

war I got hauled in to do a job for USSTAF—one which had
nothing to do with my official status as a correspondent, or
my unofficial status as a 50-caliber machine-gunner. The new
work threw me into daily, sometimes hourly, contact with
Colonel Bowman.

There was bound to be a rivalry, a conflict of opinion. As
commander of the 401st, Bowman had acquired the respect
and affection of his group which any capable commander holds.
To his mind the 401st had never done anything wrong; never
could.

My own tastes were tailored entirely within the structure
and tradition of the 305th Bomb Group (H). I had gone
there to fly when the outfit was coloneled by an intent, chunky
individual who answered to the name of Curtis Emerson Le-
May. Thus I had seen a manipulation of command and operations second to none.

Since I failed to genuflect when the 401st was mentioned,
Colonel Bowman took it upon himself to protract our little
feud from time to time. I responded heartily.

The routine was: "Just look at that bad landing! They never
did anything like that in the 305th, did they, Mack?"

Or: "I observe a pool of hydraulic fluid on the hard-stand
under that aircraft, Colonel. You never had any leaky hydraulic
equipment in the 401st, did you?"

These conflicting representations were set forth to our mutual evil delight, and probably *ad nauseam* insofar as other
people were concerned.

There dawned one particularly bright day in early May,
1945, when Bowman whispered to me, "How would you like
to take off for the United States in a B-17 tomorrow?" Which
was about like asking one of our local Siesta Key urchins
whether he'd like to go into Nan's Candy Shop and just help
himself for free. The colonel had to go to the Pentagon on
a particular little chore; he had invited me to go with him.
The blossoming chestnut trees of France shivered and danced
for joy.

Next morning before sunrise we were on our way to Orly in a staff car. It was Standing Operating Procedure, whenever a Very Big Bug needed to fly back to the States, to furnish him with an aircraft and crew from one of the groups in the Eighth AF. A rotational deal, of course. They took turns.

Our aircraft was waiting for us down at the end of the flight line at Orly, and I watched its stabilizer sticking up through the mist. "Colonel," I said. Bowman was examining some papers he'd taken out of his briefcase. "What does a triangle mean, when it's painted on the vertical stabilizer of a B-17?"

Hal said, "Means First Bombardment Division. Any damn fool knows that."

"Yes, sir," I said. "And in addition, Colonel, what does a G mean—the letter G—when it's painted in the middle of that triangle?"

"I haven't the slightest idea," said Hal. "What does it mean?"

I replied coyly, "It means the 305th Bomb Group, Colonel."

He threw his papers all over the back seat of the car. "For God's sake," he cried. "Do you mean we've got to listen to *that*, all the way across the Atlantic?"

Out of the sixty-nine available groups in the Eighth Air Force, they had picked the 305th to carry us home. . . .

Well, we got down there to the 17; our car stopped, and there appeared several happy faces . . . names like Brooks, Kleppinger, Dillon—some I knew, some I didn't. They approached, grinning as they saluted Bowman, fairly beside themselves with glee at the thought of TDY which carried them to the fabled Land of Hard-shelled Eggs and Soft-shelled Ladies. Under the circumstances they would have beamed upon Hal if his name had been Göring.

. . . They were not alone. Behind them waited a skinny major in a uniform which hung on him like a sheet on a broomstick. His name was Lenfest, and he was trying very hard to preserve soldierly deportment; but one look at that pale face, and you didn't know whether he'd fall over backward or forward.

(He had been isolated in German territory, and he'd tried to obey the old injunction which they always gave us in Briefing: at all costs avoid contact with the Hitler Youth. But that's just the bunch he ran into. He tried to get away from those little wolves, screaming after him in a pack . . . they were younger and fleeter, they ran him down. Strange thing. Those ex-*Kriegsgefangner* types all looked somewhat alike. You could tell them a mile off, at that stage of the game.)

He wanted to go to the States. Most awfully did he want to go home to the States! He had heard that someone from USSTAF was flying over in this B-17, and he thought, Maybe . . . if there was room for him. Why, maybe . . . maybe . . .

Hal heard the major's story. His face didn't change expression. You could witness the terribly disappointed attitude of the air crew. They'd been hoping that perhaps some generous-hearted commander would find room for the hitchhiker. . . .

"Major," asked Bowman, "do you have any authorization to proceed by air?"

"No, sir," said the miserable Lenfest. "I don't. Matter of fact, my orders are cut for me to proceed to a certain port, and there board a surface vessel on a certain date. But—I *have* got orders for the States, and— Well, I thought—if you had room—"

Colonel Bowman swung himself up through the waist hatch. "Most assuredly I have no authority to tell you that you may accompany me in this aircraft."

Then the genial voice came singing back out of the waist; because Hal was determined to fly the 17 himself, and was already climbing toward the cockpit. . . .

"But if I were in your shoes, Major, I know what I'd do. . . ."

Lenfest's thin face was one vast grin. I watched the boys getting him established, with an extra parachute and so on, then squeezed my way up into the cockpit. Bowman was settling himself in the left-hand seat. I sat down in the idiot seat opposite him.

Hal smiled. "We may all find ourselves peeling potatoes, when we land in the States. But at least that kid will *be there.*"

. . . I give you a toast, ladies and gentlemen.

Brigadier General H. W. Bowman (Retired) of Jupiter, Florida. God bless him.

The Idea of
Singing
1953

The book had a picture of a choir-boy on it—a boy who stood with music spread between his hands—and his open mouth showed that he was singing. I thought that the book must be very old, for it was rubbed and frayed; its paper-wrapped-board covers showed the stains of use.

But it was something which Mother had bought when she was young. She treasured the carols contained therein, and played them with mystic dignity. She found other Christmas carols printed in magazines sometimes, and she cut these out and pasted them on the book's blank pages.

Now I was twelve, and sang with an assurance I'd not owned when younger. My voice had not yet begun to grate with the roughness of puberty. I liked the sound of my voice, and sent it out lustily whenever I worked or walked. Neighbors said aloud, "Well, here comes a happy boy," which was not always true. Often I was wretchedly unhappy inside. Still I kept singing.

. . . This was a fairy-tale Christmas Eve, with ice crusting the shaggy bark of maples, and belated bobsleds jingling past, the farmers' shaggy shapes all muffled and mittened as they clutched their cold reins, the big rough dogs trotting soberly through darkness behind or ahead, as if they felt the wonder of the season.

Bring me meat and bring me wine,
Bring me pine logs hither—
Thou and I shall see him dine
When we bear them thither.

When Good King Wenceslaus had warmed and printed the path to the poor man's door, I said shyly, "I wish I could do that."

Mother sat with her big-knuckled fingers resting loosely on the keys. "You mean—take things to the poor? Do you wish that you were a saint, like Wenceslaus?"

"No, I mean, like the ancient waits that sang this song . . . sing from door to door. I wish I could do that."

"Why don't you, son?"

"Guess I will."

It seemed a daring idea. I knew of no other boy in Webster City who had gone through the snow, singing carols. Vaguely it occurred that folks would laugh, but in tasting the romance of this notion I was immune to ridicule.

Mother said that she'd walk along with me, and as long as she stayed in the background I didn't object. We went on a narrow path shoveled between tossed snowbanks, down the slope past the next street.

"Where are you going to sing? At the Halls?"

I shook my head.

"Here?" she asked presently, halting under high bare poplars in front of the Quackenbush house.

"No," and I led her on. At last I stopped in front of the Jones home, a block farther down. Partly I wished to sing here because the wide white house had always represented a manor or castle, and beveled glass around the door shone with the silky fire of diamonds. And partly because I'd heard that old Mr. Julius Jones was dying. Someone should sing to him, it seemed.

Mother hid herself in starlit wastes, and I waded up to the barberry bushes below the porch. I sang "Good King

Wenceslaus" again, and before I was well into the second stanza
I could see people coming to the windows. Relatives were there,
keeping vigil. Presently Dr. Bob Beck came out on the porch
and stood with his hands in his pockets, hearing me through.
I thought I had never sung better, and at least he was patient
about it.

When I was finished he tossed a fifty-cent piece into the
snow.

"Oh, no," I cried. Fifty cents was a very important piece
of money, but I hadn't realized that the waits of elder times
were beggars. I dug the money out of the snow and ran up
and gave it to Dr. Beck. This surprised him very much, and he
protested. But young Mr. and Mrs. Robert Jones were already
packing some candy in a cornucopia of holly paper, and they
came out and insisted that I accept the candy.

I put it under my arm with glee, and soon whistled a signal
to Mother, out in the snow. She came from deeper shadows,
and we started away.

She giggled a little. "Imagine! Dr. Beck trying to give you
money—"

"He didn't understand," I said generously. "He didn't understand that I didn't want any money. He couldn't understand
that it was—just the idea of singing Christmas carols—"

"Of course," Mother agreed heartily, breathing out frost and
spirit into the night. "Just the idea of singing."

They Loved Me
in Korea
1951

In the showery dusk of Wake Island we heard that some passengers had come in from Guam and were to board our Stratocruiser for the long flight to Hawaii; we didn't know who the passengers were.

I found out, in the middle of the night.

There are berths in those Stratocruisers but not enough to go around. Thus lucky people who booked their passages well in advance secured the berths; I was one of these. I still didn't know whether I would use the berth or not. In a war you grow accustomed to sleeping in your clothes.

After we had taken off (two hours late, because of a faulty recognition light in the left wing-tip) we still entertained hope of connecting with Flight 806 in Hawaii the next morning.

The stewardess came to check about berths. "Do you want yours made up now?"

"Thanks—I'm going to doze in the seat awhile."

She said, "I'll pull it down anyway. You can use it later if you see fit." The polished panel was tilted, and I was cautioned not to bump my head in rising from the seat.

. . . It was midnight. I had been sound asleep. I went forward to the washroom, dashed cold water on my face, and drifted down the darkened aisle toward a stairway which led to the bar-lounge. Light came up this circular staircase, and with it came the resounding voice of Al Jolson.

Jolson and his accompanist, Harry Akst, were the passengers

who had come from Guam. Akst is a genial, thoughtful man
with plump cheeks and doe-eyes. Long ago he wrote "Baby
Face"—I think—and "Dinah" and a lot of other songs.

They sat on the broad divan opposite the stair; Al Jolson
was doing nine-tenths of the talking. He still wore his pride-
and-joy—nobody could get him to take it off—a light-weight
coverall with Air Force insignia stamped on the left sleeve. He
had the suit unzipped in front: through this aperture pro-
truded folds of the gaudiest gold-black-white-and-green shirt
ever designed by wild-eyed Pacific natives.

The years had done things to him. Now he looked something like bald Jimmy Doolittle, something like that character
Bull Montana who used to act in the old films. His dome
was covered with a gloss of close-clipped gray hair, he was
deeply tanned. I don't know where on earth he got all that
sun . . . Korea was covered with clouds much of the time.

Jolson's dark eyes snapped behind their spectacles, he brandished a highball glass in his hand. The pretty little stewardess
stood enthralled. Opposite sat Frank Gibney, the Life-Time
man from Tokyo. Maybe two or three other passengers were
still extant and drinking at that hour . . . I can only be sure
about Jolson.

Conversationally he bounded like an eager puppy from the
Korean War back to Dockstader's Minstrels, from Dockstader's
Minstrels to Georgie Jessel, from Jessel to New York, to girls,
to Hollywood, to World War II in Italy, to Eddie Cantor, to
girls, to Broadway, to Korea again. People wanted to keep buying drinks but we had an awful tussle with Jolson every time
money was mentioned. He kept pressing crumpled dollar bills
upon the stewardess. When he ran out of dollar bills he cashed
a traveler's check.

"Do you know MacArthur? What, you don't know Mac-
Arthur! MacArthur's the greatest guy alive. He's wonderful, he's
fantastic. I spent an hour with him. It was really about an
hour and a half. He's a real human being. You know what
the people of the United States ought to do? Every night

when they go to bed and say their prayers (if they don't say
prayers, they ought to say their prayers) they ought to get
down on their knees and thank God three times for Mac-
Arthur!"

When he spoke it was with the rattled running accents of a
loquacious taxi-driver. He puckered his forehead in emphasis,
he worked his mouth freely and willingly . . . his mouth was
nearly a blur, he talked so fast and so much.

He said, "And Mrs. MacArthur: she's the greatest woman
alive—except for my own dear wife, God bless her heart and
soul. . . . Batting averages—imagine! Mrs. MacArthur knows
batting averages. We were talking about the Tigers, and she
was giving me their batting averages. What a woman! Imagine
her knowing a thing like that. She comes into a room, cool
and beautiful—she's got dignity like a queen. She does all the
social things the general is maybe too busy to do, or too much
occupied with other thoughts and responsibilities. She's terrific.
Everybody ought to get down on their knees every night when
they go to bed, and thank God for Mrs. MacArthur!"

He said, "They loved me in Korea. Did I tell you how many
concerts I did—how many shows? How many was it, Harry?
A hundred and forty-two, Harry says. Think of that—I did a
hundred and forty-two shows for those boys, God bless them
all."

He described his brief Korean trip with considerable richness
of detail. Before long some of the details contradicted statements
he had made previously, yet no one paid any attention to that.
Al was not a stickler for fact. He was putting on a show.

He was putting on a show the moment he rose in the morning. The show was a triumph of the past, a boast of the
present, a rousing invocation to the future. He was On, whenever he washed his face, or when he was in the can. He was
On when he was eating, On when he dozed. He knew that
he was one of the great entertainers of the world. He felt
it obligatory to entertain everyone within sight and reach, so

long as he had a flicker of consciousness. I wonder what his
dreams were like.

Proximity didn't tell me. He slept in my berth that night,
I slumbered in the seat beneath. The first thing I became
aware of, as we approached Hawaii through rippling white and
yellow clouds, was Jolson's khaki-coveralled legs sliding over
the edge of the berth, to be followed by Jolson's busy khaki
body and his tanned head.

"What a day!" he said. "What a business! They say we're
two hours late already. They say we won't connect with that
other flight for L.A. What do you bet we do? What do you
bet I get them to hold the flight?"

A throng of uniformed generals, Public Information Officers
and enlisted photographers moved toward the gate, after the
steps were pushed into place at John Rodgers airport.

Jolson danced to meet them. He moved as if taking a
perpetual curtain-call . . . applause was hauling him on stage
again. He trotted proudly from the wings—full of dynamic
nonsense, full of brags and fabrications and strange errors, but
filled also with some delightful force which made you feel
that the world was just a little gayer than you had previously
estimated it. He made you believe that life was not a care
but a plaything—a substance to be shaken and dealt and shuf-
fled and mixed, with spiciest satisfaction.

His vibrant chatter resounded; he was telling them about
Korea. Perils were getting a little worse, now—the enemy fire
a little thicker. By this time he had done "a hundred and
forty-five shows."

(Banish from your mind that picture of Jolson crawling
warily through front line mud between machine-gun nests. The
armed forces take better care of their guests than that, especially when the guests are admired and respected and—let's
face it—elderly.)

But Al had indeed strained himself in order to go and sing
to the boys. He had been flown here and there, and sometimes

there was some shooting in the areas. Harry Akst told me later that he and Jolson had much more cause to be frightened in Italy, during World War II, when American batteries fired several rounds in the direction of one of their USO transport planes.

That day in Hawaii was a comedy of errors and a cause for perpetual wonder about the kind of maintenance managed by certain commercial airlines, at least in their hard-luck seasons.

It would be impossible for us to use the reservations we held on Flight 806, people said. Jolson's outcry rose above our united protest as we lingered amid barricades of Public Health, Immigration and Customs. Flight 806 must depart on schedule; the officials were adamant. It was too bad we had been delayed at Wake, but they might not hold the Los Angeles flight a moment longer.

Accordingly the big silver chicken went ambling away while we readied our baggage for examination. We were not yet out of Customs, and Al was still holding one of his informal levees amid flashlight cameras at the door, when Flight 806 came grunting back with two props feathered.

Once again plans were hastily reorganized. Our own air-craft, on which we had flown from the western Pacific, would be prepared for departure at 2:30 P.M. Al was led away with Harry Akst, to sing to the new Purple Hearts in a military hospital. I enjoyed a nap at a small hotel near Waikiki, where a group of passengers were conveyed by the apologetic company. Returning to the field about 1:30 P.M., I found a jubilant Jolson reciting the successes of his hospital trip, and alternately swearing at these insufferable delays.

We hadn't seen the half of it yet. Through clear gold sun-light we thronged to the airplane. Most of the passengers were loaded with flowery leis, put up in cellophane packages to carry back to the States; steward and stewardesses were to have one hell of a time tagging and sorting and storing that stuff.

We taxied, we sat in sweat. The pilot and flight engineer were experiencing trouble with Number One engine; they ran

it up again and again and let it fall off. After twenty minutes
of this stewing turmoil, the captain's voice came to us apolo-
getically over the amplifier. He was sorry, he said, but he
had detected some bad spark plugs. We would have to go back
to the line while these repairs were made.

"I might add," he said, "that, as soon as we are off the
ground, the company will try to make restitution to you people
who have so patiently endured these repeated delays. The bar
will be open, and everything will be on the house."

We weren't airborne with our new spark plugs until 5:15
P.M. The ocean roared blue beneath us. Platters of delicious
Hawaiian dainties were passed around: tasty bits of pork,
toasted shrimps, and all with the accompanying fragrance of
olives, pineapple, and glazed fruits. We sat with cocktail glasses
in our hands, munching and sipping, dreaming of the landfall
to come.

There was talk of the theater. Someone invoked the name of
Walter Winchell.

"Winchell!" roared Al Jolson, brandishing his fist under my
nose. "Look! Winchell!—Walter Winchell!"

I thought he was pretending that I was Winchell, and ducked
accordingly.

"It's his hand," Harry Akst explained.

"Look at my little finger—"

The finger was bent and misshapen. It had been broken and
had healed in crooked fashion.

"Winchell," cried Al Jolson. "That's where I hit him! Didn't
you ever hear about that?" He recited details with lengthy relish. "It was when I was married to my third wife, Ruby
Keeler. It was about twenty years ago. . . . I called up my
lawyer (he was one of the best friends I had in the world)
and I said to him—just like that—'I'm going to kill a guy tonight.' 'Now, Al, don't you do anything foolish. . . .' 'I'm
going to kill a guy.' That was what I said. . . . There we were,
sitting in our seats at the fight, and Winchell came down and

leaned over me. He put his hand on my shoulder like a friend. He said, 'How are you, Al?' I stood up and swung."

(Winchell wrote a most remarkable column the day after Al died. It was too bad Al couldn't read it . . . well, maybe he did see it, somehow or other. It ended up tearfully: "There is a new star shining in Heaven tonight," or words to that effect.)

The stewardess came whispering. . . . Don't say anything now, we were told: it would be announced officially to the passengers soon. But—had we noticed?—Number Three was running rocky; they couldn't seem to do anything about it.

We were not yet at the Equal Point between Hawaii and Los Angeles. Soon we went winging back toward Oahu Island, with sunset staining our right-hand windows. We landed again at Rodgers Field about 9 P.M., with Number Three feathered.

The passengers were so filled with good cheer furnished by the company that not one of them complained within our hearing. Now we would have spent a full twenty-four hours in Hawaii before we boarded, on Wednesday morning, the Flight 806 with which originally we planned to connect on Tuesday morning.

Folks trooped down the stairway to the ground, where they were led away by a polite but harried representative of the company, to be furnished with free chits for taxi fare and overnight food and lodging. Jolson lingered aboard, where I still chatted with Harry Akst and one of the crew members.

"These airplane companies," said Al, "they're all alike. Allow me to tell a little story. It seems that the proprietor of a hotel commonly patronized by airplane pilots called up the manager of the company. 'You come over here and take care of your pilots,' said the hotel man. 'They're raising hell. They're chasing all the women guests around through the hallways, from room to room, and they're all in the nude.' 'Who?' says the airplane guy. 'The women or the men?' 'Both,' the hotel man told him. 'Well, in that case, how do you know they're my airplane pilots?' 'I know they're airplane pilots,' said the hotel

man, 'because they got the biggest wrist-watches and the smallest lalapaloozers I ever saw before!'"

He said, "Speaking of hotels, where are you going to stay?"
"I suppose the company has some place where they'll try
to send us."
"Sure they will," said Al. "Some queer little place. Come
on—let's go over to the Royal Hawaiian. It'll cost, but we'll
have comfort. It's a beautiful place. You ever been there before?
It's a beautiful place. Hell, you and I went to the war on our
own dough, didn't we? O.K.—let's stay at the Royal Hawaiian
on our own dough tonight." (We didn't; I wonder if Al ever
knew the difference. When we checked out in the morning we
found that the airplane company had generously taken care
of our rooms for us.)
The rooms were high-ceilinged, wide-windowed. You could
look out over arching thin palms to the fabulous dark beach of
Waikiki. We had three connecting rooms in a row: they were
spacious, and we could yell and wander back and forth.
By this time Al looked exhausted. He didn't want any
more drinks; he said he wanted to get in the sack, but he was
still bubbling to all he met.
"A hundred and fifty shows I did for those kids out there.
They break my heart when I think of them—those kids in
Korea."
He began to laugh again, thinking of the story he had
told about the pilots, back in the airplane. "You know who told
me that story?" and he named a popular contemporary come-
dian. "Do you know him?"
"Yes."
"Do you like him?"
"Yes," I said. "I'm very much indebted to him. He went
to great trouble one time to get me out of a jam when he didn't
really have to."
"I love the guy," said Al. "He's a dear, sweet, wonderful
guy. He's a sweetheart and I love him. But—" He meditated

momentarily. "He'd seduce his own grandmother." Al considered again. "And no doubt *has*," he added contentedly.

"Harry, think of it!" He seemed beating his weary breast as he gazed at the palm trees and the rich fabric of mid-Pacific night beyond. "Think of it! We did a hundred and fifty-two shows out there for those kids. And tomorrow night I will be meeting the most wonderful woman in the world—my dear little wife. 'California, here I come—!'"

I went to bed much later than Al and Harry. I had called friends, and we absorbed drinks, we went here and there to batten on shrimp and pineapple and spareribs. When I woke up there seemed to be leis scattered all over the place.

A car was promised us at 8:00; thus I left my call for 6:45 A.M. and ordered a light breakfast sent up while I took a shower. Sampling this breakfast as I dressed, and hearing no sounds from the rooms beyond, I felt impelled to beat on Jolson's door.

He yelled a welcome. I went in and found him sitting cross-legged in his bed, clad in undershirt and shorts. He was chirping merrily at Akst, who soon came wandering fully dressed from the room beyond.

"It's a beautiful day," said Al. "And this is a beautiful place, this Hawaii. But you can only take it about so long; and right now I have had it long enough. Let's go down and grab some breakfast before that taxi gets here."

He leaped out of bed and into his coveralls. You could see how he fancied those coveralls—official insignia and all. He pulled the zipper up affectionately, he touched the cloth with appreciative hands.

He peered over his black-rimmed spectacles. "Mack, did I tell you how many shows we did out there? I wore this suit all the time. How many was it, Harry?" He didn't give Harry Akst time to say anything. "Something like a hundred and sixty-five shows," said Jolson. "Come on—let's grab a bite."

I told them that I'd see them downstairs, and went back to

pack the small bag I had brought from the airplane. By the time I had visited the hotel desk and paid a bill for extras (and had been surprised by the indulgence of our host, the airplane company)—by the time I had done these things and drifted to the dining room, Jolson and Akst were nearly done breakfasting.

The head waiter had placed them at a strategic table in the wide sunny room with its huge picture-windows. Other guests were regarding their idol with appreciation. I sat down for coffee, and complained about a hangover.

"You got no business to complain about hangovers at your age," Al said. "How old are you? What, only going-on-forty-seven? You're a boy, you're a baby. Look at me—I'm sixty-four—would you believe it? But let me tell you something: I can run the hundred in twelve. Believe it or not, I can run the hundred yards in twelve seconds! Ask Harry here, if you don't believe me."

Harry Akst smiled with his blue-brown eyes. You could understand that he loved Al Jolson; he was happy merely being with him—happy playing his accompaniments—happy listening to the eternal ebullient flow which would have exhausted lesser people or less patient ones.

"If you *can* run the hundred yards in twelve," I said, "you oughtn't to."

Now we were walking away from the dining room toward a distant corner of the lobby where our baggage waited.

"Look at those stairs," said Al. "Look at that guy—he's walking up those stairs. Me—I run up stairways. I go up a stairway—I can't walk up—I got to run. Want to see me run up those stairs?" We restrained him.

The bright morning, the prospect of Los Angeles at night: these were a tonic to Al. He poured out the tale of Korea again; he went back to World War II and traveled twenty-two thousand miles through the South Atlantic, the Mediterranean, the many Pacific islands . . . he went further into the past

. . . he was with the Shuberts . . . he was earning ten thousand dollars a week in Hollywood. . . .

At John Rodgers Airport he bounded from the car. Smiles broke loose behind the counters, among passengers and others in the lobby. It was fascinating, but tiring. Part of it I think was jealousy: a lot of us ordinary mortals were bound to be envious of anyone who could function on all cylinders through every tour of duty, like the engine of a New York police car. . . . Never a rest, never a let-up. Life poured the gas into him; he kept running on.

I spotted three Air Force personnel in grimy coveralls, standing near a souvenir counter in the lobby, and went over to speak to them. They turned out to be some of Buster Briggs' boys from the 307th Bomb Group at Okinawa. They were en route to the States on emergency leave. The tallest man—I took him to be the aircraft commander, though he wore no insignia on cap or coveralls—told me soberly that his father was dying of cancer; but brightened to tell also that he would be greeting a new son in Tampa; the baby had been born after he left Mac-Dill Field.

Jolson came circulating near us, slapping a folded newspaper against his leg, humming as he walked.

"How would you guys like to meet Al Jolson?"

"Boy!"

I called Al over to us. I began the introductions, and then realized that I didn't know the names. "Mr. Jolson, these are B-29 people, just going back to the States from Okinawa. This is—" I looked at the tall young man questioningly. "Major—?" I began.

"Just a sergeant." Grinning, he took the hand Al extended.

"You're a major to *me*," said Al Jolson.

This time we made it to the American mainland. Through long evening hours we droned into the northeast. Our dinner was served on trays. We sat in the forward compartment be-

yond the washrooms. A rumor had reached us that the Louis-
Charles fight would be picked up on the radio.

Harry Akst recited tales of elder Tin Pan Alleys. Jolson devoted himself to a little pocket edition of my novel *Wicked
Water*, which I had picked up at the airport newsstand. He
wanted it autographed.

"I'll send you one of the regular editions."

"No, you won't," said Al. "You'll forget. Authors are always
forgetting to send the books they promised they would. You
autograph this right now," and so I did.

The fight was broadcast as promised. The radio operator managed a skillful hook-up between his outside channel and the
interior amplifying system. We sat or stood, peering intently at
the little cup in the ceiling from which the broadcast issued.

Al had taken our bets. I can't remember how Harry bet, but
Jolson bet me three dollars to one, on Louis. He insisted that
these were the prevailing odds. It sounds a little phony, now
that I think of it.

His forehead was more corrugated than ever; he gasped,
grunted, groaned, shook his head repeatedly as he heard the
hammering the aging Joe Louis received.

"It's the death of a champion," said Jolson. "It is an awful
thing to see a champion die. You know, one of the fighters I
used to own, he—" Then the next round would begin to sputter
from the amplifier. Jolson would hear the bell, and would follow
operations intently, seeming to lead and feint and clinch with
the distant toiling fighters.

We were very nearly landed at Los Angeles Municipal Airport before the fight was over, and before Jolson dug up two
crushed dollar bills from the recesses of his zipper-suit to pay
me off. "This is all I got. I owe you a buck."

*California, here I come . . . come on! Open, open, open up
that Golden Gate. . . .* He was back again, safe and active,
bursting with the triumph of his ordeal.

"Listen," he said, "it was the most wonderful thing I ever
did to myself, to go to Korea! They said they couldn't fly me out

there; Secretary Johnson had made some kind of a rule or something. I said, 'Listen, I'll tell you what I'll do: my marijuana crop did pretty well this year, and I got the dough. I'll buy our own tickets, that's what I'll do.' I'm sure glad I went. Those are wonderful boys out there. I wish you could have heard them in that place where I opened up with 'Sonny Boy.' You should have heard those kids. . . . Did I tell you about General MacArthur? I spent two hours with him. He's got a wonderful wife, too. Well, so have I—I've got a wonderful, wonderful wife. She will be here at the airport to meet me, God bless her pretty little face! I guess I don't deserve anything as wonderful as she is—not an old guy like me—sixty-two. But I am not sixty-two years old in body. I'm pretty nearly like a kid. Did I tell you—I can run the hundred in eleven-five! A guy has got to keep in shape, or he couldn't do what I've just done: go out there to Korea and Japan and sing pretty nearly two hundred shows!"

The landing, the final taxiing, the steps against the side. Then a crowd, huddled and breaking apart and running forward as Jolson skipped to the ground, bare-headed, brisk in his treasured coveralls. Everyone was beaming amid the puff of flashlight bulbs. We saw the little adopted son in his cowboy suit; we saw the pretty young wife; we heard Jolson's voice yapping in ecstasy.

There was a momentary tangle at the last steel gate, once we had passed through the underground ramp. Al Jolson's face worked close in the press. His eyes sparkled behind their lenses, his voice was rapping glad and shrill.

"So long!" he cried. "I'll see you in New York. I'll pay you that buck I owe you!"

But he won't.

Layne's Pink Lady
1964

Never yet have I observed what I would consider incontrovertible evidence of the survival of the human entity. I do believe in apparitions, because I have had such experience; but I believe along with the late Harry Price that the charge and power of a human being may be locked in surrounding inanimate materials during life—in walls, floors, trees, ceilings. Then it could emerge in visual or auditory form, after the subject has died and when the right sensitive comes along, and circumstances are favorable for the recapturing—or explosion, if you will—of an original charge.

Thus, if I were to go back to a certain bomber base in England and see the figure of George McClintock or Jerry Price walking along the road in coveralls, I would still not believe that necessarily showed the survival of an individual entity. The force of magnetism (or whatever you want to call it) of this particular personality— These may have been lodged in the area during lifetime, and might emerge under favorable conditions later on.

For what it's worth, however, I will tell of an incident occurring in our family many years ago.

Late 1930 to early 1932 we lived at 1417 Germania Drive, Des Moines, Iowa: my wife, our daughter Layne, and myself. Our son Tim was not yet born. Also we had with us, in the later months of 1931, my mother, Effie M. Kantor. An accomplished journalist, she had been publishing a small maga-

zine in another town, but failing health caused her to come
and live in our home.

There were two bedrooms in the house. My wife and I had
the one at the front; then there was a bathroom in between,
giving on to a little hall; and then the back bedroom. The
maid lived out. My daughter Layne, not yet four years old,
slept in a good-sized crib in the back room. She had her little
desk there, her toys and baby things. Although there was a three-
quarter-sized bed in the room, Layne still preferred her familiar
crib.

My mother came in the fall, ailing from a heart condition,
but not too weak to enjoy her granddaughter. They shared the
room for a while. Layne's greatest delight was to get into bed
with her grandmother and listen to the wonderful stories which
Granny could tell her: all about black cats going on picnics,
dogs who flew airplanes, dogs and cats who ran restaurants
together . . . I don't know what all.

However, on Thanksgiving Day my mother suffered a painful heart attack, and from then on she was undergoing constant
medical treatment. Layne's crib was moved into our own bedroom and Layne joined us there.

This was the way things stood on December 26th, 1931,
when my mother died after two or three days in a coma.

One of the first things I did was to indulge in a little personal
therapy, a general exorcism of the Death Angel, and clean up
my mother's room. After she was taken away that afternoon,
I stripped the bed, went out and beat the mattress in the cold
winter sunlight; all that sort of thing. My wife joined me in this
work, collecting Mother's clothing to be given away, and clear-
ing the dresser and table of medicine bottles.

When Layne came home from nursery school she found
Granny gone, and her things being installed in her favorite old
room. Granny had gone to Heaven; we tried to explain this
as best we could, since neither one of us then believed very
firmly in the idea of Heaven (and later lost what shreds of
belief still clung to us from sectarian childhood). Layne cried

at first: she wondered who was going to make her dolly-clothes,
and who would tell her stories. But we pointed out that Granny
was so sick and tired, and that she would be much happier and
more comfortable in the place where she had gone. Layne agreed
that she must and would accept the facts. (Pretty good, for a
gal still a month or so short of her fourth birthday.)

So that night Layne slept in her old room (later for a time
Granny's room, the room where Granny had died). She slept
there that night and the next night and from then on, as long
as we stayed in that house.

A few nights after Mother's death, my wife was preparing
Layne for bed, pulling on her pajamas and so on—as well as
she was able, with the child dancing all over the bed.

"Oh, I love to go to bed!"

"Do you?"

"Yes. I like to come to this room and get into my nightclothes
and get into bed. For then the Pink Lady comes."

Irene was silent for a moment. "What is the Pink Lady?"

"Oh, she comes. She comes to see me after the lights are out,
before I go to sleep."

Irene was certainly wondering about all this; but she tried to
appear casual. "Well, just who *is* the Pink Lady?"

"She's lovely. She's real nice to me."

"What does she do?"

"Oh, she sits on the bed, or she stands by the bed, and she
talks to me and tells me stories. I just *love* the Pink Lady."

"Why do you call her pink?"

"Because she *is* pink."

"Is she anybody you know?"

The child was humming to herself happily. "Oh, she's just
the Pink Lady," she reiterated. "I *like her*," and that's all Irene
could get out of her then or later.

Not many weeks after that we moved away to the East. No
more Pink Lady.

After Layne was a little older we tried to question her about
this incident again; but she couldn't remember it. Odd, too,

because she had and has an exceptionally vivid recollection extending in patches into babyhood. I know this: that she never expressed any fear of the Pink Lady.

. . . Dream, infantile fantasy, apparition? You tell me.

A Speech About
Saucers
1962

Some twelve or fourteen years agone I was doing a little peacetime job for the United States Air Force and, in the course of activities, had to squat down at Lackland AF Base—San Antonio, Texas—for a while. This was in the days when Unidentified Flying Objects were very much in the news.

Major General Charles W. Lawrence commanded Lackland then, and one of his right bowers was a colonel named Hix, who had been in command at Godman AF Base in Kentucky on that sad day when a young KNG officer named Mantell was killed when he came too close to a saucer at high altitude. Thus UFOs figured in dinner-table and bunk-flying conversation, just as this entrancing subject was of high conversational priority elsewhere in the country.

The San Antonio Rotary Club had been pestering Charley Lawrence, wanting him to come and make a luncheon speech; and of course the general was trying to dodge. Finally one day a committee waited upon General Lawrence and practically nailed him to the wall. He knew that he had to come up with a speech—whether he delivered it himself or not.

(O.K., so I said Rotary Club. Could have been Kiwanis, Lions or even the Chamber of Commerce. Doesn't matter—they *all* bother *me* about speeches which I just won't make. So we'll still blame the Rotarians.)

Being by his own admission chicken-hearted when it came to

such public appearances, Charley dragged in Colonel Stuart, his executive officer, the moment the committee had departed.

"Look here, Stu. I've got too damn much to do, and I'm not going around yakking to luncheon clubs. So you're the baby."

Colonel Stuart groaned; but brightened a little when Charley told him what the subject was to be.

"You see, they want to hear a talk about Unidentified Flying Objects. You know a lot about that stuff; so you ought to have fun with the speech."

. . . Stu told me later, pridefully, that he really thought he'd put together a very good speech indeed. He went around combing all the files, hunting for any material which wasn't Classified, or even previously Classified material which was now Down-Graded.

"I had never seen a flying saucer," said Stu. "And I had never heard anyone else give a speech about flying saucers; but, with due modesty, I am convinced that I delivered just about the best lecture on flying saucers, ever delivered in San Antonio or anywhere else."

Seems like the Rotary Club thought so, too. After that fateful luncheon at the Gunter Hotel, all the appreciative Rotarians were coming up and shaking Colonel Stuart's hand, and telling him what a good speech it was indeed—how very informative, how thrilling, how conducive to inquiry and speculation.

Flushed with victory, our colonel decided that he might treat himself to a few hours off. By this time it was near the middle of the afternoon, anyway, and the thought of his ranch house amid hills far to the northwest of San Antonio was something that soothed and beckoned. He called up the Base . . . everything was under control, his secretary assured him.

"You tell General Lawrence," said Stu, "that I have just delivered the greatest speech about flying saucers, or UFO's or whatever you want to call them, that was ever uttered by mortal lips. Tell him not to be too jealous, however, because he didn't succumb and deliver the speech in my stead. Now I intend to take the rest of the day off, and shall go out and die pleasantly on my own terrace."

Our colonel tooled his car along into the sun-baked open spaces, and eventually fetched up in the driveway of his charming ranch home. Mrs. Stuart came hastening in welcome, delighted at having a husband who was home early instead of dragging wearily in at 10 P.M. from a rough day at the Base, as happened so frequently.

"Let us relax," said the Stuarts. "Let us have martinis! Let us delight in limpid breezes, and forget the woes of the world, and especially those gruesome woes of United States Air Force."

Accordingly the colonel's lady buzzed off to work miracles with gin, vermouth, ice, and olives; while the colonel sprawled on the terrace with his long legs extended, and the little portable radio played soft music beside him.

Suddenly he raised his eyes to the southwestern sky—

"Honey," he called weakly to his wife. "Honey. . . ."

"Yes, Stu?" said that dulcet voice from the kitchen.

"Honey. I see—a flying saucer—"

Mrs. Stuart approached the terrace in a Gray Lady mood and went over to feel her husband's head. The colonel was collapsed in his chair, pointing one quivering finger at the southwest horizon.

"Now, dear," said his wife, "you've had an exhausting demanding day. You just take it easy and relax, and you'll feel better soon."

"But—" said Stu. "There *was* a flying saucer. Honest!"

"Where, dear?"

"Right over there. It went streaking off behind that hill. It was headed north. Just before you got out here. . . ."

"I know, I know," crooned Mrs. Stuart. "What an exhausting ordeal! And when I think of all that stuff about UFOs that you had to read and absorb and evaluate! Why, it's enough to make *anybody's* mind crack! Now just rest quietly, and I'm going to bring you a nice big double martini; and as soon as you've had that, I know that you'll feel a thousand per cent better—"

The colonel lay weakly, still trying to point with his palsied finger.

At that moment the radio beside him went clack-clack-beep-beep, and the next moment a voice cut in to say: "We interrupt this program to bring you an important announcement. An Unidentified Flying Object has just been sighted sweeping above Sheppard Air Force Base—"

(I seem to remember that Sheppard is maybe three hundred miles north of San Antonio.)

That's the true story. Even in retirement, which he is enjoying these days, I doubt that Stu is the man he was before that historic afternoon. I doubt that he will ever be the same. Neither will anybody remotely connected with the occurrence, including members of the San Antonio Rotary Club.

The Marchers
1955

The new motel at Americus was clean and comfortable, the bed smooth; still I could not sleep. Too many forces would not let me sleep. Again I looked at my watch: a little after 4 A.M., so it would be hours before the February sun appeared. I got up and dressed. I drove into northeast blackness along that road grown so familiar—Georgia State Highway Number 49. The road brought me, eleven miles away, into a dark unpopulated valley where water trickled from a certain storied spring.

For a time I parked near that spring. Frogs were singing like birds along a tiny watercourse where new grasses tufted fresh as salad leaves. There was the thought of monuments looming, thought of a bareheaded boy made of bronze who stands, cap in hand and eternally youthful face uplifted, amid a low forest of white marble slabs. But the graves were yonder, to the north. Now I did not wish to go there—I was heartily afraid to go, although I had gone many times before in daylight, and on occasion illegally in darkness. Regulations declare that a United States Military Cemetery may not be visited at night; yet on occasion I had sinned so, and had not felt myself a sinner; I'd felt that I belonged there. Almost I might wish to lie there eventually, could it be permitted. I felt that I was nearer to those dead than I was near to a breathing, sleeping world of mortal men and women.

About five o'clock I drove up the south slope of this valley and parked near the summit. Barely in gloom could I make out the few naked markers which approximate the position of the old Andersonville stockade. Actually I stood within the stockade area—the South Gate would have been over here, to the left; the gallows directly ahead, the raiders' pavilion ahead to the right. Still that constant spurting symphony of frog voices cried in the pretty ravine, the ravine I could scarcely distinguish in its mystery.

Clouds were thick, oppressive, blocking the light of even a single star. An owl spoke among underbrush masking the ancient Island. All fifty-odd thousand of you, I thought. Where do you drift now? Guards and prisoners alike—Henry Wirz with the rope mark on your dusty neck—sniveling child and hulking bully, serene martyr and master-of-the-hounds . . . I thought (in that intense awareness of one's own dream, the egoistic concentration which impels one to tell the story which he feels must be told)—Men and boys, I am here, waiting. Where have you gone?

I heard them coming. They twitched in a whispering rank from woods at the north, they rose up beyond statues and the superintendent's house; they came walking, massed and steady. Gently, gently they traveled through and over and under distant trees, came out into open ground where little circular fences protected the wells and tunnels they had dug—black pits drilled down through colored layers of clay. The marchers passed the fences easily, pacing nearer and nearer. There would be no resisting them.

I turned in panic, and stumbled back to my car, I flung myself into the front seat, heard the frightened slam of the car door go banging off through haunted distance. It was no illusion—I *heard* those soft-footed thousands walking ever closer. Now their phalanx was pressing down the opposite slope, passing Providence Spring. I had summoned them, their reply was in their implacable approach.

Why was I afraid—I, who had called them brothers for so long in my mind, who dared to feel that I belonged in their

misty column? It was not solely a fear of ghosts, a quailing
away from the Dead. I had been close to death on a number
of occasions in two wars, had walked within Buchenwald, had
climbed into trucks loaded with dead, had tripped across their
stiff outflung arms when they lay upon the ground. It was
something more. In the next moment, as that unseen soft-
treading horde pressed over the crest of the Sweetwater branch,
I recognized the answer.

They had come to tell me that there must be no compromise.
I had invoked their name and thought for nearly twenty-five
years; they were thronging at last to force me to the task.

I was crying. I had not cried in many years, but now I was
crying. Get out of the car, I said. You must show them that
you have fear no longer, that you are ready to accept orders.

My feet were on the grass, the door clicked shut behind me.
I stood waiting. The wide rustling rank moved fairly in my
face. Then they were touching me, they were all around me,
brushing my face and hands, the hair of my head.

Rain.

A thin slow-speaking, slow-stepping rain had formed somewhere among miles and ages of darkness before dawn. So it
had moved on many small feet from the direction of the
cemetery, had walked open glades, put its coolness on monuments, now it was touching me. I was glad to be brushed by
it, glad to feel it on my lips.

At this time I had written perhaps twenty-five thousand
words on *Andersonville*, and knew that I must write at least
three hundred thousand more. Often the recollection of that
rain walking the late hours of a Georgia night came to prod
or sustain me. The next fifteen months were a strange confusion from which only the book itself emerged in clarity. I
worked here, there, everywhere. There were several very good
reasons why I must be abroad a great share of this time;
but never was the country or the place or the room where
I sat of first importance. A great deal of the time I worked
near our Spanish home in Andalucía, alone in mountain foot-

hills. I had secret hideaways carefully surveyed: the promontory where I rolled stones to free a path for my car—another hill near the road to a lonely village called Benilmadena, where I was free from the incursions of herdsmen and gypsies alike. For several years I'd worked habitually in the car, with portable typewriter set up on a folding chair for a table; it was my peripatetic office, complete with books, briefcase—a basket of bread, cheese, olives, and sausage, a bottle of thin country wine. It didn't matter where we went or what we did; I was working each day from the 16th of December, 1953, until the 25th of May, 1955. I mean working each day.

Nights were frequently the worst part of the whole business. It is a mean experience to labor within the stockade all day— say alongside Father Peter Whelan—and then to have Veronica Claffey stalking into her tomb, and you going with her, through all the remembered hours of exhausted sleep.

They say that Carcassone is fabulous, that the Cité crusted on its little mountain is a sculptured wonderland. I do not know. I have been there, and my wife and my dog went walking and exploring and painting for days (Irene did the painting, Lobo the exploring), but my memory of Carcassone is of a double-door where wind rattled across a balcony, and where I sat with that same gray typewriter before me, and where I was writing about—was it Willie Mann in Missouri, Judah Hansom up in York State? Oh, no—that was in the Hyde Park Hotel in London, and what a noise the buses made outside. . . . No, it was Naz Stricker and Coral Tebbs. No, that was in Copenhagen. . . . Oh, yes. No, no! It was in mid-Atlantic—Laurel Tebbs and Sergeant Sinkfield—and the smoking room is cold and deserted at six in the morning, and for hours afterward; and you keep your typewriter and the smallest of the several portable bookcases in the steward's locker, and sometimes there is a storm, and you have to hold your typewriter fast to the table with one hand while you type with the other— Was it the *Empress of Australia* or the *Mauretania?* Why, it was both.

(Folks tell me that a Trans-Atlantic voyage is a good way to take a rest cure. Interesting, indeed. I must try it sometime.)

I should not on these pages attempt to set down what I feel or felt or believe about *Andersonville*. If I have not told such things in the novel itself, then the book is valueless and should remain unread. But let me say this: that only once before have I felt so many people breathing down my neck while I was at work, no matter where I worked—and that was when I was writing *Glory for Me,* which in time came before the world as a motion picture which told the story of war veterans—*The Best Years of Our Lives.* And the breath of these Andersonville people was especially compulsive; it came cooled by the ice of ninety years, ninety years to the minute.

The book was not written chronologically—few books of such scope could be written chronologically. Nevertheless, it was begun ninety years from the month when the stockade was first reared; and Providence Spring burst forth exactly ninety years from the week when Providence Spring did burst forth; and the last tattered relics were conveyed from the pen in May, 1865; and the last word of this novel was written in May, 1955, and strangely the last word happened to be *Andersonville.*

Frankie
1966

So this is 1966, and it is fifteen years since the Bravest Woman in America left off living, and I wonder how many people have forgotten her, and how many still remember.

Her name was Mary Frances Housley. She was a stewardess for National Airlines until she relinquished her job (you might say) in 1951.

Frankie Housley—friends called her by this nickname—was twenty-four years old at the time. So, if she were among those present today, she'd be thirty-nine.

(You can guess how her warm little voice would cry Lord-a-Massy at the idea. When ladies are twenty-four they just can't imagine being thirty-nine. Why, that's practically *forty* . . . practically *old age*.)

But, if she were with us now, I picture her toiling and rejoicing like Longfellow's blacksmith . . . although she wasn't built like any blacksmith in this world. No, no, she was dainty and rustly and silky, and properly giggly when occasion demanded.

. . . Envision her residing today in a fairly new ranch-style house in a suburb of Jacksonville or Knoxville or Asheville or Nashville or some other *ville*. In the South . . . she'd always lived in the South.

She'd be arguing with her thirteen-year-old daughter about whether the little critter should or should not wear stretch-pants to a Go-Go-Go dance in the junior high school gym. She

would be sternly ordering her eleven-year-old son to move his
half-completed original model of a lunar vehicle from the living
room to his *own* room. And maybe comforting a nine-year-old
of either sex who had been indulging in fisticuffs with the little
boy down the block.

Oh, well. Or some of those things.

And there would have been the jaunty husband to come
slamming in from the driveway and cry, "What do I *smell*?
Don't tell me, darling, you're cooking spareribs! Boy oh boy!"

"Yes! *Barbecued!*"

. . . And nights when Bob or Bruce or Bud or whoever her
husband was— He'd be taking her out for dinner. Later they
might even stop for an evening drink and a little dancing.
Frankie loved to dance.

Perhaps the orchestra would play that old one, the one she
had sung years before, the one she used always to request . . .
she'd hum it with her head against her partner's shoulder.

This song was about a man who was waltzing with his darling, when an old friend he chanced for to see, and the wicked
old friend stole his true love away from him. It was called the
Tennessee Waltz, and it had a haunting air. Somehow it seemed
especially appropriate to Frankie Housley's heart and imagination. Born and bred in Tennessee. . . .

Stewardess Housley was 5 ft. 3½ inches tall. She weighed
about 120 pounds, all carried in the right places. She had
tender brown eyes and a lovely soft mouth, and a lovely soft
roundness to her chin. She did all right with her lovely soft
brown hair, too.

Let's have no wisecracks, *à la* Shelly Berman, concerning
Coffee, tea, or milk. Not right now.

The date was Sunday, the 14th of January. The plane was a
DC-4, NAL 83, the Norfolk shuttle, proceeding on the first leg
of its journey: Newark to Philadelphia. The aircraft had been
delayed for minor repairs at Newark, while air over much of

the northeastern United States thickened with rain and sleet in that early afternoon.

Shortly after 2 P.M., the airplane approached the field south of Philadelphia close to the Delaware River. It was a coach trip with only a crew of three: pilot and co-pilot, Captain Harold Barwick and Edward Zatarian; and Mary Frances Housley, stewardess. Twenty-five passengers in the cabin looked out at the driving storm and some of them spoke their trepidation. The smiling Miss Housley reassured them, as she had calmed the fears of hundreds of other novices in months past. In truth, Mary Frances was no veteran herself. She had been flying only four months.

The airplane went lower . . . some of the passengers were soldiers and sailors, there was a Marine, there were mothers and little girls, and two babies in arms.

Visibility was reduced close to minimum conditions. The weather report at 2:09 recited a horizontal visibility of one mile and a ceiling of six hundred feet. Regulations said that a DC-4 might land when there was a mile of visibility and a four hundred foot ceiling, so Captain Barwick was directed to bring his aircraft down on Runway Number 9.

Ice and snow plastered the surface. At 2:13 P.M. the wheels touched the runway. They kept on touching, sliding, and skidding; the DC-4 thrashed from side to side as Barwick fought to bring his braking action to bear. Off the end of the runway, smashing through a fence, the halting airplane bridged a ten-foot ditch and lurched to a stop with grinding pressure and a scream of ripped metal. The concrete abutment of a beacon light had torn a hole in the left wing, and high octane gas began to spew, and the first flames bloomed.

The next day your correspondent felt it incumbent to begin an investigation of Frankie Housley's life and works. I didn't know quite how to find out what made her tick. Relatives, teachers, boy friends, girl friends? I tried them all.

Let's start in Knoxville, Tennessee, where she was born, 12th of October, 1926, right smack in the middle of the Libra sign. I found that there was always a hill in her life, or a height. While she was still a baby, her father, momentarily successful, moved his family to a handsome brick house on a peak of the North Hills area. And in Knoxville, at that time, to live in North Hills was something.

Neighborhood snapshots show Mary Frances as a chubby grinning child with tousled hair. When she smiled, her wide mouth allowed the smile to spread clear across her face.

The neighbors remembered, too, that John Housley, Sr., owned a cigar company, and that Mary Frances's mother spent a great deal of time working in her flower garden. They recalled that the brother, John, Jr., was nine years older than Mary Frances.

Later I became acquainted with Brother John. I gained the impression that Mary Frances most resembled her father: she was more or less of his pattern in personality and human attitude. She wasn't much like her mother. And they called her Mary Frances all through her childhood, though when Little Sister grew older she liked the name Frankie and tried to adopt it, as girls do. She didn't get away with that until she left home to find momentary disaster in teen-age matrimony, and eventual freedom in Jacksonville.

Mr. Housley had lost out on things, back in the middle Depression years. He no longer owned the cigar company, and had to work as a salesman. The family moved to another house on another hill at the outskirts of Fountain City, next door to Knoxville. It was a quite different house and a quite different hill. When I went out there in 1951, Forest Avenue was a bumpy unpaved sluice. On the east side, at Number 300, a narrow roadway crossed a brimming ditch which one time might have been a cool brook; but you could look down, and the water was dark and turbid and you could see tin cans and broken bottles. High on a ridge beyond, the once-Housley house stared gray and forbidding.

Maybe an explorer would seek in vain for the nucleus, the

bright silver core of greatness amid such surroundings. Maybe
the germ lived elsewhere. I drove over to Central High School
of Fountain City.

Sure enough—another hill, this time the most beautiful hill
where Frankie Housley's years were passed. The big pink brick
building rose amid sheltering oaks. It stood on the exact site of
an old normal college, so Fountain City boys and gals had a
regular college campus. And in that building, sweetened by
apple-green walls and olive-green rows of recessed lockers, there
flourished vigor and ambition.

. . . Mrs. Pace Moore Johnston had a cool voice with a
surprising undercurrent of strength. Her dark eyes were serene
behind their spectacles.

"Yes, I taught Latin to Mary Frances Housley. But I have
never contented myself with teaching Latin as a language. I
try to correlate the exploration of this study. We examine the
economics, the political factors of Rome. Often I have taken
my classes to the courtrooms downtown, that we might learn
something by comparison with the structure of an ancient
State."

She smiled calmly. "Sometimes I have been criticized for
this. People have said, 'If you are teaching Latin to young
folks, you should be merely teaching Latin.' But on the day
when I may not include the wider and more important studies
of humanity in my courses, I will walk out of this classroom."

It would seem that Mrs. Johnston included those studies of
humanity. Frankie appeared to have picked up some ideas along
that line.

Although perhaps she gained them also from the principal,
Miss Hassie K. Gresham.

. . . In the deserted auditorium, rows of opera chairs seemed
peopled with boys and girls who sat in the many general as-
semblies since that building was erected. A marble tablet, high
in the wall, bore the names of seven Fountain City boys who
died in World War I. Above the list was engraved a paraphrase

from John XV, 13: "Greater love have no men than this: that they lay down their lives for their friends."

Folks said that Hassie Gresham used to hold her student audiences spellbound as she told, with challenge and sympathy, little incidents from the lives of those servicemen who once attended Central. In the quiet of the big bare room you could very nearly hear Miss Gresham's voice . . . you could see her standing before the old wine-colored curtain which draped the platform.

In searching amid fancied rows of attentive teen-agers, it was possible to pick out Mary Frances Housley, her face breaking into vivacity when her full lips spread in their smile, when Miss Gresham said something funny and made everybody laugh.

Greater love—

Up on the second floor was a narrow study hall. Not much in there: just rows of desks where kids could work when they had a free period, and a place for the monitoring teacher to sit and keep her eye on them. On its big stand waited the un-abridged dictionary with leaves stained and torn by countless young fingers.

In its biographical index were lined the Greats of the past—inventors, artists, kings, poets, heroes. There were even the names of a few heroines, like Florence Nightingale and Grace Darling. I looked for Molly Pitcher but she wasn't there.

Odd thing, though, about Grace Darling of the Farne Islands, the one who saved those shipwrecked people in 1838. Her middle name was Horsley. That's pretty close to Housley.

So the record continues. Mary Frances scrambled into youthful matrimony, and very shortly scrambled out of it again. By that time she found herself in Jacksonville. Still bruised from her divorce, she took a job as secretary for the Visiting Nurses Association. She stayed there only six months, then went to work for a succession of doctors as (in each case) office assistant. She was with Dr. J. G. Lyerly in the Greenleaf Building, and then for two years with Dr. Frederick H. Bowen; and after that she worked for Dr. Harold S. Levin.

And then—bang—it was 1950, and Dr. Levin was recalled for active duty with the Navy.

Frankie surveyed the situation. There were several other young doctors for whom she might have gone to work; but they were trembling in their boots for fear that they too might be called back into the Service.

That was how it came about that, on September 6th, Frankie filled out an application to work as a stewardess. The very next day she was hired by David H. Amos of National Airlines. It seems that Mr. Amos had interviewed a great many applicants in his lifetime, and very quickly could he separate the sheep from the goats, the Right Girls from the spooks.

Frankie fibbed a little on that application. She had written the word *Single* in her marital status blank . . . well, after all, she really *felt* single. She didn't like to think of herself as being divorced; she thought that she was a young woman still peering hopefully into the future, and not a disillusioned old hen with rusty relics of emotional wreckage still clinging.

Home, these days, was at an address in Vernon Terrace. There were six small apartments in that building, away over on the west side of Jax . . . immediately in front the St. John's River glinted warm and bright. The furniture wasn't much, but it served. It was nice to be high, nice to be up on a hill again.

She had lived for several years with a friend named Anne Davis. But about this time Anne was enabled to set up housekeeping in a location where she could have her young son with her. So a pretty gray-eyed girl named Peggy Egerton, another fledgling stewardess, succeeded Anne in the Vernon Terrace apartment.

. . . *Life,* said Anne and Peggy. *How she loved it! People. Life and people.*

Every moment, every waking moment—the adoration for people, the desire for them, and that same echo recited by Foun-

tain City neighbors rose again. Frankie's smile, her laugh . . .
when she laughed, she laughed all over her face. . . .

And it's as if she were laughing all the while?

No, oh no—those few times when you saw her face in repose,
when she was sleeping, it was a sad face, strangely beautiful,
strangely sad.

But people, people, people, every waking minute.

"Oh, I'm in love," Frankie would cry, coming in at Heaven
knew what hour. "Anne, wake up! I've got to tell you all about
it. He's the most wonderful man! I'm in love!"

She wasn't happy unless she was in love. She looked for
love everywhere.

The Lobster House knew her well, that hearty restaurant
built on a rambling pier across the river from the business
district. Drinks bubbled briskly, smells of steak and shrimp
drifted from the door, men and girls sat with their glasses and
platters before them; they listened to the pianist, they chatted
with Ducky the landlord, they hummed the *Tennessee Waltz.*

Eddie George sat there with me. He was of Syrian extraction,
and a B-24 pilot during World War II. (Another thing about
these stewardesses: they really go for the fly-boys. So many of
their dates and their romances are with the Air Force or the
boys off the flat-tops.) Eddie was tall, good-looking, his hair as
black as heavy flak.

"There was one night when I called up Frankie and asked
her for a date, and she had already promised somebody else.
I was tired and rather sore at the world. You see, I'm in the
confectionery and tobacco business, and keeping track of all
that tax data is really a job. I had been struggling with tax
details for a long time; this was the last night. I was due to
send the stuff in the next day, but I just bogged down."

He turned the glass in his hand and looked down at it,
smiling gently the way all her friends smiled when they spoke
of Mary Frances Housley.

"Came in here, sat down at the bar, looked around, and there
was Frankie. She left her party and came over to me right

away. 'Eddie, have you finished the tax?' I told her it was too much for me, I guessed I'd have to be delinquent. 'But you *can't*,' she said. 'You're supposed to have that done by tomorrow!' I said, 'The hell with it,' and she went back to her party. Next minute here she was by my side again. 'Come on, Eddie. We're going.' 'Going where?' 'We're going over to your place to work on the tax, and I won't take no for an answer. I've told my date goodbye. Now come along.' It took almost all night. She'd grab a list of figures out of my hand, look at it. 'Why, you haven't got this right—it isn't right at all. Here, these should go in the other column,' and so on."

"Was she in love with you, Eddie?"

"Not me especially. She just loved people."

. . . She'd go into a strange restaurant with one of her pals and even then she'd feel lonely because there were people laughing and talking at a table, and she didn't know them, and couldn't join in their fun. She wouldn't let such a state of affairs last very long, however. She'd go right over to the table.

"Hello, don't I know you? And if not, why not? I'm Frankie Housley. Who are you?" and soon she'd have a half-dozen fine new friends. There was something about her that brought out all the warmth and sincerity that men and women owned. Some of them may have owned very little, yet Frankie managed to find it and let their best be revealed.

But I think that she was lonely when she flew long and high at night, and the passengers were asleep. Then she might have cuddled in her rear seat, fragile cheek against the pane, eyes watching low distant crystals of light which marked the towns hiding amid wide darkness two miles and more below. All those towns and all those folks who dwelt within each affectionate core of light, and all the millions of other folks who slumbered in space where no lights showed.

This was America beneath, and Frankie Housley loved America, and wore that love upon her sleeve. Of late she had been having delightful dates with a Navy pilot. Now they were more or less engaged; and so she would think of Bob, and wonder whether perhaps he was flying too in this same midnight extending its mystery beyond her vision.

On Saturday, January 13th, Frankie called Peggy Egerton from the stucco wing adjoining the main station at Jacksonville airport. That was the place where stewardesses checked in for their flights.

". . . Darnedest luck," Frankie lamented. "I've got to work, so no double-date tonight. June"—she meant June Long, the superintendent of stewardesses—"had to use me after all. Some girls were sick, and so on, and there was a foul-up."

"Where are you going, Frankie?"

"Oh, up to Newark. Then tomorow I've got to work the Norfolk shuttle; I'll be back in Jax on Monday. In case you're not working Monday night, maybe we can have that double-date then?"

"I'll do my best to save Monday night," said Peggy, and she said other things about the date, and Frankie's laughter jingled through the telephone.

Thus she flew on her last trip North. She proceeded in Flight 83 to Philadelphia on Sunday, January 14th, and she went into the flames.

She forced open the door of the cabin. It was a ten-foot drop to the sleety ground outside. Had she willed, Frankie could have taken that drop then and there, and no one would ever have blamed her. But here were her passengers, and many were hallooing, and the children were wailing, and one woman was screaming louder than the rest above a popping of fire, a distant whine of approaching sirens: *My baby, my baby—!*

People were twisted in the seats. Some of the safety belts seemed jammed from impact, the gasoline flames swathed nearer. Frankie hauled a dazed passenger to the door and shoved him into space. Another. The next was a woman, her coat was on fire . . . Frankie got her out.

People heard the stewardess's voice. "Just be calm," she was telling all and sundry. "Just take it easy, and everybody will get out. There's nothing to worry about." She pulled another woman toward the door—

Why count the words or breaths or steps? What need to guess at the temperature of the blaze, or the few seconds which would elapse before the entire fuselage was puffing?

Frankie Housley went back into that cabin eleven times.

Ten passengers she released, and dragged to the miraculous coolness of the hatch opening. The pretty enamel on her nails suffered as her fingers clawed at metal fastenings of the safety belts. Surely there were spots on her dove-gray uniform which no cleaner could ever take out or would need to.

A woman tells it—a woman who found herself mauled through seething space, and realized that the door was before her, and then wrenched loose from her savior's hands. "No," the woman cried, "you go first!"

Frankie looked at her wide-eyed . . . maybe her tender hair would have stood on end with amazement, except that by this time Frankie Housley's hair was all burned off. "I've still got some passengers back there!" and the force of her little body shoved the woman out through the door which opened on life itself.

She had ladled out another wailing young mother, and a little girl too. Some of the soldiers and sailors had been helping, dragging less able people through the hatch, but they were outside now—bruised and cut, most of them—from the ten-foot fall. It was ninety seconds since the DC-4 came to broken rest across that ditch, and a high octane gasoline fire doesn't wait for anybody, even the prettiest stewardess you ever wanted to make a date with.

There were still four women tangled in the forward section of the cabin. Frankie plunged into the reek on her eleventh trip, and there were two babies up there somewhere, and one of them was named Brenda Joyce, and she was four months old. And Brenda Joyce was the one they found in Frankie's arms after the wreckage had cooled and after foamite from the extinguishers was freezing on the ground.

You fly to Tennessee on a warm sunny day, and the willows rim a quiet section along North Broadway and wave their pliant fingers at anyone who passes by.

You go through an arch marked "Lynnhurst," and birds are thick and flowers too; you follow a long drive out into the west and you come at last, past perils of mockingbirds and roses, to an area where you can stand and see hills on many sides.

Toward the north, sheathed in a grove, is the hill where Central High School looms and where Miss Gresham used to talk about heroes. Less than a mile over east, as the cardinal flies, was that gray home at 300 Forest Avenue whence Frankie fled to Jacksonville and eventually to National Airlines. Then, maybe three miles away to the southeast, is the opulent house where she spent the first nine years of her life, and that is on a hill also.

Frankie is on a hill now. Away off beyond the environs of Fountain City and Knoxville, bigger ridges stand purple; of course they are Tennessee ridges; you might imagine that Frankie was up there somewhere, waltzing.

She could be, too. Could have been dancing with her darling, and snuggling delightedly with him in bed, during five thousand nights of these past fifteen years. Could have been bearing babies, and running through life with all the verve, all the perplexity, the heartbreak and exultation of our traditional Young American Wife & Mother.

Except that something made her go back into that airplane cabin eleven times, and eleven times was just one time too many.

The world, thank God, owns many heroines. Women who sacrifice themselves daily, working when truly they're not able to work . . . the uncomplaining angel who tends a snarling, exasperating invalid . . . that lame nun wading through snowdrifts to nurse her tribe of gaunt little Indians . . . mothers toiling day and night—alone, obscure, ignored and neglected by more fortunate neighbors—carrying cruel loads in the face of every agony from toothache to cancer. Each of us has known some such candidate for the Medal of Domestic and Community Honor.

But flames are something else.

. . . *Yes! Barbecued!*

A crashed airplane is strictly for the stalwart men in asbestos suits and masks. It is not for the petite little Miss Pretty, not for any brown-haired Jeanie To-Be-Dreamed-About.

Not unless she is a Mary Frances Housley. Then she has such benevolence in her heart (a Love Which Passeth All Understanding, a Love for the Entire Human Race) that no high octane explosion can ever blast it out.

She lies in Lynnhurst, the fir tree makes a long shadow when sun is low in the west, but morning sun can find her sod . . . as brave a woman as ever breathed. There she lies. Always a hill for Frankie.

The Larks of April
1967

We were a khaki-clad column, marching in disorderly route-step along a country road. A suggestion of bugle notes lifted ahead.

We are at war, we are at war.

The next day would be Easter, with its story of a Rising and an Eternal Promise.

But— *We are at war.*

Those light bugle calls were sounded by early larks, and blue-birds added their own melody. Our khaki clothing was inter-mingled with flannel shirts, old sweaters, denim overalls. We were not soldiers, were not tall enough to be soldiers. We were Boy Scouts. In our minds there had been no necessity for soldiers. Until now.

"You mean— It's true?"

"Bet your life. Didn't you see it, in the *Register* this morning?"

"No, my folks don't take the *Register*. But did the President actually sign a declaration of war?"

"Congress passed it, early yesterday. The President signed the bill in the afternoon."

We are bugles now, the meadowlarks seemed to say. *No longer little pipes of Peace.* The rich black earth shone fresh-turned in rolling fields past which we strode; bluebirds whistled anew. And there would be trilliums showing pale beauty in the woods ahead, and other flowers heartening in their very frailty.

I remember looking toward the east, trying to imagine that

guns sounded beyond that feathery horizon, and that we might hear them. But there were only happy bird cries, and the yell of a farmer directing his team of horses.

No voice of a Great Authority spoke from the mild sky, and said, "In this hour comes the end of an America and a World which have lived long in their sameness. Stand to Attention, children! You are not hiking merely to the woods and the river today. You walk into a new and fearsome half-century, and everything will change. Everything!"

Because the Power of Universes never speaks coherently to tell us what is ahead. We could not dwell as humans, were we to know. But we can recall that which is past; and thus I remember spring birds, and the first piercing greenness putting its vigor into our own green bodies.

The day was Saturday, the 7th of April. Fifty years ago.

John F. Kennedy is not living today, nor was he living then. Instead there could be found a young woman named Rose, in Brookline, Massachusetts, who was seven months pregnant and who undoubtedly—as becomes the pathetic whim of mothers-to-be—was a bit irked by the whole business, and longed for the day when she would be rid of her tender burden. But that wouldn't happen until May 29th.

Senator Bobby Kennedy, Senator Teddy Kennedy? Undreamed and unperceived, not even figments of an imagined future. Like uncounted millions of others—sung and unsung, recognized and unrecognized—who would precede or follow them into the realm of the Alive.

In our Boy Scout troop of that period were Charles Mason, who swung along on crutches; and Bill Plumb, whose leg-brace jingled as he limped. They might be considered representative of a vast hobbling throng who were Born Too Soon. Because, in the nervous springtime of fifty years ago, there was only a two-and-a-half-year-old boy playing with his toys in New York City; and a two-and-a-half-year-old boy can't do anything about infantile paralysis even if his name does happen to be Jonas E. Salk.

Everything will change.

Back in the Iowa county seat town we had left behind us, young men (and boys in the upper teen-age brackets) were calling back and forth with self-conscious raillery.

"Well, I guess *this* time the National Guard won't just set on the Mexican Border."

"Hell with the INGs. I'm going to join the Navy."

"Honest?"

"Sure. Going down to Des Moines day-after-tomorrow."

A big dark fellow named Jim Wedding talked earnestly with his brother about who was going to join what. For Jim, existence would terminate in another eleven months. A shell striking deep in Champagne . . . what was Champagne? Something rich folks drank in the movies, wasn't it?

Sixty or seventy miles distant, in another town named Glidden, people knew a certain youth, Merle Hay. Folks in our county had never heard of him. But they would, come next November—the entire Nation would. 16th Infantry, 1st Division. Photographs reproduced on the recruiting posters . . . *Hay, Enright, and Gresham.* The first three to die in the American Expeditionary Forces.

Farther away than Glidden and in quite another direction, a brawny Tennesseean, aged twenty-nine, was giving serious attention to his plowing. No warfare for him, he thought . . . he liked to shoot at a target, but didn't believe in killing other men. He reckoned that if anybody wanted him in that dang war, they'd have to draft him.

They did. His name was Alvin C. York.

Draft? There hadn't been any such thing since Civil War days. Draft card? It would be something dangerous and ominous: a small oblong chunk of Official importance, to show that you had registered with the local board, to prove that you had taken the first step toward accepting your sacred responsibility as an American.

. . . Burn it? *Burn* a draft card? As well talk about burning the Flag.

Everything will change.

Let's say that Aunt Edna was bedridden or at least housebound. So she read until she wore out her ancient eyes; then, after it hurt her to read small type, she could look out of the window—if she were fortunate enough to have a window within range. Or she could be read to. Failing these possibilities, she just lay or just sat.

Let's say that Aunt Edna was of pioneer experience and pioneer metal, and she had suffered and sacrificed, and Gone Without, and Done For Others, her life long. Surely she was deserving of a better final decade than the one awarded her. She'd loved church, loved the preaching and the hymns . . . kind soul, she was easygoing, she welcomed new ideas and new horizons. She wished to observe and enjoy and appreciate; and above all she loved to have that enraptured feeling of *being there.*

Walls of the little house on Elm Street were tight, the place was a jail and a tomb. Aunt Edna had done nothing to deserve being entombed before her time. But she was too uncomplaining to even lift her tired old hands and beat against the coffin-lid.

Then suppose that magicians had come along, and they had perfected a miracle not only for Aunt Edna but for all the Uncle Ralphs as well . . . For all the Grandma Smiths and Grandpa Clarks who were caged within their tight cells; and for younger prisoners also.

And the sorcerers said, "Here is our Enchanted Box. Twist the knob, listen, and gaze. You shall be a part of life again . . . and all life, and all time! You shall go to church, and to the opera, and to the ball game . . . you will climb mountains . . . drink in the fierce glory of waves which never broke for you, move in cities where you never walked. Veldt and iceberg, tundra and tower, White House and Taj Mahal: all shall be yours. And more."

The wizards did not appear, fifty years ago. They couldn't, for the Enchanted Boxes weren't yet ready for distribution. So Aunt Edna sat, and hoped that maybe someone would come to read to her. And she tried to wave at the children as they came dancing home from school.

In winter it was apt to grow rather chilly in that room, because Aunt Edna's nephew was working at his job all day; and his wife might forget to run down and put those extra shovelfuls of coal on the furnace fire; or maybe she'd be gone away, doing errands—going to the grocery store, to the milk depot, to the butcher shop, to the bakery, to the drugstore (they were all separate, and rather far apart). The furnace fire would die, kind of.

The whole family wished that they could afford an automatic stoker. Folks told about the rich folks over on Boone Street who owned an automatic stoker . . . you had to wind up a kind of clock thing, and set it; and then little buckets of coal were carried along on a kind of chain thing, and dumped into the furnace. But it also was told that the device was pretty clumsy and undependable.

And, come summer, it was apt to grow hot in that room, because the windows were small, and air didn't circulate very well; and during daytime the red mercury in the thermometer oozed up past the 100° mark . . . maybe at night no breezes would develop, though you prayed for even a weak breeze. Aunt Edna prayed. It was torture, lying there against crushed baked pillows, her flesh weary from the scrape and squeeze of a sweaty nightdress. . . .

The magicians just weren't around. Wouldn't be, not for many years.

So the coal was shoveled, the fans were waved . . . huge chunks of ice carried to the refrigerator and boosted in, with newspapers stuffed around to make the ice last longer.

And in merciless Julys and Augusts the seasonal fear came

annually . . . it always came with the heat. Little Mae or Lorene had a fever and then— And then complained of *pains in the legs*—

The mothers and fathers, hovering by the beds. And the doctors— How many times did they cry, "Oh, *God*," in their souls? We did mention that Jonas E. Salk was only two-and-a-half, in April, 1917.

There used to be a thing called diphtheria, too.

A number of smaller boys were busy and breathing in that same springtime, but they lived in other States and— Let's face it: we wouldn't have paid any attention to them if they had been able to trot along after us, right there in Hamilton County. We were scornfully disinterested in smaller fry. And no one had ever heard of a Cub Scout program.

Take an eight-year-old, away down there in Texas. Lyndon B. Johnson was his name, and we would have cared more about the fact of *Texas* than the fact of LBJ.

Or another eight-year-old by the name of Barry Goldwater. Phoenix, Arizona, was his home. Little Barry wouldn't have mattered a mite to us. But, gosh— Arizona? *Apaches!*

As for a four-year-old in Yorba Linda, California, who liked to stand in his yard and watch the Santa Fe trains roaring past— Well, we might have been a trifle sympathetic with *him*. Little Dick Nixon dreamed blissfully of some day becoming a locomotive engineer; and even the eldest of us could recollect his own infancy, a whole decade and more ago, when he too entertained that childish and universal ambition.

Soldiers counted for a lot more, just then. Some of the bigger Scouts who hiked on that day would themselves put on new uniforms in the next year or so. Yes, and there would be a few gold stars on the service flag soon to hang in dignity, in our Scout hall.

. . . Consider a lieutenant less than two years out of West Point: an energetic blond guy, Dwight Eisenhower. We'd never heard his name, but might have been impressed profoundly by

his views on the intricacies of modern warfare. He declared that
airplanes and *tanks* were going to be *the* definitive factors in
campaigns of the future. Just imagine. And we would have respected his longing to accompany the 57th Infantry overseas,
and would have groaned along with him when he was welded
grimly into the training program instead.

Overseas . . . queer events going on there, besides the regular
battles and ship-sinkings. These mysteries were referred to every
now and then—briefly—in Iowa newspapers, but we boys
didn't bother to read about them. The Czar of Russia, for instance, had been placed under restraint, along with his whole
family. The Russian kingdom or empire or whatever they called
it— They were holding the first All-Russian Conference of
Soviets, right that month (but the big Bolshevik revolution
wouldn't happen until next November). How could that ever
concern us, away over here in the United States? The Western
Front was what counted.

And Germany counted, very much so. The Germans were
now our declared enemies. Pity the plight of that tall French
captain who'd become a prisoner of war in Germany—pity all
six-feet-four-inches of him. He'd been seriously wounded about
thirteen months previously, but already he was being disciplined
in camp after camp. They said warningly, "Captain De Gaulle,
if you try to escape *again*. . . ."

So in our contemplations we ignored what were typified as the
far corners of the Earth, although they did take up considerable
room on the maps. Places like India (tigers and Rudyard Kip-
ling), Siberia (salt, and cold weather), Australia (kangaroos),
Siam (twins, and white elephants), Mongolia (idiots), and
China itself (firecrackers; and something called chop suey which
city people were supposed to eat if very bold. Allegedly it was
fabricated from rats, mice, and puppy-dog tails).

We considered that we knew a lot about China, however.
Because, right there in Webster City, we had first-hand ac-
quaintance with an honest-to-goodness Chinaman. He was called
Ding Sam, and he operated a laundry. We supposed that all

China was one extensive series of laundries . . . also there was tea, and the Great Wall. We had no way of reckoning that, to those of us who survived the next fifty years, a certain Chinaman (no one ever said, "A certain *Chinese*") would loom importantly. He was then a zealous student at the Changsha Normal School, and had just published an article on body-building. The pen-name he used was, "The Man of Twenty-eight Strokes," because it took twenty-eight marks with the Chinese brush to write his name: Mao Tse-tung.

Speaking of Chinese and firecrackers and such, we'd observed an occasional magazine story in *Popular Mechanics* or some similar publication, about a real nut: fellow from Massachusetts who was always fooling around with rockets. He actually believed that rockets might prove to be of military importance—maybe even more so than a Zeppelin, or a water-cooled machine-gun, or a bayonet charge by the Black Watch.

He must have been singing *The Star-Spangled Banner* a little too frequently! You know—"the rocket's red glare, the bombs bursting in air," and so on. Ha, ha.

. . . It was about this time that Robert H. Goddard considered craftily that it might be wise to switch from black powder as a propellant . . . suppose that you were to employ a mixture . . . say 40 per cent nitroglycerin and 60 per cent nitrocellulose . . . what about that? If only he had more funds for experimentation. . . .

Nine years would elapse before Goddard could launch the first liquid-propellant rocket which ever soared.

Only five years *had* elapsed since (in an episode quite unrelated, apparently, to any sort of rocket whatsoever) a baby was born in East Germany.

"Such a fine boy! What name shall you give him, Baroness Von Braun?"

"Wernher."

So we boasted no space vehicles; the only radios were primitive instruments with dots and dashes; we had no television, no air conditioning, no automatic heating systems, no electric This or electronic That. The advantages of 1967 could not be ours. We possessed no Social Security, and thus anyone with a few employees was denied the patriotic ecstasy of keeping books for the Government.

There was something around called Income Tax—had been, since 1913—but that affected solely the remote wax figure of a Morgan or an Astor or a Vanderbilt. In the beginning the top rate was 6 per cent, and you had to have a yearly income of $500,000 in order to pay *that*.

The woods where we boys walked on this Good Saturday were unbenefitted by spraying, and our placid river unfrothed by detergents. In our homes we suffered the hostility of house-moths and ants, because there were no poisons encased under pressure in can-shaped bombs, to waft a lethal mist into our antiquely innocent air.

And no calcium propionate had been added to a single morsel of food we bought in the stores, "to prevent spoilage." When something was going to spoil it just had to go ahead and spoil.

We lived essentially through the same young years our parents and grandparents had lived, and amid much the same appurtenances. It was taken for granted that the telephone, the automobile, and the cinema had wrought enormous changes in the mode and even the mores of civilization; yet no one knew exactly how, or what the changes actually were. When people wanted to get down to Des Moines they took the eight o'clock train on the Chicago & Northwestern. People had been doing that ever since the railroad was built.

By this time many of us Scouts were grown into high schoolers, and here was an Easter vacation. War or no war, we would enjoy parties—maybe an early picnic or two. We could savor the social proximity of the fair sex . . . how very fair they were. They smelled perfectly delicious when, hot-faced and gawky, we were enabled to sit close to them. Their mothers were quaint old-fashioned women who believed that girls should wash their hair (and wear shoes, to keep their feet clean). And

never was the hair chopped off like a man's, but it grew long
and luxuriant; and of certain young ladies it was said that they
could "hide behind it."

The Devil had not yet invented those wire-and-plastic rollers.
But as soon would a girl have appeared before her swain in her
camisole, as to have greeted his sight when disfigured by *kid
curlers*.

And if Cousin Fanny Fatsworth had squeezed her bulging
loins into a pair of shorts, and waddled down the street before
the eyes of all— She would have been hung.

It is obvious that the America of fifty years ago was populated
by a naïve race, subject to traditional whims and inherited limitations, and staggering under a burden of delusion.

When we returned to school on the Monday following vacation, everyone would gather in the assembly room for Chapel
service, and Mr. Kelly would read from the Bible. You see,
the Bible had not yet been outlawed; so we were compelled to
listen to it—and that went for Abie Stein and Harry Brin and
Herman Dvorsky, as well as the young Protestants and Catho-
lics.

I rather think that, this time, Mr. Kelly read from the
Third Chapter of Ecclesiastes. It was one of his favorites.

> *To every thing there is a season, and a time*
> *to every purpose under the heaven. . . .*
> *A time to mourn, and a time to dance. . . .*
> *A time to love, and a time to hate; a time of*
> *war, and a time of peace. . . .*

Have I made it plain that our Chapel service in the school
assembly room was compulsory? Then, having been subjected
to such nefarious preachment, we might even end up with a
Pledge to the Flag.

Herein lay the seeds of Fascism beyond any doubt. Yet we had
never heard of a Fascist, and wished only that Cookie Clark and

Paul Nickerson and the rest of our heroes in Company C would hurry up and get over to Europe, and make that old Kaiser stop sinking our ships. The entire community, including German-named kids from the country, wished the same thing. Anybody who didn't feel that way would have been put in jail. The big grinning red-cheeked Fritzes and Guses trooped to enlist, and some of them would die at sea or at Croix Rouge Farm, before it was over.

We were ridden by fallacies. We believed that policemen were put on Earth to watch over us. True: but also we believed that policemen represented the Law, and thus you ought to do what the Law told you to do. The Great Society had not yet spread its wings. Economic injustice was rife. Let me cite an hallucination commonly entertained in most circles: that *a man got out of life exactly what he put into it.*

. . . You should be industrious. You should work hard, because that was the way to get things done, and it made you feel good to know that you had worked hard. If you desired luxuries then you had to go ahead and earn the right to possess them.

It is distressing to survey the lacks and limitations of that fargone era. There were no airplane strikes (and scarcely any airplanes). No stretch-pants, no Beatles, no frug, no nylons, no computers. No camps and salaries and high-priced administrators for high school drop-outs. If anybody quit high school he went and got a job. If he couldn't get a real good job then he took one which was not so good. Simple. If he preferred to sit on his can, then he could do that too; and no one grew very anguished about it. No one thought that the fellow should be psychoanalyzed or expensively counseled. There might be secret opinion to the effect that what he needed was a good swat on the rear end. . . .

For we were primitives of a low order. We still believed in black and white, right and wrong. To us, as to our parents, there were scarcely any gray areas. Our society failed to make a hero out of a hot-blooded rapist or a cold-blooded murderer; instead we considered him a monster. Bad people were bad, and good people—Good.

Small boys were apt to be naughty—and big boys, too, on Halloween. If apprehended in the commission of a misdemeanor they were punished. But local freebooting consisted mainly of larceny in relation to melons; and vandalism was limited to the upsetting of privies, the dislocation of porch furniture, and the misplacement of a pig such as the one discovered occupying the 7th Grade classroom of Miss Anna Petersen, a maiden preceptress who never won any popularity contests.

Nevertheless had a band of teen-agers gone into a house or a school and systematically wrecked the place, and declared that "they did it for kicks," they would have received the kicks. Plenty of them. Then they would have been booted off to Glenwood, where a Home for the Feeble-minded was located.

It is unlikely that any other such crew would have attempted to emulate them, but that is beside the point. The point is that people who did nasty things were attended to with despatch, and in no mean way. Which, as any modern parole board can tell you, is all wrong.

Stand to Attention, children! You walk into a new and fearsome half-century—

But the Voice did not resound, nor did warning howitzers fire their shells within our hearing.

A boy asked, "Hey, Waldo, you going to the Orpheum with me tonight to see the new Beverly Bayne and Francis X. Bushman picture?" and Waldo replied in disgust that he was going to have to stay home and dye Easter eggs for his little sister. "I promised Mom," he said . . . that was typical of our artlessness. A promise given must be fulfilled—no two ways about it.

It is conceivable that the meadowlarks of April, 1917, might have descried what was going to happen, and that was why they were so insistent in their miniature bugling. But they spoke lark language, and we spoke and understood only our own.

And perhaps they knew even more than that which we elders have learned in the fifty years gone by . . . much more than we know now. Perhaps the larks glimpsed a remote future (remote today, still, in 1967) in which the advances in physics and technology will be correlated with the conscience and spirit of America, and even the whole World.

It will be a time wherein moral codes and principles may be fetched from forgotten storage heaps. Moss will be scraped from them, and their power and soundness revealed.

Letter to Canella
1966

Miss Canella Bales,
c/o Mr. and Mrs. Bob Bales,
10806 Lindbrook Drive
Los Angeles, California 90024

Dear Canella:

It was thoughtful of you to send a Christmas Card to our own Bill Dog. Trouble is, I've been unable to give it to him, because he is no longer living here.

Bill has gone very far away.

I don't even know his address, and can't forward any mail to him. But doubt not that we treasure every memory of your visit here. You, *tres charmant* in pearl collar and blue hair ribbons, as befitting any toy poodle of femininity and station— And Bill Dog, all brindles and uplifted ears and sharply wagging tail—a bucolic mixed-breed, full of snorts and sneezes, but bound to welcome every guest as if that guest were the gift of God.

Now, this business about Bill Dog going away— It sounds rather as if it were something he did deliberately, perhaps even in naughtiness or, save the mark, in malice. Yet that is untrue: it is a retreat in which every Dog indulges eventually, and we HB's (Human Beings) have never become generally accustomed to the idea.

People go into fits over Abandonment by Dogs. Some of

them refuse to talk about it, some threaten to jump out of the window, some lock themselves in their rooms to weep. All and sundry act as if they were enduring a phenomenon unparalleled in the experience of other HB's.

Of course you and I know the falsehood of such an idea. But still it is difficult for many persons to adjust themselves to the actuality.

Come to think of it, this is just about the only heart-breaking thing that a Dog ever does to an HB. *People* do dreadful things to people: they did yesterday, are doing so today, will do so tomorrow. Dogs couldn't possibly behave as wickedly as people! They work only this final little cruelty on the heart, because they can't avoid doing so. . . .

That does seem like a very sad state of affairs, to have Dogs giving any pain at all; but it must be so. (This circumstance should be corrected in some future environment where a great many other reforms are crying to be made.)

Canella, do you know what some silly folks do, when such a thing happens? They beat their breasts and cry against the Lord and the stars. They yell, "I will never have another Dog."

Can you imagine anything so absurd?

It is like saying, "I owned a supreme friend. He gave me laughter, courage, tenderness, power. He gave me all those things, and more—yet now he is gone. Therefore I want never to have another friend."

There is some sort of distorted inverse reasoning here which I can't follow. Seems like sitting on the beach at the bliss of sunrise (as I am sitting now, with gulls calling and flying for their breakfasts over the satin Gulf) and declaring, "I find wistfulness and mystery and medicine in this day. So I decline to see another day. I never want to live again."

Or— Shall we mention love? Suppose one says to a lover, "We formed an almost unbelievable union. We were sustained and invigorated. We dwelt in a perfect amalgamation of our mutual flesh and spirit; we strode the clouds with all of Beethoven resounding around us, with all of Michelangelo hung upon our wall . . . the very tapestries of Heaven came floating to wrap us when we wearied. We owned such a pride and such an undiminishing treasury. Ergo— What is the verdict? We desire never to make love again."

. . . *The apple was delicious, so I don't want to eat another apple.*

. . . *The bone was joy, so I don't want to chew another bone.*

There's no profit, Canella, in detailing any further lunacies.

Irene and I have to get ready to go on a little trip, ourselves; but this is one from which we hope to return. We'll come back to the house where last you visited us, and where Bill Dog's collar is hung in reverence and in style, and where a few of his hairs may still be discovered here and there. Were you present, you would find his jovial scent, I know.

But, fact is, it will be replaced when we return from our trip. Funny thing: we *know* that it will be replaced, but by *whom* we can't yet tell. We can't even describe him physically . . . still we know he will be with us soon.

Because there is no proper answer to the Departure of a Dog except the Advent of Another Dog. You Dogs have brought this about very cleverly, all by yourselves, without any help from us. So we are in your debt.

Canella, please visit us again before too long. We will wish you to meet the new Dog who is coming— No, of course not: not to *replace* Bill! No Dog can ever replace another.

But one Dog can take over the responsibilities and duties of another, and I'm glad to say that somewhere they are doing so, every hour. Dogs have a keen sense of fitness and propriety.

Our best HB love to you, Canella, and to Peggy and Bob.

Affectionately,

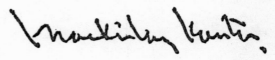